D1179871

This is a book in the series

STUDIES IN PHYSICS AND CHEMISTRY

Additional volumes in preparation

STUDIES IN PHYSICS AND CHEMISTRY

Number 6

SPECIAL RELATIVITY

by

A. SHADOWITZ

SPECIAL RELATIVITY

A. SHADOWITZ
Department of Physics
Fairleigh Dickinson University
Teaneck, New Jersey

1968

W. B. SAUNDERS COMPANY

PHILADELPHIA • LONDON • TORONTO

W. B. Saunders Company: West Washington Square
                          Philadelphia, Pa. 19105

                          12 Dyott Street
                          London W.C. 1

                          1835 Yonge Street
                          Toronto 7, Ontario

Special Relativity

© 1968 by W. B. Saunders Company. Copyright under the International Copyright Union. All rights reserved. This book is protected by copyright. No part of it may be duplicated or reproduced in any manner without written permission from the publisher. Made in the United States of America. Press of W. B. Saunders Company. Library of Congress catalog card number 67–17454.

TO HELEN DUKAS

Portrait of Albert Einstein—by Josef Scharl.
Courtesy of Galerie St. Etienne, New York.

FOREWORD

The Theory of Relativity has been of the utmost importance in the development of physics, and its concepts have penetrated the public consciousness to an unusual degree. The basis of the theory is inherently simple; nevertheless there remains an impression that the topic is of a forbidding difficulty, and that the acquisition of some understanding of the theory requires an onerous intellectual effort. To a large degree this is a pedagogical problem in that full advantage has not been taken of more efficient methods of presentation. This difficulty occurs in every branch of physics, as one can see by comparing books of fifty years ago on electromagnetic theory to those published today. The shrubbery of mathematics can be pruned to allow a quick approach to the trunk of the theory and more easy access to the distant branches. Therefore it is a pleasure to read this refreshing exposition of relativity by Dr. Shadowitz, which should be of use to anyone who wishes to improve his understanding of physics.

RICHARD STEVENSON

PREFACE

This book on special relativity is based largely on the recently developed space-time geometries of Professors Loedel and Brehme, especially the former. The great advantage of a geometric approach to relativity is that it minimizes the demands on abstruse thought and insight demanded by a strictly algebraic treatment. It is, incidentally, in keeping with Einstein's attempt to reduce all physics to geometry.

Two old space-time geometries—the complex rotation diagram and the Minkowski diagram—were proposed soon after the birth of relativity, but time has proved both to be inadequate. Some of the reasons for this are discussed in the second chapter; here it is sufficient to point out that, as a consequence, none of the scores of texts available on special relativity approaches the subject geometrically. Yet the geometric approach is probably the most fundamental one; certainly it is the simplest.

The two new space-time geometries of Loedel and Brehme suffer from none of the inadequacies of the old diagrams. All quantities are real and in proper proportion; no conversion of scales is necessary; no hyperbolas are required for measurement. My preference of the Loedel over the Brehme diagram is based on experience in using both types with students; the Loedel diagram seems to require a shorter learning period.

The geometric approach has its chief advantage in 2-dimensional space-time because of the ease with which the drawings can be made. This is sufficient for almost everything in special relativity. In the 4-dimensional space-time of general relativity the chief advantage of any drawings is suggestive—for detailed computation the analytic treatment is just as simple. The analytic approach employed here in conjunction with the diagrams is identical with the Minkowski 4-vector and 4-tensor formulation. This makes the transition simple for those readers who wish to go on to general relativity.

This monograph is intended for use both as a text and as a reference manual. Because of the simplicity of the mathematics and the sophistication of the ideas, a strange situation exists with respect to special relativity: it is taught at the freshman level, at the graduate level, and at all levels in between these two. My aim has been to write a book which will serve not only as a straightforward textbook for students but also as a unifying reminder to those for whom the subject was learned, fragmentarily, many years ago.

At the end of the book there are problems based on the material in each chapter. Only in Chapter 8 is it necessary to employ a knowledge of calculus, either in the text or in the problems (though there are a few problems in other chapters, so indicated, which also require this). Despite the elementary mathematics employed, the geometric approach enables me to treat virtually all the topics usually covered in graduate level courses.

I would like to thank a number of students at the Geophysical Institute of the University of Alaska for suggestions which were incorporated in the text—in particular Sue Ann Bowling, William Stringer, and Theodore Young. I also wish to express my thanks to Keith Mather for extending to me the hospitality of the Institute, where much of this book was written. It is a pleasure to acknowledge the efficient typing of Mrs. Ruth Cluggish and the meticulous draftmanship of Leo Kantrowitz. I am grateful to Wallace Arthur and Harold A. Rothbart for making available various facilities of Fairleigh Dickinson University. I owe a great debt to Professor H. Fröhlich for providing a Research Fellowship and the ideal working conditions at the University of Liverpool, where this text was completed. Finally, I am happy to mention the contribution of my wife, Edith, who not only helped in the proofreading but also prepared the index.

ALBERT SHADOWITZ

CONTENTS

Nomographs

Derivation of Steady-State Values of Charge Density and
Drift Velocity for the Case of Reflected Waves

The Case of Parallel Conductors for Real (Nonideal)
Metals

CONTENTS

Chapter I WHAT IS RELATIVITY?

I. COMMON SENSE

One of the basic axioms of relativity, now verified many times by experiment, contradicts common sense, as we shall see subsequently. In defying common sense, Albert Einstein was following in the footsteps of two great earlier physicists—Isaac Newton and Galileo. This is not to suggest that it is necessary only to contradict the obvious to be outstanding. Rather, the original thinkers change the nature of what seems obvious.

Consider Newton, for example. When a ball is rolled along the ground it first slows down and then comes to rest. Before Newton it seemed perfectly obvious that it would require force to keep the ball going indefinitely with its original velocity. According to Newton, however, a force was not necessary to do this: the ball's changing speed was caused by a force, the force of friction. (Actually, Galileo suspected this not long before Newton was born, but the latter was the first to write the relation quantitatively.) If this frictional force were removed, the ball's velocity would remain unchanged without the application of further force. Now we apply this principle every day, even using huge space rockets instead of small balls.

Before Galileo and Copernicus everyone thought the sun went around the earth once a day. Today we all accept the fact that this is not so but that, rather, the earth spins on its axis. Before Copernicus one interpretation seemed obvious, after Galileo quite another.

By the early 1920's most scientists accepted relativity as a closer approximation to the truth than that given by the classical theory. The layman could not really be expected to change his common sense views as readily as the scientists. It was not until 1945, when the atom bomb exploded, that the public was ready to accept relativity as proved by life. The atom bomb was based, after all, on the simple law $E = mc^2$, now almost folklore. This law, first predicted by relativity, said that mass could be considered a form of energy. If a given mass, m, were to disappear then an equivalent energy, E, would appear. The square of the velocity of light, c^2, is a huge number so a little mass would give a lot of energy. This is just what the atom bomb showed; a large amount of energy was created, energy not explainable by prerelativistic theories.

2. RELATIVE VERSUS ABSOLUTE

Relativity concerns itself with the nature of space and the nature of time. Such subjects were of interest, before Einstein, to philosophers but not to most scientists, although there were some philosopher-scientists, such as Ernst Mach and Isaac Newton, who did devote thought to these matters. The notions prevalent before relativity could be called the theories of absolute space and absolute time. These classical beliefs seemed so obvious and self-evident that scarcely anyone questioned them. Was it necessary to argue that if two events occurred simultaneously for Mr. X they also occurred simultaneously for Mr. Y? It was assumed that time went at the same rate for all people: time was absolute, not relative. Similarly with space—an inch was an inch. It could not be an inch for one man, a foot for another. Space had absolutely the same value for all people.

Both these ideas were successfully contradicted by relativity. According to it, time may indeed go at different rates for different observers. We are speaking here of real, objective, time—the time intervals measured by accurate clocks—not the apparent, subjective time of the mind. Space, likewise, is flexible according to relativity. What X would call one square foot might be one square inch for Y, yet both might be correct. Space and time were shown to be relative quantities, not immutable and absolute.

Unfortunately, although the mathematics involved in relativity is simplicity itself, the ideas behind the mathematics violate common sense and everyday life. This is so because the physical facts, which relativity was designed to explain, violate ordinary experience. Our ideas of common sense are still in the process of changing from what they were before Einstein to what they must become, of necessity, after Einstein. But the theory of Einstein has one serious disadvantage compared to those of his predecessors Newton and Galileo—their ideas pertained to phenomena which were common occurrences and could be seen and reasoned out in the course of natural events. The ideas of relativity do not predict different answers from those given by classical physics in situations with which we are ordinarily concerned. Special circumstances not usually encountered, such as speeds of thousands of miles per *second*, are required for the two theories to give results which differ appreciably. The practical experience to fall back on, which ordinarily eliminates incorrect assumptions and conclusions by direct evidence, is lacking here in daily life. So errors in reasoning are still being discovered to this day.

The considerations which led Einstein to propose a revision of classical thinking about space and time were twofold. Einstein made these the two mathematical legs on which he rested the entire body of logic called the Theory of Special Relativity. This was proposed in 1905 for the case of different observers having a constant velocity relative to each other. In 1916 Einstein introduced General Relativity, which applied to all observers—even those accelerating with respect to each other. The present exposition limits itself to the case of special relativity, which will simply be called relativity.

3. THE ETHER

To describe the motion of a body it is necessary to pick some reference system with respect to which the body is moving. I may be walking in a train; then I am moving—relative to the train. But the train itself may be moving in such a way that I could be standing still relative to the earth. Am I then really moving or really standing still? Before answering this one must consider the earth itself. The earth revolves about the sun; the sun moves with respect to the center of our galaxy, the Milky Way; our galaxy moves with respect to other nebulae; etc. How is it possible to tell whether I am really moving or really standing still? To learn whether a body is really moving it is necessary to find a reference system which is fixed in space. Then if a body is not moving relative to this system, it is really at rest; if it moves relative to this system, the body is really in motion. All that is necessary is to find the fixed reference system.

Before embarking on a search for such a reference system we ask: Is there such a system? If there is some one star, perhaps, that is really standing still, how do we pick it out from, the myriad of other stars? No known star seems so exceptional as to be a likely candidate for this distinction. Perhaps, instead of one isolated body, the stationary reference system pervades all space. Such a concept proved attractive after James Clerk Maxwell found in 1864 that an electromagnetic wave would propagate with a speed close to that experimentally obtained for the speed of light. (Heinrich Hertz obtained the same result for the speed of radio waves some 20 years later.) This indicated that light is but one form of electromagnetic wave. But if light is a wave there should be some medium to do the waving. For a sound wave the medium is air. It seemed plausible that the medium for the electromagnetic waves might be the stationary reference system with respect to which all motion could be measured. This system was given a name, the ether, and a search was initiated to find it. Since light goes through a vacuum, however, the ether must exist in a vacuum. This, of course, is a contradiction in terms, which poses a slight dilemma.

There is another alternative—that it is not possible to tell whether one is "really" moving. Suppose there is no reference system which is fixed in space. Then it is only possible to give the velocity of A with respect to B, which would be equal and opposite to the velocity of B with respect to A. It is not possible to say whether A or B is really moving; "really moving" would, in fact, have no meaning. Just as there is no star or other heavenly body which we can recognize as fixed, this alternative would mean that, in addition, there is no all-pervasive medium that is fixed in space. But if there is no ether, what serves as the medium for electromagnetic waves? This, too, is a problem.

If there were an ether fixed in space then an observer at rest with respect to the ether, an observer really at rest, would be picked out from all other observers moving with respect to him—an aristocrat, so to speak. It would not be too surprising if the laws of nature would prove to be especially simple in this one reference frame, the highest caste system. On the other hand, if there were no ether then the laws of nature should be equally valid for all observers, since no single system would be fundamentally different from, or more important than, any other system; the observers would form a democratic system. How do the laws of nature actually behave experimentally—are they the same or are they different for different observers? We will wish to clarify this in just a moment but here let us state, first, the surprising fact that some laws remain the same while others do not. Newton's laws are invariant, they are identically the same for all observers. On the other hand, the wave equation for light, based on Maxwell's laws, changes its form completely for different observers. Something is wrong— either there is an ether or there is not an ether.

There are two qualifications that must be made in connection with this remark. First, when we speak simply of two observers moving relatively to each other we will always imply uniform motion; that is, motion with constant speed in a straight line—no acceleration (bumps, jerks, turns, etc.). The reason for this restriction is that we know from experience that the laws of nature are not the same for two observers if one is accelerating relative to the second. An astronaut in free fall, accelerating toward the earth, apparently has a different law of gravitation than that which applies on earth: when the astronaut releases an object it does not fall relative to him but stays, relative to him, where he left it. Again, let a sphere rotate with constant angular velocity about an axis through its center. Those of its constituent parts not on the axis are thus accelerating perpendicular to this axis. (The motion of these parts, although uniform, is not in a straight line.) The laws of mechanics are not quite the same for an observer on the surface of the sphere as they are for a stationary observer: a so-called fictitious inertial force—the centrifugal force—must be introduced for the rotating observer if he is stationary relative to the surface. If the rotating observer is moving relative to the surface an additional inertial force is required, the Coriolis force.

We wish to avoid the necessity for inertial forces, real or fictitious. Then Newton's law $F = ma$ would apply for all bodies having sufficiently low velocities, with F the sum of all noninertial forces. An observer will be called a Galilean observer (an inertial observer) when it is not necessary to introduce inertial forces into F in order to make Newton's second law valid. All observers who move with constant velocity relative to a Galilean observer are also, themselves, Galilean observers. The contrary is not true, however. Two observers who move with constant speed relative to each other are not necessarily Galilean since they may both be accelerating relative to a third, Galilean, observer.

Just what distinguishes a Galilean observer from a nonGalilean observer? According to Mach's principle there exists between any two masses an inertial force, in addition to the Newtonian gravitational force $G \dfrac{m_1 m_2}{r_{12}^2}$. The inertial force is also proportional to $m_1 m_2$; it is some function of r_{12}; and it is also a function of the relative acceleration between the two masses. When the total inertial force on a mass, m, produced by all the other masses in the universe is zero, then that mass (or an imaginary observer moving with that mass) is Galilean. The exact expression for this inertial force, however, has never been determined quantitatively.

The second qualification concerns the means by which different Galilean observers compare their results. If A is a rocket ship moving toward the right along the X axis with constant velocity, v, relative to B, the earth, then an x measurement made in A will be different from the corresponding measurement, X, made in B. From Figure 1 we see that, if the two origins O_A and O_B were coincident at $t = 0$, then $X = x + vt$ and a body resting at P in A, say with $x = 3$, will be moving to the right relative to B. Since $X = x + vt$, in fact, the X position will be increasing linearly with the time. The distances measured perpendicular to the direction of relative motion, on the other hand, will be the same for A and for B: $Y = y$ and $Z = z$. Finally, the time of any event occurring at P will be the same whether measured (a) by an accurate clock moving with

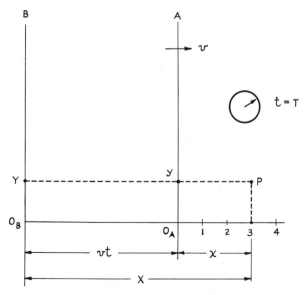

Figure I. The Galilean transformation.

A or (b) by an accurate clock, at rest with respect to *B*, located at the position in space where the event occurred. These considerations are nothing more nor less than common sense and are based on our innate feelings of absolute space and absolute time. Together, they are known as the Galilean transformation:

$$\begin{cases} X = x + vt \\ Y = y \\ Z = z \\ T = t \end{cases} \quad \text{or} \quad \begin{cases} x = X - vT \\ y = Y \\ z = Z \\ t = T \end{cases}$$

Any law which is given in terms of x, y, z, t for observer *A* may be transformed by the aid of these equations to the corresponding law (involving X, Y, Z, T) that pertains to observer *B*. The reverse is also true.

If there were an ether there would be an absolute space and absolute time—the distance intervals and time intervals measured by an observer at rest with respect to the ether. All laws of physics, then, ought to be stated as they would apply for an observer in this preferred system. For other observers the laws might be different. For instance, when dealing with sound waves we would want to formulate all the laws as they applied to the case of the air at rest. If there were a strong wind we would simply transform conditions to a system, moving with the wind, in which the air was at rest. After the necessary calculations the results could be carried back, by the Galilean transformation, to the conditions of the moving air.

If, on the other hand, there were no ether then absolute space and absolute time would lose all meaning. Only distances and times relative to a particular system would have any significance, and it would not be correct to emphasize the measurements of any one observer over those of any other. The particular coordinates of any one event would differ from one Galilean observer to another but the laws, themselves, should be the same for all observers.

Utilizing the Galilean transformation it was not possible to find any indication of an ether from Newton's laws, for they are identically the same for all Galilean observers. By the same transformation the wave equation for light, based on Maxwell's laws, actually changed its form for different observers. It was a particularly simple law for one system; for all other observers the law became more complicated.

It appeared that the alternatives were to discard either Newton's laws or Maxwell's laws. But Einstein came up with a different suggestion—that we modify the Galilean transformation.

4. THE VELOCITY OF LIGHT

In 1887 two American physicists were the first to "succeed" in the search to find the ether, the preferred system or medium that was really stationary in space. It was a negative success, however, for their experiment seemed to show that there was no ether. The Michelson-Morley experiment, which has remained world-famous to this day, seemed to say there was something quite unique about light or other electromagnetic radiation—light waves did not behave like sound waves, or water waves, or elastic waves, or any other kind of waves known. For those waves the velocity in the transmitting medium varied between one Galilean observer and another; but for light waves the velocity in vacuum turned out to be identically the same for all Galilean observers, making it quite impossible to pick out any preferred observer.

The Michelson-Morley experiment, employing light waves to determine the velocity of the earth through the ether—the light-transmitting medium—yielded a zero value for the speed of the earth through the ether. The velocity of light with respect to the earth is, consequently, the same as its velocity with respect to the ether; and the velocity of light with respect to an observer moving on the surface of the earth is, then, also the same as its velocity with respect to the ether. The latter, however, is presumably a constant whose value is fixed by the nature of the transmitting medium (as in the case of all other types of waves).

Figure 2 shows the paradox this presented. It did not seem possible to understand how the velocity of a light wave could be the same for the two observers, A and B, moving relative to each other. If an outgoing spherical light pulse was emitted when the two observers were coincident, then at some later time A would find, with his instruments, that the light wave was a sphere centered about A and moving radially outward with velocity c. B, with his clocks and rules, would find that the light wave was a sphere centered about B and moving radially outward from him with velocity c. Both A and B could not be correct, thinking along the lines of absolute space and absolute time. Yet experiment showed that they were, indeed, both correct.

The first tendency in attempting to resolve the paradox of the light spheres is to question the correctness of the Michelson-Morley experiment. This experiment, however, had been performed very carefully. It duplicated, with much greater accuracy, the results of an earlier experiment carried out by Michelson alone in 1881. Also, when the experiment was repeated by others the same results were obtained. The velocity was always the same; for all observers; in all directions.

In the years 1893 to 1895 two physicists independently suggested that the Michelson-Morley experimental null result could be explained if it were arbitrarily assumed that any body moving relative to the ether contracted its length in the direction of motion. In our final chapter, in which the Michelson-Morley experiment is considered in detail, it will be seen how simply such a suggestion gives the null result. This was called the Lorentz-Fitzgerald contraction hypothesis.

No reason was given, at first, to explain the contraction. It was an

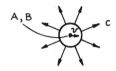

(a)   B APPROACHING A

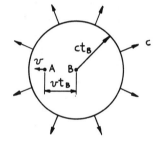

(b)   LIGHT PULSE STARTS AT TIME
$t_A = t_B = 0$ WHEN A & B COINCIDE

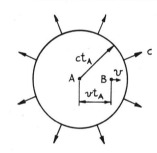

(c₁) LIGHT PULSE SPHERE AT A
LATER TIME, t_A AS SEEN BY
"A" AND HIS EQUIPMENT –
CENTERED ABOUT "A"

(c₂) LIGHT PULSE SPHERE AT A
LATER TIME, t_B AS SEEN BY
"B" AND HIS EQUIPMENT –
CENTERED ABOUT "B"

Figure 2.   The paradox of the light spheres.

ad hoc proposal, designed only to yield the results, not to understand them. Subsequently H. A. Lorentz did derive the contraction, starting with the assumption both of an ether and of the exclusive existence of electrical forces. Since the mere existence of the electron seemed to show that there must be nonelectrical forces present—to keep the electron together—this derivation was not convincing and it remained for Einstein to give an explanation that could be accepted.

Another attempt at reconciling theory and experiment was provided by the ether drag hypothesis which assumed that the earth dragged the ether along with it, automatically explaining the Michelson-Morley experiment. This hypothesis was contradicted, however, by an experiment of Fizeau's on the velocity of light in running water. It was also contrary to an astronomical effect, aberration, which could not exist if the hypothesis were true.

Still a different explanation assumed that the velocity of light might be affected by the motion of the source. This is demonstrably not true for sound (only the characteristics of the air determine the velocity of sound) but possibly, it was suggested, it might be true for light. Here, too, observations have disproved the hypothesis. The gamma rays emitted by fast-moving pions which decayed in flight were found to travel with a velocity that was independent of the velocity of the pions; also, the light emitted by eclipsing binary stars did not show any effect on the light velocity caused by the motion of the stars.

There was no way out: the Michelson-Morley experiment was correct. It violated common sense by stating that the velocity of light in a vacuum, c, was the same for all observers. But it was true.

5. THE TWO AXIOMS OF RELATIVITY

Einstein was able to settle these questions by a series of imagined experiments, using logic based on only two axioms. The reason the experiments were imagined rather than real was that there were no feasible means, in 1905, of obtaining test velocities close to the speed of light. Not until a third of a century later did technological developments proceed sufficiently so that an actual test could be performed. By then it was also possible to verify a number of predictions which were a consequence of the theory.

The first of Einstein's axioms was that there was no ether. All Galilean observers were to be treated as equals and the basic physical laws of nature were to be the same for all of them. We wish to stress the presence of the word Galilean. Without it one would be justified in saying that it is the sun that moves around the earth once a day rather than saying that the earth spins on its axis once a day. Shades of Galileo! But this would be incorrect, since the axiom applies only to Galilean observers—those moving in a straight line with constant speed relative to each other. A revolving sun or a rotating earth, each is nonGalilean.

The name Principle of Relativity is often given to this first axiom. Based on ordinary experience using the Galilean transformation this axiom required courage, since sound waves did not obey this principle. Adoption of this axiom left open the question of why Maxwell's wave equation was different for different Galilean observers.

The second axiom was that c, the velocity of electromagnetic waves in a vacuum, was indeed a constant for all Galilean observers. At the time it was made this was a very bold step, for the experimental evidence in favor of this was not then overwhelming, as it is today. Then, as now, it was contrary to common sense. This axiom accepted the experimental evidence as fact. It left open the need to explain the paradox of the light spheres.

Based on these axioms and the imagined experiments, Einstein was able to reconcile all the experimental results with the theory. The price it was necessary to pay for this was the abandonment of the Galilean transformation based on our common sense notions of absolute space and time. Einstein found that often the Galilean transformation gave results which were essentially correct; but for velocities approaching that of light the common sense results were quite incorrect.

Although Einstein's special relativity has eliminated the concept of the ether, it has not removed the restriction to Galilean observers, i.e., inertial frames of reference. Special relativity sheds no light on the question "What is exceptional about observers who are nonaccelerating, presumably with respect to the center of mass of the universe?" This is precisely the question to which Mach's principle addresses itself. Einstein's general relativity also addresses itself to the question posed above. Both Mach's principle and general relativity, however, are outside the scope of the treatment here.

BIBLIOGRAPHY

American Association of Physics Teachers: Special Relativity Theory. New York, American Institute of Physics, 1962. Paperback collection of papers, especially on the paradox of the twins.

Bondi, H.: Relativity and Common Sense. Garden City, N.Y., Doubleday & Co., 1964. Paperback, part of Science Study Series.

Born, M.: Einstein's Theory of Relativity. New York, E. P. Dutton & Co., 1924. An elementary treatment by an outstanding physicist.

Einstein, A., Lorentz, H. A., Minkowski, H., and Weyl, H.: The Principle of Relativity. New York, Dover Publications, Inc., 1958. A collection of original memoirs on the special and general theory of relativity. Paperback reprint of a 1923 Methuen translation.

Gamow, G.: Mr. Tompkins in Wonderland. Cambridge, Cambridge University Press, 1939. Contains a classic popularization of relativity based on a then-prevalent erroneous supposition.

Katz, R.: An Introduction to the Special Theory of Relativity. Princeton, New Jersey, D. Van Nostrand Co., 1964. Paperback.

Lieber, L. R.: The Einstein Theory of Relativity. New York, Reinhart, 1945. For the layman.

Ney, E. P.: Electromagnetism and Relativity. New York, Harper and Row, 1962. Paperback.

Rosser, W. G. V.: An Introduction to the Theory of Relativity. London, Butterworth & Co., 1964. A recent college-level treatment.

The following books have more comprehensive treatments:

Eddington, A. S.: The Mathematical Theory of Relativity. 2nd ed. Cambridge, Cambridge University Press, 1952.

Fock, V.: The Theory of Space Time and Gravitation. 2nd ed. New York, Pergamon Press, 1964.

Frank, P.: Einstein—His Life and Times. New York, Alfred A. Knopf, 1965. A biography of Einstein by a scientist who was his close friend, this book contains a wealth of background material of a personal nature and also depicts the ferment of ideas from which the theory of relativity was born.

Møller, C.: The Theory of Relativity. New York, Oxford University Press, 1955.

Pauli, W.: Theory of Relativity. New York, Pergamon Press, 1958. New edition of 1921 treatment.

Schilpp, P. A. (ed.): Albert Einstein: Philosopher-Scientist. New York, Harper and Bros., 1959, 2 vols. Paperback reprint of a 1949 edition published by the Library of Living Philosophers. It contains an autobiography by Einstein, as well as essays contributed by many world-famous physicists, discussing a multitude of topics both in physics and in philosophy.

Synge, J. L.: Relativity: The Special Theory. New York, Interscience Publishers, Inc., 1956.

Tolman, R. C.: Relativity, Thermodynamics, and Cosmology. New York, Oxford University Press, 1934.

Weyl, H.: Space, Time, Matter. London, Methuen & Co., Ltd., 1922. Dover paperback reprint of 4th edition.

Whittaker, E. T.: A History of the Theories of Aether and Electricity. Revised ed. New York, Harper and Bros., 1960. (Torchbook series) Vol. 1, The Classical Theories; Vol. 2, The Modern Theories.

The following articles are all from the American Journal of Physics:

Ahrens, T.: Aether Concept Versus Special Relativity. *30:* 34, Jan., 1962.

Fox, J. G.: Experimental Evidence for the Second Postulate of Special Relativity. *30:* 297, Apr., 1962.

Fox, J. G.: Evidence Against Emission Theories. *33:* 1, Jan., 1965.

Haseltine, W. R.: Second Postulate of Special Relativity. *32:* 173, Feb., 1964.

Holton, G.: On the Origins of the Special Theory of Relativity. *28:* 627, Oct., 1960.

Komar, A.: Foundations of Special Relativity and the Shape of the Big Dipper. *33:* 1024, Dec., 1965.

Schwartz, H. M.: A Note on Poincaré's Contribution to Relativity. *33:* 170, Feb., 1965.

Scribner, C., Jr.: Henri Poincaré and the Principle of Relativity. *32:* 672, Sept., 1964.

Chapter 2 SPACE-TIME DIAGRAMS

I. INTRODUCTION

A generation ago there was a widespread belief that only three men in the entire world understood the Theory of Relativity proposed by Professor Albert Einstein. Presumably it was called a Theory to distinguish it from accepted fact. The Theory itself, introducing an imaginary fourth dimension, led to equations which predicted that lengths would shrink, that time would expand, that mass could disappear. Almost everyone felt the subject was fascinating, but just too difficult for all but a few isolated geniuses to comprehend.

Times change. Today relativity is taught in some high schools. It has long been recognized that the mathematics involved is particularly simple, requiring nothing more than a little algebra, geometry, and trigonometry.

Soon after the birth of relativity in 1905 it was noticed that even the equations, simple as they were, could be eliminated by the use of a geometrical approach. Two different types of diagrams were employed, the Minkowski diagram and the complex rotation diagram, but both types were defective for use in introductory treatments. In the second of these figures it was necessary to employ great care in comparing two magnitudes since a line that looked obviously smaller than another might, as often as not, turn out to be actually larger. The first type required a scaling factor in going between scales, making comparisons for different observers somewhat indirect. The geometric approach never became popular, therefore, leaving the interpretations only to algebra. The latter, however, often proved tricky.

In 1948 a simple geometric procedure was suggested by Enrique Loedel. His diagram had no distortion and all quantities were real. Because the article appeared in an Argentinean journal the method remained unknown to the English-speaking world until 1955, when it was independently proposed by Henri Amar. In 1962 Robert W. Brehme, unaware of either Loedel's or Amar's work, suggested a diagram which was related to Loedel's but was, nevertheless, different from it. For simplicity we will refer to these

12

two related space-time geometries as the Loedel diagram and the Brehme diagram. The present treatment is based largely on the Loedel diagram. *For succinctness, whenever we refer to just a space-time diagram we will imply the Loedel diagram.*

A generalized geometric approach, not limited to any one special type of diagram, has been utilized by the mathematician John L. Synge in a number of well known books on mechanics and relativity. His work, more than that of anyone else, has served recently to emphasize the benefits of the geometric approach. In one sense both the Loedel and Brehme diagrams could be referred to as Synge diagrams. Actually, however, the chief credit for all space-time diagrams belongs to Hermann Minkowski.

Even though the mathematics is simple, it nevertheless remains true that relativity has only a remote relevance to common, everyday affairs. Why, then, should students attempt to master it, even with a ready-made geometric approach? There are several reasons we can offer. The first is the importance that relativity has in science today. From atoms to x-rays, there is scarcely a nook in physics which has not had light shed on it by relativity. In fact, relativity is second only to quantum mechanics in important contributions to the physics of the twentieth century. Second, even aside from its great technical importance, relativity is of interest as a study in logic—a self-consistent but noncommon sense system of consequences based on two axioms. In this respect it could be learned the way non-Euclidean geometry is learned. Third, relativity is worth learning if only to watch seemingly unrelated facts fit together, like the pieces of a jigsaw puzzle, into a unified picture of great beauty. Finally, relativity seems to arouse a great curiosity in many, many people. There is evidently a psychological factor involved. Some people would undoubtedly have a higher self-image if they knew they could understand a subject so reputedly abstruse as relativity. Since we are in favor both of self-esteem and of curiosity we consider this an excellent reason.

2. THE BREHME DIAGRAM

Figure 3*a* shows a graph giving the coordinates (x, y) of one end point, P, of a line, the coordinates of the other end point, O, being at the origin. The length of the line is given by $l = \sqrt{x^2 + y^2}$. The line OP might extend, say, between a lighthouse and a ship. The coordinates would be the measurements taken on shore along the two sets of axes, Ox and Oy. To find the coordinate x a perpendicular is dropped from P to Ox. The y coordinate is similarly obtained.

The coordinates of P might just as well have been determined along another system of axes, say Ox' and Oy' in Figure 3*b*. Then the coordinates (x', y') would be different from (x, y). The length of the line would now be given by $l = \sqrt{(x')^2 + (y')^2}$. Since the length from lighthouse to ship is

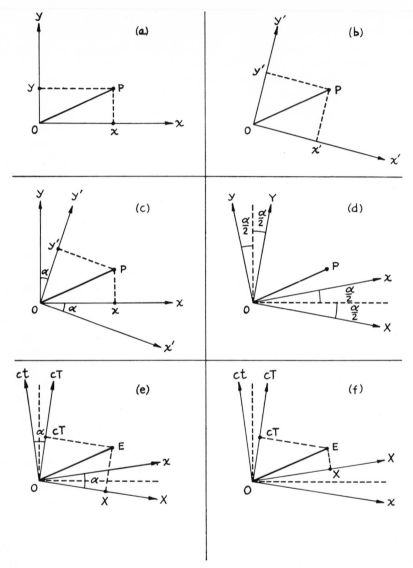

Figure 3. Evolution of the Brehme diagram.

unaffected by the choice of the particular set of axes used for the measurement, the two values obtained this way must be equal:

$$x^2 + y^2 = (x')^2 + (y')^2.$$

Figure 3c contains the two sets of axes combined into one diagram. To find the coordinate of P along any axis it is necessary only to drop a perpendicular to that axis. Ox and Oy are at right angles to each other; Ox' and Oy' are also perpendicular to each other. The angle between the first set of coordinates and the second, α, is a measure of the difference in angular attitude of the two observers who are performing the measurement. The set of coordinates (x, y') could serve just as well as either of the first two in fixing the position of P with respect to O. The axes Ox and Oy' no longer form an orthogonal set, however, and the length $l \neq \sqrt{x^2 + (y')^2}$. For this reason there is ordinarily a disadvantage in employing a nonorthogonal set of axes.

Figure 3d differs from the previous diagram in having the axes rotated counterclockwise through the angle $\frac{\alpha}{2}$. This makes the diagram symmetrical with respect to imagined horizontal and vertical lines. In addition, the Oy' axis has been relabeled OY while the Ox' axis has been changed to OX. The axes Ox and OY have an acute angle between them; OX and Oy have an obtuse angle between the axes.

So far the graphs have been employed to fix the geometrical position of the point P. The z axis has been ignored by assuming, implicitly, that the z coordinate is fixed. Suppose, now, that we wish to determine on a graph the position and time of an event. For simplicity let us ignore y and z by assuming they are constant. We could then plot the event on a graph, similar to Figure 3d, with the y axis replaced by the t axis.

In addition, it is possible to change the scale along any axis by multiplying the values on that axis by a constant. For example, $792t$ could serve for the time axis if that were desirable for some reason; so could ct and ct', where c is any constant. If, furthermore, c also has the dimensions of velocity, then ct will be a distance, similar to x. The distance ct represents the distance traveled in the time t by an object moving with velocity c. Figure 3e shows this change of axis designation. The point is now labeled E, instead of P, since it designates an event rather than a position. Here

$$X^2 + c^2 T^2 = x^2 + c^2 t^2.$$

For c we will take the velocity of light in vacuum, 3×10^8 meters/second or 186,000 miles/second $= 5.9 \times 10^{12}$ miles/year, which experiment shows to be a constant. A convenient nomenclature may then be employed for ct. If t is 1 year then the distance ct (5.9×10^{12} miles) is called one light-year. Similarly, if $t = 1$ sec. then $ct = 1$ light-second (a distance equal to 186,000 miles); for $t = 1$ microsecond or 10^{-6} sec. the distance ct (300 meters or 982 feet) is 1 light-microsecond. Thus, time and light-time (a distance) are equal numerically.

The change from a time scale to an equivalent distance scale is common practice on the screens of radar sets. The horizontal distance between two pips on the radar scope—the transmitter pip and the receiver pip—is actually a time measurement, accurately determined by the speed of the electron dot which is moving horizontally across the face of the radar scope tube. It is calibrated, however, in feet, yards, or miles representing the distance radar pulses (electromagnetic radiation, like light) travel in that time.

Finally, in Figure 3*f* a most important step has been taken—the Ox and OX axes have been interchanged. This figure is called the Brehme space-time diagram. Instead of the relation applicable to Figure 3*d* we now have $X^2 + c^2t^2 = x^2 + c^2T^2$. X and cT are the coordinates, for one observer, of the event E; x and ct are the coordinates of the same event for another observer. Thus, here we have the important relation

$$X^2 - c^2T^2 = x^2 - c^2t^2.$$

The significance of this equation will be discussed in the following section. It is central to everything in special relativity.

In finding the coordinate of an event, as seen by one observer, the procedure is to drop a perpendicular to the particular axis, say the OX axis, from E. Since the set (X, cT) is not orthogonal, but has an acute angle between the two axes, it follows that EX is not parallel to the cT axis; instead, since the ct axis is perpendicular to the X axis, EX is parallel to the ct axis.

3. THE INTERVAL

The basis for the construction of the Brehme diagram above was the equality $x^2 - c^2t^2 = X^2 - c^2T^2$. (x, t) characterizes an event for one observer, while another observer designates the same event by (X, T). A light pulse emitted at $x = t = 0$ would be received at (x, t) if $x = ct$; similarly, if the second observer assigned $X = T = 0$ to the emission then the reception would occur at (X, T) if $X = cT$. The application of the equation

$$x^2 - c^2t^2 = X^2 - c^2T^2$$

to two events connected by light signals becomes the identity $0 = 0$.

We may generalize the situation, first, by employing all three dimensions instead of just the x axis and, second, by letting the light emission occur at an arbitrary point of the space-time diagram instead of at the origin. Then

$$(x_2 - x_1)^2 + (y_2 - y_1)^2 + (z_2 - z_1)^2 - c^2(t_2 - t_1)^2 = 0$$

expresses the fact that the velocity of light is c for the first observer. The second observer would write

$$(X_2 - X_1)^2 + (Y_2 - Y_1)^2 + (Z_2 - Z_1)^2 - c^2(T_2 - T_1)^2 = 0$$

to describe the fact that the velocity of the wave is also c for him. All the unusual consequences that will result from the application of the space-time diagram stem ultimately from the fact that the velocity of the light wave is the same for the two observers. In the next section it is shown that the Brehme diagram applies to two observers who are moving with respect to each other with relative velocity $v = c \sin \alpha$. The experimental fact that the two observers each measure c for the velocity of the wave, though they are moving relative to each other, is a fact which violates common sense.

The interval, s_{12}, between any two events E_1 and E_2 is defined by $s_{12} = \sqrt{c^2(t_2 - t_1)^2 - \{(x_2 - x_1)^2 + (y_2 - y_1)^2 + (z_2 - z_1)^2\}}$. If the two events are connected by a light wave then the interval between them is zero for both observers. What happens if the two events are arbitrary—not connected by a light wave? If

$$c^2(t_2 - t_1)^2 > \{(x_2 - x_1)^2 + (y_2 - y_1)^2 + (z_2 - z_1)^2\}$$

then the interval will be a real number; if the reverse inequality holds, the interval will be an imaginary number. If two events are separated by a distance which is less than the distance which light can travel in the time between the two events then the interval is real and is called time-like. If the separation is by a greater distance than this, the interval is imaginary and is called space-like.

We seek a relation between an arbitrary interval, s_a, recorded by observer A and the interval, s_b, between the same two events as measured by observer B. By an arbitrary interval we mean one between two arbitrary events, not necessarily connected by light, by cause and effect, or by any other means. Observer B is assumed to be moving relative to A with velocity v_{ba}, which is the negative of v_{ab}, the velocity of A relative to B. Suppose

$$s_a = f_0 + f_1 s_b + f_2 s_b{}^2 + \cdots,$$

where the coefficients f_0, f_1, f_2, etc., could be functions of the space-time coordinates of the two events and of the magnitude and direction of the relative velocity.

In general, we would have

$$s_b = g_0 + g_1 s_a + g_2 s_a{}^2 + \cdots,$$

where the g's are different functions than the f's. But if

    a. space is homogeneous,
    b. space is isotropic,
    c. time is homogeneous,

then the f's and the g's cannot depend on space or time coordinates or on the direction of the relative velocity between A and B. The only quantity on which the f's and g's can depend is the magnitude of the relative velocity between A and B. Since $\mathbf{v}_{ab} = -\mathbf{v}_{ba}$ then $|\mathbf{v}_{ab}| = |\mathbf{v}_{ba}|$. Consequently, the f's and g's must be identical and we have, for the second observer:

$$s_b = f_0 + f_1 s_a + f_2 s_a{}^2 + \cdots.$$

Putting one expression into the other and using s for either s_a or s_b:

$$\begin{aligned} s &= f_1(f_1 s + f_2 s^2 + \cdots) + f_2(f_1 s + f_2 s^2 + \cdots)^2 + \cdots \\ &= [f_1{}^2]s + [f_1 f_2(1 + f_1)]s^2 + \cdots \\ &= A_1 s + A_2 s^2 + \cdots. \end{aligned}$$

We have set $f_0 = 0$ since $s_a = 0$ when $s_b = 0$. The A_n contains only the coefficients f_1 through f_n. For $n > 1$ the term in A_n which contains f_n is $(f_1 + f_1^n) f_n$. Thus, if the quantity in parenthesis does not vanish, the term itself can only be zero if $f_n = 0$.

We must have $A_1 = 1$; also, $A_n = 0$ for $n \neq 1$. The first condition gives $f_1 = +1$ and $f_1 = -1$. If $f_1 = +1$ then $A_2 = 0$ requires $f_2 = 0$; the vanishing of A_3 then makes $f_3 = 0$; etc., for all f_n with n greater than 1. We leave as an exercise the ruling out of the other possibility, $f_1 = -1$. Consequently,

$$s_b = s_a.$$

The invariance of an arbitrary interval for all observers moving relative to each other with constant velocity, as expressed in this equation, is the starting point for all the subsequent discussion.

The Brehme space-time diagram is a construction based on the supposition $c^2 t^2 - x^2 = c^2 T^2 - X^2$. This condition is identical with the demand that the interval be invariant for the special case $y = Y$, $z = Z$. Since invariance of the interval is the mathematical expression for the constant velocity of light in vacuum for all observers nonaccelerated with respect to each other, the Brehme diagram is seen to depend on this experimental, non-common sense fact.

4. WORLD-LINES

In Figure 4 we have taken $\alpha = 53°$ to obtain simple numbers for $\sin \alpha$ and $\cos \alpha$: $\sin \alpha = 0.8$ and $\cos \alpha = 0.6$. In addition, a line aa' has been drawn perpendicular to the Ox axis. This means the x coordinate is constant for all events along aa'. Suppose the Ox axis is fixed with respect to a rocket ship. The Oct axis also pertains to the rocket ship—different events on aa' occur at different times, t, but they all occur at the same place, x.

Two events, E_0 and E_1, lie on the line aa'. Let E_0 represent the birth of a radioactive particle in a laboratory on the rocket ship while E_1 represents the death of the same particle. Any line which joins different events associated with a given object will be called a world-line. Thus, aa' is the world-line of the rocket ship and $E_0 E_1$ is the world-line of the radioactive particle.

The time interval between two events that occur at the same place is called a proper-time interval. When viewed by another observer moving with respect to the first, the two events do not occur at the same place. The time interval between the two events as measured by the second observer is a nonproper-time interval. For example, a man starting and ending a meal on a jet plane would have a proper-time interval for an observer on the plane, since for this observer the meal occurred at one place: a given seat on the jet. For an observer on the ground, however, the start of the meal may have occurred over one city, and the conclusion of the meal over another. The

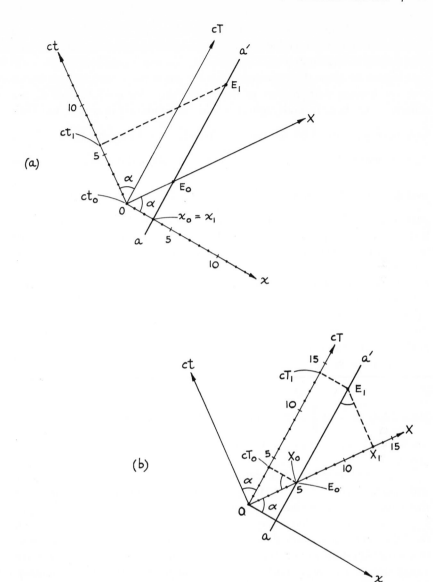

Figure 4. Significance of α in a Brehme diagram.

ground observer would record a nonproper-time interval. To measure a proper-time interval only one clock is needed. To measure a nonproper-time interval two clocks are necessary, stationary with respect to each other: one at the point at which the start of the interval occurs and one at the point at which the interval ends.

Figure 4a gives the coordinates of the two events, E_0 and E_1, as seen by a rocket ship observer. Here $x_0 = 3$ and $ct_0 = 0$, obtained by dropping perpendiculars from E_0 to the x and ct axes, respectively. Similarly $x_1 = 3$

and $ct_1 = 6$. If the units are light-microseconds for distance, this gives a proper-time of 6 microseconds between the birth and death of the particle, both events occurring at $x = 3$.

Figure 4*b* gives the coordinates for the same two events as seen by an observer moving with respect to the rocket ship, for now X_0 and X_1 are different. Ordinarily both figures would be combined into one, but they have been separated here for clarity. From the small triangle $X_0 = \dfrac{x_0}{\cos \alpha}$ so $X_0 = 5$, while $cT_0 = x_0 \tan \alpha = 3\left(\dfrac{0.8}{0.6}\right) = 4$. Also, directly from the large triangle, one finds $\sin \alpha = \dfrac{X_1 - X_0}{cT_1 - cT_0} = \dfrac{v}{c}$. When the world-line of the particle moves from a to a' the value of X increases as T increases. From this it is seen that the particle (and also the rocket observer) is moving toward more positive X relative to the earth observer with velocity $c \sin \alpha$. Or, what is the same thing, the earth is moving toward more negative x relative to the rocket with this speed. The significance of the angular shift, α, in Figure 4 between the x and X axes or between the ct and cT axes is this: $c \sin \alpha$ gives the relative velocity between the two observers. This is quite different from the case of Figure 3*c*, where α represented just a rotation through a fixed angle between the two observers.

The value of $X_1 - X_0$, from the large triangle of Figure 4*b*, is

$$X_1 - X_0 = (ct_1 - ct_0) \tan \alpha.$$

Here this is $(6 - 0)\dfrac{4}{3} = 8$. Since $X_0 = 5$, the value of X_1 is 13. Similarly, the value of $cT_1 - cT_0$ is, from the same triangle, $\dfrac{ct_1 - ct_0}{\cos \alpha}$ or $\dfrac{6 - 0}{0.6} = 10$, giving $cT_1 = 14$.

A world-line that is a straight line represents an object that is moving with constant velocity: comparing different events on the world-line shows that equal intervals of time correspond to equal intervals of distance. If the slope of a world-line changes at a point from one constant value to another, then the object has suddenly altered its velocity from one constant value to another constant value. If a world-line is curved rather than straight, the object does not have a constant velocity but is accelerating continuously. If a world-line ends, the object has disappeared. If a world-line becomes perpendicular to a space axis, then the object has come to rest for the observer corresponding to that axis.

5. THE LOEDEL DIAGRAM

The Brehme diagram of Figure 5*a* may be easily altered to yield the Loedel diagram of Figure 5*b*. Start from E and let the line which, in the Brehme diagram, is perpendicular to the x axis terminate, instead, at its intersection

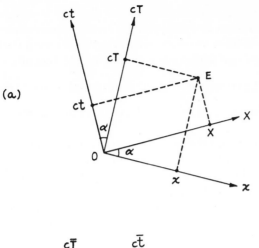

(a)

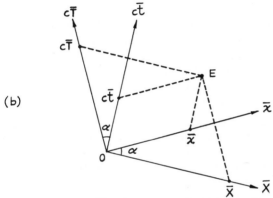

(b)

Figure 5. Conversion of the Brehme diagram to the Loedel diagram.

with the X axis. Designate the termination $\bar{x}$. Similarly, the line from E perpendicular to the X axis is extended to intersect the x axis, the termination being labeled $\bar{X}$. By the same means the coordinates $c\bar{t}$ and $c\bar{T}$ are obtained. The $(\bar{x}, c\bar{t})$ system now has an acute angle, while the $(\bar{X}, c\bar{T})$ system has an obtuse angle. A coordinate, say $\bar{x}$, may be obtained by drawing a line from E parallel to the $c\bar{t}$ axis until it intersects the $\bar{x}$ axis. What enters now is not a perpendicular to an axis but a parallel to the mating axis. ($\bar{x}$ may also be obtained by drawing a line perpendicular to the $\bar{X}$ axis but terminating on the $\bar{x}$ axis.) Of course, if the axes were orthogonal, a perpendicular to an axis would be identical with the parallel to the mating axis. For the non-orthogonal axes here, however, it is seen that $x = \bar{x} \cos \alpha$, $ct = c\bar{t} \cos \alpha$, $X = \bar{X} \cos \alpha$, $cT = c\bar{T} \cos \alpha$. Since $c^2t^2 - x^2 = c^2T^2 - X^2$ then, also,

$$c^2\bar{t}^2 - \bar{x}^2 = c^2\bar{T}^2 - \bar{X}^2.$$

The interval is, thus, an invariant in the Loedel diagram; the utility of the diagram rests entirely on this fact.

The obtuse $(\bar{X}, c\bar{T})$ system applies to an observer moving toward negative $\bar{x}$, along the common $\bar{X}$, $\bar{x}$ axes, relative to the observer whose system is the acute one $(\bar{x}, c\bar{t})$. This is just the reverse of the condition in the Brehme diagram. It is also seen that if the unit length along the axes of the Loedel diagram is larger by the factor $\dfrac{1}{\cos \alpha}$ than the unit length in the Brehme diagram, then the coordinates of an event will have the same values in the two diagrams.

The Brehme diagram and the Loedel diagram are quite similar to each other. In this book we will chiefly employ the Loedel diagram. In the Loedel diagram the world-line of a particle which is resting at the origin of the $(\bar{X}, c\bar{T})$ observer lies along the $c\bar{T}$ axis; the time intervals for this observer may then be read directly at a given point of the world-line. In the Brehme diagram, on the other hand, the world-line of a particle which is at rest at the origin of the (x, ct) observer lies along the cT axis; the time intervals for the (x, ct) observer must be obtained by dropping perpendiculars from the appropriate points of the world-line to the ct axis. Thus, additional auxiliary lines are required in this diagram compared to the Loedel diagram. Moreover, it is somewhat confusing to have the world-line on one time axis but to have its measure on the other time axis.

In a later chapter we will discuss the distinction between contravariant and covariant vectors. The Loedel diagram is actually the space-time diagram for a contravariant vector while the Brehme diagram is the representation of a covariant vector. Since the ordinary three-dimensional space vector is contravariant, by usual definition, it is also more appropriate to employ the contravariant Loedel diagram for ordinary space-time. The system we have adopted here of designating a contravariant vector and its components by a bar above the letter is in keeping with the usual practice of employing superscripts for contravariant components and subscripts for covariant components. The usual practice is awkward when it becomes necessary to raise a contravariant component to a power higher than unity. By using the bar above the letter to imply the superscript, while keeping the symbol actually as a subscript, this difficulty is eliminated. *When there is no danger of confusion we will make the bar over the symbol implicit, for simplictiy.*

6. THE COMPLEX ROTATION DIAGRAM

The most straightforward attempt at a geometric interpretation of the invariance of the interval, and one dating from the earliest days of relativity, is obtained by introducing the variable $\tau = ict$, where $i = \sqrt{-1}$. Then $s = \sqrt{c^2 t^2 - (x^2 + y^2 + z^2)}$ becomes

$$s = i\sqrt{x^2 + y^2 + z^2 + \tau^2}.$$

The interval is related by a constant, i, to the radius vector

$$r = \sqrt{x^2 + y^2 + z^2 + \tau^2}$$

in the 4-dimensional space x, y, z, τ. τ is the imaginary fourth dimension which was so intriguing in the popular expositions of relativity during the first few decades of this century.

Two observers moving relative to each other with constant velocity, v, will assign, as we have seen, the same value to the interval between the two events. Let the relative motion take place along the common x and x' axes with the y and z coordinates the same as the y' and z' coordinates, respectively. Then, if the two observers have a common time origin and a common space origin, the invariance of the interval is equivalent to a rotation of the axes in the (complex) x, τ plane through the angle ϕ. In Figure 6a the coordinates of the event E for one observer, employing orthogonal axes, are (x, τ); for the second observer the coordinates are (x', τ'), also using orthogonal axes. The interval between O and E is given by i times the length of the radius OE, which is the same for both observers.

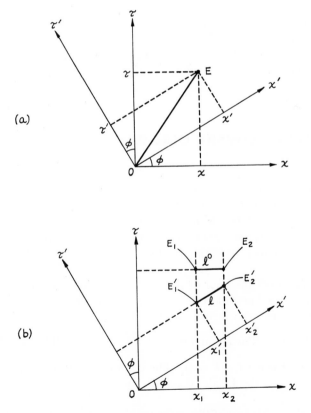

Figure 6. The complex rotation diagram.

Difficulty in the use of the complex rotation diagram stems from the fact that the angle ϕ is not real but is imaginary. To see this one need only consider a point on the τ' axis with coordinates $-x$ and τ for Σ, the unprimed observer. Then $\tan \phi = \dfrac{-x}{\tau} = i\dfrac{v}{c}$ where v is the speed of Σ, the (x, τ) system, toward more positive x' of Σ', the (x', τ') observer. But $\tan(i\delta) = i \tanh \delta$. Thus ϕ is a pure imaginary: $\phi = i\delta = i \tanh^{-1}\left(\dfrac{v}{c}\right)$.

In Figure 6b we consider a rod, stationary for the (x, τ) observer. The two dotted vertical lines are the world-lines of the ends of the rod; the length of the rod, $x_2 - x_1 = l^0$, is determined by this observer at some specific instant, for example the instant common for events E_1 and E_2. The second system or observer, (x', τ'), must "see" the same world-lines for the ends of the rod. These will not be perpendicular to the x' axis, since the rod moves with respect to this observer. When the (x', τ') observer measures the rod at some specific instant, say at E_1' and E_2', he obtains $x_2' - x_1' = l$. From the diagram it would appear that $l^0 = l \cos \phi$ (l^0 seems less than l). But ϕ is imaginary; so, with $\phi = i\delta$, $\cos \phi = \frac{1}{2}(\varepsilon^{i\phi} + \varepsilon^{-i\phi}) = \frac{1}{2}(\varepsilon^{-\delta} + \varepsilon^{\delta}) > 1$. Thus $l^0 > l$, despite appearances.

Consequently, caution is required in the interpretation of the complex rotation diagram. Much use has been made in the past of this complex 4-dimensional space with three real axes and one imaginary axis but it seems destined to be abandoned because of this important shortcoming, among others.

7. THE MINKOWSKI DIAGRAM

The Minkowski diagram also dates from the earliest days of relativity. It is simpler than the complex rotation diagram (which was also introduced by Minkowski) in that only real quantities enter into it; but it is more complicated in that one set of axes is nonorthogonal and requires a different scale than the other, orthogonal, set of axes. In Problem 12, Chapter 2, we suggest a method for the derivation of this diagram. Here we will merely summarize some results.

Figure 7a shows the axes of the Minkowski diagram. (x, ct) are the orthogonal axes for one observer; (x', ct') are the nonorthogonal axes for the second observer, who is moving toward more positive x relative to the first with velocity v. The angle δ is given by $\tan \delta = \dfrac{v}{c}$. The two observers have $x = x' = 0$ when $t = t' = 0$. The coordinates in the (x', ct') system are measured, as in the Loedel diagram, by drawing parallel lines to the mating axis.

If the scales on all axes of Figure 7a are identical we obtain the following

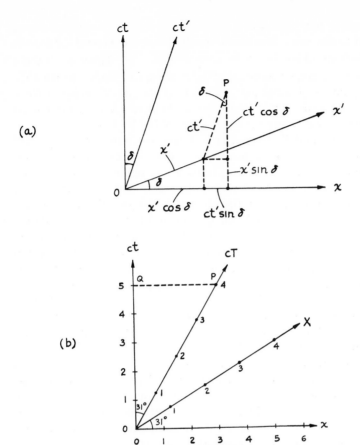

Figure 7. The Minkowski diagram.

equations between the coordinates of an event P:

$$x = x' \cos \delta + ct' \sin \delta,$$
$$ct = x' \sin \delta + ct' \cos \delta.$$

Then $s^2 = c^2t^2 - x^2 = (\cos^2 \delta - \sin^2 \delta)(c^2t'^2 - x'^2) = \left(\dfrac{1 - \beta^2}{1 + \beta^2}\right) s'^2$, where $\beta = \dfrac{v}{c}$. Consequently, if the scales are the same for the two observers a given event, P, will yield different intervals with respect to the event O for the two observers. To make the intervals equal it is necessary to use a scale factor such that $ct' = \sqrt{\dfrac{1 + \beta^2}{1 - \beta^2}}\, cT$ and $x' = \sqrt{\dfrac{1 + \beta^2}{1 - \beta^2}}\, X$. The units along the (X, cT) axes must be spaced farther apart than the units along the (x, ct) axes so that the measure of a distance along X, say, will be smaller than along x'.

As an example let $\beta = 0.6$. Then the scale factor is $\sqrt{\dfrac{1 + 0.36}{1 - 0.36}} = 1.46$

and the angle $\delta = \tan^{-1} 0.6 = 31°$. In Figure 7*b* the axes have been drawn to correspond to this case. It is readily verified that the interval OP has the same value for both observers: $\sqrt{5^2 - 3^2} = \sqrt{4^2 - 0^2}$. However, it is not correct to assume from the diagram that $OQ = OP \cos 31°$ since $5 \neq 4(0.857)$. The correct result is obtained in (x, ct) only if the (X, cT) value of OP is multiplied by the scale factor 1.46. For a check in (X, cT), the correct result is obtained by dividing the (x, ct) value of OQ by 1.46.

In the Loedel and Brehme diagrams the two observers are treated symmetrically. Neither is given preference over the other; neither's space-time diagram can be used alone but, to have any significance whatsoever, requires the presence of the axes for both observers. Both observers employ an identical scale for all axes. In the Minkowski diagram the observers are treated asymmetrically. Not only do they have different scales; only the observer with orthogonal axes has a scale which is independent of velocity. The extension to 4-dimensional space-time is particularly simple for this observer: all his axes are not only orthogonal but also employ the same scale. In applying the Minkowski diagram to general relativity it is convenient to employ only this observer with the orthogonal axes of identical scale, no reference being made to the other observer. While this is uniquely possible only to the Minkowski diagram, it must be admitted that there is no physical distinction between the two observers.

The orthogonal axes with identical scale can, nevertheless, also be employed in the Loedel and Brehme diagrams. Here, and also in the case of the Minkowski diagram, such axes may be considered to represent two Galilean observers who move with infinitesimal speed relative to one another. A pair of observers, rather than only one observer, constitutes the reference system and takes the place of the classical ether.

The requirement of a scale factor between the two observers in the Minkowski diagram is a complication, though not one which is serious. This method of Cartesian coordinate measurement is not the one, however, which is generally employed in connection with the Minkowski diagram. Minkowski, himself, introduced a method of measurement employing a family of hyperbolas. Though this method is convenient for the comparison of intervals, it is a cumbersome one for obtaining coordinates. Because this technique is so different from the usual, Cartesian, method of measurement, the hyperbolas have undoubtedly limited the acceptance of this diagram for introductory treatments.

BIBLIOGRAPHY

Amar, H.: New Geometric Representation of the Lorentz Transformation. Amer. J. Phys. *23:* 487, Nov., 1955.

Brehme, R. W.: A Geometric Representation of Galilean and Lorentz Transformations. Amer. J. Phys. *30:* 489, July, 1962.

Brehme, R. W.: Geometric Representations of the Lorentz Transformation. Amer. J. Phys. *32:* 233, March, 1964.

Loedel, E.: Aberración y Relatividad. Anales de la Sociedad Científica Argentina *145:* 3, Jan., 1948.

Loedel, E.: Geometric Representation of the Lorentz Transformation. Amer. J. Phys. *25:* 327, May, 1957.

Chapter 3 TIME

I. TIME DILATION

The chief difficulty in reconciling the ideas of relativity with common sense stems from our ingrained ideas about the nature of time. This chapter is devoted to exploring a few of these differences between the usual way and the relativistic way of looking at time. They all depend on the fact that the velocity of light does not change for a moving observer.

Imagine an experiment being performed in a rocket ship, completely enclosed by windows, moving at a constant speed v with respect to the earth. In Figure 8 a sonar set has been modified so that it may transmit sound pulses in air rather than in water. A short air-sonar pulse, consisting of a compact group of sound waves in air, travels across the width of the ship L and is reflected back to the transmitter. The velocity of the sonar pulse, determined by the pressure, composition, and temperature of the air, is $c_s = 0.2$ miles/second. The proper-time interval between emission and reception at the sonar set is

$$\Delta t^0 = \frac{L}{c_s} + \frac{L}{c_s} = \frac{2L}{c_s}.$$

Figure 8a shows the two paths slightly displaced from each other, for clarity, although they actually coincide.

The same two events, transmission and reception, are shown in Figure 8b as noted by two observers fixed in space with reference to the earth. The ship is moving with respect to these observers so the two events occur at different places for them, giving them a nonproper-time interval. The velocity of the sonar pulse with respect to these observers is determined by the Pythagorean theorem to be $c_R = \sqrt{c_s^2 + v^2}$. The total path traversed is, similarly, given by $L_R = 2\sqrt{L^2 + \left(\frac{v\,\Delta t}{2}\right)^2} = \sqrt{4L^2 + (v\,\Delta t)^2}$. Here $\frac{1}{2}\Delta t$ is the time required for the pulse to travel from transmitter to reflector and also from reflector to receiver, so Δt is the nonproper-time interval.

SONAR PULSE

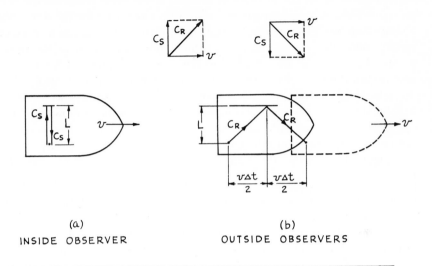

(a)

INSIDE OBSERVER

(b)

OUTSIDE OBSERVERS

RADAR PULSE

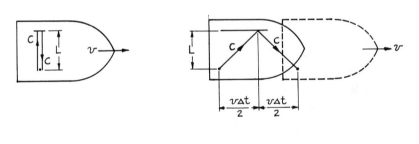

(c)

INSIDE OBSERVER

(d)

OUTSIDE OBSERVERS

Figure 8. Time measurements using either sonar or radar.

Then $\Delta t = \dfrac{L_R}{c_R} = \dfrac{\sqrt{4L^2 + (v\,\Delta t)^2}}{\sqrt{c_s^2 + v^2}}$ and $(c_s^2 + v^2)(\Delta t)^2 = 4L^2 + v^2(\Delta t)^2$

giving

$$\Delta t = \frac{2L}{c_s}.$$

In this case, therefore, the two earth-stationary observers measure a nonproper-time interval which is identical with that obtained inside the ship. The outside observers will say that the pulse traveled a longer distance than merely twice the width of the ship. The pulse velocity increased in proportion, however, so the total elapsed time measurement is the same as that obtained by the single observer inside the ship.

So far this has been an exercise in common sense. The results, however, depend critically on the increase in velocity of the sonar pulse for the two observers outside. Suppose we now substitute a radar set for the sonar set. Radar waves are electromagnetic and travel through vacuum at a speed of $c = 186,000$ miles/second, almost a million times the speed of the sonar waves. In the air of the rocket ship the speed is diminished by a slight amount but this may be ignored. We are now no longer free to assume that the velocity of the radar pulse will be greater for the outside observers than it is for the inside observer. All experiments, in fact, have shown just the opposite—the velocity is the same for all observers. Consequently, it should not be too surprising that different results are obtained here.

Figure 8c shows that the inside observer now measures $\Delta t^0 = \dfrac{2L}{c}$ for the proper-time interval between transmission and reception. For the outside observers, Figure 8d now gives an increased total path between the two events but not an increased velocity. Consequently, the elapsed nonproper-time measurement between the two events must be larger than in the case of the proper-time measurement. Here c is the resultant velocity of the pulse. Also, $\sqrt{4L^2 + (v\,\Delta t)^2}$ is, as before, the total distance traversed by the pulse. Then

$$\Delta t = L_R/c = \frac{1}{c}\sqrt{4L^2 + (v\,\Delta t)^2}, \quad \text{or} \quad \Delta t = (2L/c)/\sqrt{1 - (v/c)^2}.$$

If, as is usual in relativistic formulas, we set $\beta = \dfrac{v}{c}$, then

$$\Delta t = \frac{\Delta t^0}{\sqrt{1 - \beta^2}}.$$

If we are going to demand that a velocity be the same for any two Galilean observers, then it follows of necessity that the two observers will measure different time intervals between two given events. Only if the two velocities differ for the Galilean observers can the time intervals be the same. For sonar waves the velocities differ for the inside observer and the outside observers; the time intervals are then the same. For radar waves the velocities are the same for the inside observer and the outside observers; the time intervals are then different.

Let us return to the Brehme diagram in Fig. 4, p. 19. This summarized the measurements for the birth and death of a radioactive particle in a rocket ship moving with a velocity $0.8c$ with respect to the earth. Figure 9 presents the same information in graphic form. It will be noticed that the duration of the time interval is different for the two observers: for the one on the ship $ct_1 - ct_0 = 6$ light-microseconds while for the two on earth $cT_1 - cT_0 = 10$ light-microseconds. The time interval $\Delta t^0 = t_1 - t_0 = 6$ microseconds is a proper-time interval occurring at the fixed position 3 light-microseconds (i.e., 900 meters) from the origin of the x axis in the rocket ship. The time interval on earth, ΔT, is a nonproper-time interval, equal here to 10 microseconds. From $\Delta t^0 = \Delta T\sqrt{1 - \beta^2}$ we have a value for Δt^0 of

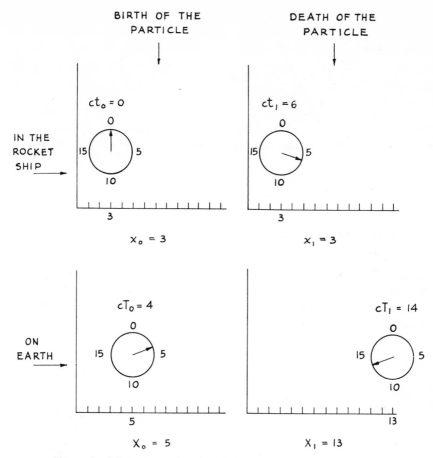

Figure 9. Measurements in two systems moving relative to each other.

$10^{-5}\sqrt{1 - (0.8)^2}$. The diagram of Figure 4, therefore, gives the same results for the comparison of the light intervals as does Figure 9 and the imagined experiment just above.

This equation, of course, is not to be interpreted to mean that a time interval in the rocket ship is always less than the corresponding time interval on earth. Rather, the proper-time will always be less than the nonproper-time interval. If the two events defining the interval occurred at one spot on earth, rather than at one spot in the rocket ship, then $\Delta T^0 = T_2 - T_1$ while $\Delta t = t_2 - t_1$. Figure 10 shows the relation, by means of a Loedel space-time diagram (the bars are implicit), between two events occurring at one place on the rocket, as in the Brehme diagram of Figure 4. Figure 11 uses the space-time diagram for two events occurring at one place on earth. We repeat here our earlier statement that when we use the term space-time diagram without modification we are referring to the Loedel diagram.

The name time dilation is given to the phenomenon that makes a nonproper-time interval larger than a proper-time interval. Because β is

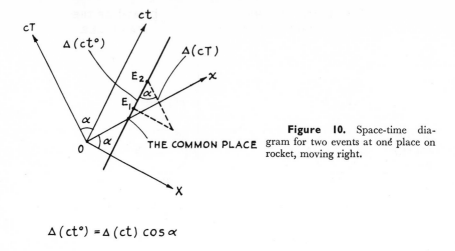

Figure 10. Space-time diagram for two events at one place on rocket, moving right.

$$\Delta(ct^\circ) = \Delta(ct) \cos \alpha$$

usually so much less than unity it is an effect not ordinarily observed. Nevertheless, it is a very real effect and its existence has been verified in the laboratory. An experiment giving such a verification is described in a later chapter.

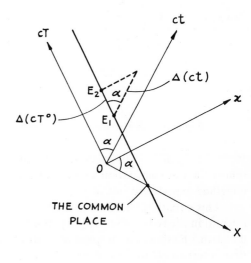

Figure 11. Space-time diagram for two events at one place on earth, moving left.

$$\Delta(ct^\circ) = \Delta(ct) \cos \alpha$$

2. SIMULTANEOUS EVENTS

The world-line of a light beam going toward $+x$ has been drawn in Figure 12 and on it an event E_1 has been selected. O may represent the place and time where the beam originated while E_1 represents its reception at some distant

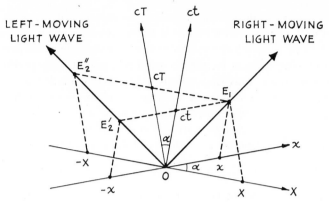

Figure 12. Simultaneous events; resolution of the paradox of the light spheres.

place to the right at a later time. The coordinates of E_1 are (x, ct) for an observer moving toward a more positive coordinate with velocity v relative to another observer. For the latter observer the coordinates are (X, cT). Similarly, a second world-line has been drawn for a beam going toward $-x$. On this world-line the event E_2' represents the reception of the left-going beam at some point at some time. E_2' occurs simultaneously with E_1 for the (x, ct) observer; for this observer the place where E_2' occurs is as far to the left of the origin as E_1 is to the right of the origin. For the (X, cT) observer, however, E_2' occurs first and it occurs nearer to the origin. To avoid confusion, this time coordinate has not been drawn on the diagram.

The case of E_1 and E_2'' is similar: E_1 and E_2'' are simultaneous for the (X, cT) observer but not for the (x, ct) observer. For the latter, E_1 occurs first.

Consequently, it is possible to say only that two events are simultaneous for a certain observer. For an observer moving relative to the first the two events are not simultaneous. Simultaneity is no longer an absolute quantity but is relative to the observer. What is the physical meaning of such noncommon sense behavior?

We have actually been discussing the case of the paradox of the light spheres, restricting ourselves to events along the direction of relative motion of the two observers; the diagram which explains the relative nature of simultaneous events serves, as well, to resolve the paradox of the light spheres. At O the light pulse was emitted; at some later time, t, the instruments of the (x, ct) observer record simultaneous reception of the wave at equal distances to the left and to the right of the transmitter, the wave traveling with velocity c. The (X, cT) observer, however, also has the wave moving relative to him with velocity c. Because he is moving toward $-x$ relative to the other observer, the event E_2' to the left occurs, for him, at a closer distance, and sooner, than the event E_1. The (X, cT) observer would say that the event E_2'' was the proper one to compare with E_1: at T the instruments of the

(X, cT) observer would record simultaneous reception of the wave at equal distances to the left and to the right of the transmitter, the wave going with velocity c. The (x, ct) observer, however, will record the event produced by the right-moving wave as having occurred first and at a closer distance.

The conclusion that simultaneity is a relative matter is a necessary consequence of the fact that the velocity of light is the same for different Galilean observers. Two events that occur simultaneously for one observer do not occur simultaneously for another observer, moving at constant speed relative to the first, because the velocity of light is the same for both. The effect is large in Figure 12, where $\dfrac{v}{c} = 0.33$; when the relative velocity of the two observers is much less, however, the two sets of axes practically coincide and the effect becomes so small it is not ordinarily noticed. The paradox of the light spheres is resolved by recognizing that what one observer considers as two simultaneous events, the reception of the right- and left-moving waves, are not simultaneous for the second observer. The measured interval for each observer is zero. But the two observers measure completely different events. Consequently, it is possible for each to contradict the other, yet for each to be correct.

3. SYNCHRONIZATION OF CLOCKS

Suppose three observers (A, B, C), resting at three different places in a rocket ship, synchronize their clocks. Thus, in the space-time diagram of Figure 13, the events A_1, B_1, and C_1 each have $ct_1 = 0$ with $x_{A_1} = -l$, $x_{B_1} = 0$, $x_{C_1} = +l$. This is the viewpoint of A, B, and C, synchronization being made by them. (x, ct) is the coordinate system for the three rocket ship observers. The synchronization of clocks for A, B, and C takes place at a common time for them; so A_1, B_1, C_1 lie on the x axis, which corresponds to a fixed value of ct.

As time goes by the three observers generate three individual world-lines, each parallel to the ct axis. At some later time, for them, the three observers will be characterized by the events A_2, B_2, C_2.

Now let there be an observer, D, on earth such that the rocket ship moves to the right in real space relative to him with velocity v. D's system is so chosen that D synchronizes his clock with B, the middle man, when D is immediately adjacent to B. Thus $x_{B_1} = ct_{B_1} = 0$ is the same event as $x_{D_1} = ct_{D_1} = 0$: B and D have synchronized their clocks to start from zero at the instant when B in the rocket ship is infinitesimally close to D. One would normally assume that if B is synchronized with A and C, and B is also synchronized with D, then D must be synchronized with A and C; but this turns out not to be so.

It is seen from Figure 13 that on D's time axis at the instant of synchronization the three rocket clocks have the following readings: $-\Delta$, 0, Δ

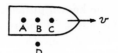

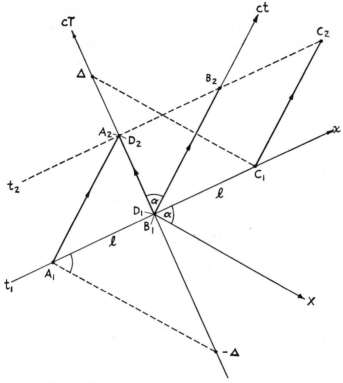

Figure 13. Synchronization (rocket's viewpoint).

where $\Delta = \Delta(cT)$. In other words, clocks A and C on the rocket ship are not synchronized with clock D on earth. The difference in synchronization, Δ, may be obtained from Figure 13:

$$\Delta = l \tan \alpha, \quad \text{or} \quad c(\Delta T) = l\left[\frac{\beta}{\sqrt{1 - \beta^2}}\right], \quad \text{so} \quad \Delta T = \frac{\dfrac{lv}{c^2}}{\sqrt{1 - \beta^2}}.$$

When x on the rocket ship is positive with respect to the origin then the clock there seems to have its zero moved ahead with respect to the clock at the origin on earth, as regarded by the latter. When x is negative the clock there seems to have its zero moved backward, as measured from $X = 0$.

This behavior also arises from the fact that the velocity of light is the same for B and D. B can synchronize himself with D when they are contiguous. B can also then synchronize A and C with himself by sending radio pulses to each, the same known distance away, and making allowances for the travel times of the pulses. B will record the pulses as reaching A and C simultaneously, but D will not. Consequently, A and C will not be synchronized for D.

It is instructive to follow the world-line of D until D and A meet. The events A_2, B_2, C_2, D_2 are indicated for this occurrence on the space-time diagram of Figure 13. The table below gives the coordinates from the viewpoint of A and B, and also of D, as calculated from the geometry of Figure 13.

	A	B	D
t_1	0	0	0
t_2	$\dfrac{l}{v}$	$\dfrac{l}{v}$	$\dfrac{l}{v}$
T_1	$-\dfrac{lv}{c^2\sqrt{1-\beta^2}}$	0	0
T_2	$\dfrac{l}{v}\sqrt{1-\beta^2}$	$\dfrac{l}{v\sqrt{1-\beta^2}}$	$\dfrac{l}{v}\sqrt{1-\beta^2}$

In Figure 14 the space-time diagram has been made from the viewpoint of D, who does not share the view of the rocket observers concerning the conditions for initial synchronization. D agrees with the world-lines of

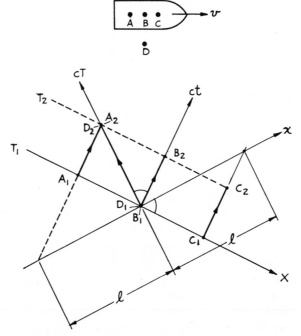

Figure 14. Synchronization (D's viewpoint).

Figure 13; but he does not agree that A_1, B_1, C_1 on the world-lines of Figure 13 were simultaneous. For D the proper way to synchronize those three observers is shown in Figure 14. The following table gives the coordinates for this case, D's viewpoint:

	A	B	D
T_1	0	0	0
T_2	$\dfrac{l}{v}\sqrt{1-\beta^2}$	$\dfrac{l}{v}\sqrt{1-\beta^2}$	$\dfrac{l}{v}\sqrt{1-\beta^2}$
t_1	$\dfrac{lv}{c^2}$ ✓	0	0
t_2	$\dfrac{l}{v}$ ✓✓	$\dfrac{l}{v}(1-\beta^2)$	$\dfrac{l}{v}$

Suppose we compare the two single-checked items in the two tables: $t_1(A) = 0$ for A and $t_1(A) = \dfrac{lv}{c^2}$ for D. The former gives A's time by his own clock, the latter gives D's estimate of A's time by A's clock; both are for the condition when D is at B, so that D is separated from A. The two values are different. As time goes by, D finally meets A. The double-checked items in the two tables show that then $t_2(A) = \dfrac{l}{v}$ for A's time by his own clock and $t_2(A) = \dfrac{l}{v}$ for A's time by D's estimate. When the two are together the estimate agrees with the clock. Similarly, when comparing B and D, agreement would be obtained at the start but not at the finish.

Thus, the following situation exists—when A and D are separated spatially, then A's own time does not agree with D's estimate of A's time; further, as time goes by, time intervals for A and D run at different rates; but whenever A and D meet, the estimate D has of A's time agrees with A's actual value!

4. THE DOPPLER EFFECT

So far we have considered proper-time intervals (measured at one place) and nonproper-time intervals (measured, simultaneously for them, by two observers at rest with respect to each other but at two different places). Now we consider a third type of time measurement, using one clock not actually at the place where either event occurred. Merely to designate this type of measurement we will call it an apparent-time interval.

A traveler on a rocket ship has a radio transmitter, as does an observer on earth. The ship moves with constant velocity v to the right in real space, first approaching the earth observer and then receding from him. At some moment the rocket ship observer starts broadcasting the ticks of his clock,

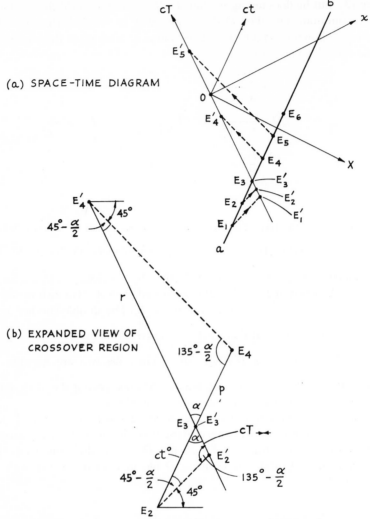

(a) SPACE-TIME DIAGRAM

(b) EXPANDED VIEW OF CROSSOVER REGION

Figure 15. The communicating travellers; the Doppler effect.

identifying them in sequence 1, 2, 3, and so on. The line *ab* in Figure 15*a* represents the world-line of the rocket ship: on it all points have the same value of *x*, i.e., the transmitter is stationary at some point with respect to the origin inside the rocket ship. The points E_1, E_2, etc., designate the transmitted ticks of the clock. E_1 and E_2 occurred with $X < 0$: the rocket ship was to the left of the earth observer and approaching him. E_3 occurred when the transmitter was immediately adjacent to the earth observer; E_4 and E_5 took place after the rocket ship had passed him and was moving away.

From each of the events E_1 through E_5 a world-line is drawn for the radio pulse leaving the transmitter. Each pulse travels with the speed of light so its world-line is a straight line, at 45° for the right-going pulse and at

135° for the left-going pulse with respect to the horizontal toward the right. From E_1 through E_5 the world-lines E_1-E_1', E_2-E_2', etc., have been drawn as dotted lines, all terminating at the position $X = 0$ where the earth receiver is located. The events E_1', E_2', etc., designate the received ticks of the clock.

From this figure it is seen that the time interval between E_1' and E_2' is equal to that between E_2' and E_3' (on the cT axis); but this interval is less than the corresponding time interval between E_1 and E_2, etc. (on the ct axis, or on ab). After the transmitter and receiver have passed each other the received time intervals E_3'-E_4' and E_4'-E_5', though equal in magnitude to each other, do not equal the previous value. Now the received time intervals are larger than the transmitted time intervals. An observer at the receiver would say, first, that the transmitter clock was going too quickly and the received time intervals were too short; then he would say the transmitter clock had changed its rate and was going too slowly, with the received time intervals too long. The two clocks, one at the transmitter and one at the receiver, do not maintain the same relative values when they are approaching as when they are receding. It is clear that the physical basis for this effect comes from the time it takes the pulses to go from the transmitter to the receiver. When approaching, a later pulse has a smaller distance to go than an earlier one; when receding, a later pulse must go farther than a previous one.

What happens if, instead of the rocket observer broadcasting the ticks of the rocket clock, the observer on earth starts broadcasting the ticks of the earth clock to the rocket ship as the two are approaching each other? This could be shown on Figure 15 by drawing a world-line parallel to the cT axis, and placing several equally spaced events e_1, e_2, . . . , along it. Drawing the radio pulse world-lines from these points to the ct axis in the space-time diagram (where $x = 0$) would give the recorded events e_1', e_2', ... Where, previously, the earth observer said the rocket clock intervals were too short, now the rocket clock observer would say the earth clock intervals were too short. They would not agree with each other: each would say, when approaching, that the other was broadcasting too quickly. Similarly, after they pass each other and are receding, the rocket observer would say the earth clock was going too slowly and the intervals between the ticks were too long. The results are, consequently, symmetrical between the two.

The effect described here is actually the Doppler effect, usually described in terms of the apparent frequency of a continuous received wave. It is a common sense effect and takes place also with sound waves. The relative lengthening or contraction of the time intervals predicted by relativity is different from the values predicted by Galilean considerations, however, and will now be calculated from Figure 15b, an expanded view of the cross-over region.

In the lower triangle the proper-time interval measured by the rocket traveler between the ticks of his watch E_2 and E_3, when receiver and transmitter are approaching each other, is given by the distance between E_2 and

E_3 as ct^0. The apparent-time interval measured by the earth observer between the ticks E_2' and E_3' on his receiver is given by $E_2'E_3' = cT_{\rightarrow\leftarrow}$. The law of sines gives

$$\frac{ct^0}{\sin\left(\dfrac{270° - \alpha}{2}\right)} = \frac{cT_{\rightarrow\leftarrow}}{\sin\left(\dfrac{90° - \alpha}{2}\right)}$$

or

$$cT_{\rightarrow\leftarrow} = ct^0 \, \frac{\sqrt{\frac{1}{2}\{1 - \cos(90° - \alpha)\}}}{\sqrt{\frac{1}{2}\{1 - \cos(270° - \alpha)\}}}.$$

So

$$cT_{\rightarrow\leftarrow} = ct^0 \, \frac{\sqrt{1 - \sin\alpha}}{\sqrt{1 + \sin\alpha}} \quad \text{or} \quad T_{\rightarrow\leftarrow} = t^0\sqrt{\frac{1 - \beta}{1 + \beta}}.$$

The apparent-frequency of the approaching received signals, $f_{\rightarrow\leftarrow}$, is related to the proper-frequency of the transmitted signals, f^0, by $\dfrac{f_{\rightarrow\leftarrow}}{f^0} = \dfrac{t^0}{T_{\rightarrow\leftarrow}}$. So

$$f_{\rightarrow\leftarrow} = f^0\sqrt{\frac{1 + \beta}{1 - \beta}}.$$

When the travelers are approaching each other, the received apparent-frequency is greater than the transmitted proper-frequency.

Similarly, in the upper triangle when the receiver and transmitter are receding from each other, the proper-time interval $ct^0 = p$, while the apparent-time received interval $cT_{\leftarrow\rightarrow} = r$. Figure 15b then gives

$$\frac{p}{\sin\left(\dfrac{90° - \alpha}{2}\right)} = \frac{r}{\sin\left(\dfrac{270° - \alpha}{2}\right)}$$

or

$$r = p \, \frac{\sqrt{\frac{1}{2}\{1 - \cos(270° - \alpha)\}}}{\sqrt{\frac{1}{2}\{1 - \cos(90° - \alpha)\}}} = p\sqrt{\frac{1 + \beta}{1 - \beta}}.$$

So

$$T_{\leftarrow\rightarrow} = t^0\sqrt{\frac{1 + \beta}{1 - \beta}}.$$

The apparent-frequency of the receding signals, $f_{\leftarrow\rightarrow}$, is given by

$$f_{\leftarrow\rightarrow} = f^0\sqrt{\frac{1 - \beta}{1 + \beta}}.$$

When the travelers are receding from each other, the received apparent-frequency is less than the transmitted proper-frequency.

It is interesting to compare the Doppler effect for light with that for sound, where there is a medium and the principle of relativity is not obeyed. For the case of sound waves the Doppler formula for the frequency depends on (1) the velocity of the transmitter, v_t, relative to the ground (stationary air); (2) the velocity of the receiver, v_r, relative to the ground; (3) the velocity, w, of any wind (actual velocity of air relative to hypothetical stationary air, or to the ground); and (4) the velocity of sound, c_s, relative to stationary air. For the case of transmitter and receiver approaching each other with a wind blowing from transmitter to receiver, e.g., the formula is

$$f_{\to\leftarrow} = f^0 \left[\frac{c_s + w + v_r}{c_s + w - v_t} \right].$$

For $f_{\leftarrow\to}$ the signs before v_r and v_t become reversed; if the wind blows the other way the sign before w becomes negative. The case of sound is seen to be much more complicated than the relativistic case.

For $v_r = w = 0$, when $\dfrac{v_t}{c_s} \ll 1$

$$f_{\to\leftarrow} = \left[\frac{1}{1 - \dfrac{v_t}{c_s}} \right] f^0 \approx \left[1 + \left(\frac{v_t}{c_s} \right) + \left(\frac{v_t}{c_s} \right)^2 \right] f^0.$$

Similarly, for $v_t = w = 0$, then

$$f_{\to\leftarrow} = \left[1 + \left(\frac{v_r}{c_s} \right) \right] f^0.$$

The relativistic case for $\dfrac{v}{c} \ll 1$ gives

$$f_{\to\leftarrow} \approx \left[1 + \left(\frac{v}{c} \right) + \frac{1}{2} \left(\frac{v}{c} \right)^2 \right].$$

To the second order in $\dfrac{v}{c}$ this is seen to be just midway between the two cases for sound above.

Another difference exists between the relativistic and nonrelativistic cases. For sound the only component of either the transmitter or the receiver velocity which is pertinent is that along the line connecting transmitter and receiver. There is no transverse Doppler effect caused by a transverse component of relative motion. But, relativistically, there is such an effect.

Consider the situation of Figure 16 which shows a transmitter sending a light beam to a receiver that is moving with velocity v relative to the source. A pulse just leaving T when the receiver is at R_1 in Figure 16a arrives at the receiver when the latter is at R_2. This depicts the view of the process from the transmitter reference frame, for the special case when $\theta_T = 90°$. Figure 16b shows this process from the receiver reference frame, the pulse leaving the transmitter when it is at T_1 and arriving at the receiver when the transmitter is at T_2. In both cases the separation between receiver and transmitter is a minimum when the pulse is received; in the second case, however, the pulse seems to arrive at an angle θ_R instead of at 90°, as in the first case.

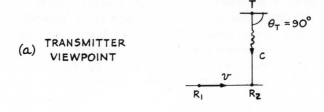

(a) TRANSMITTER VIEWPOINT

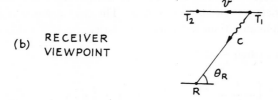

(b) RECEIVER VIEWPOINT

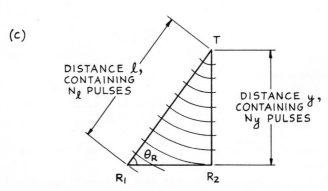

(c)

Figure 16. The transverse Doppler effect.

Suppose the pulse frequency to be f^0 for an observer stationary at R_2 in Figure 16c. During a time t, for him, N_y pulses are received; so $f^0 = \dfrac{N_y}{t}$. But, during the same time t the moving receiver goes from R_1 to R_2 and, in so doing, receives N_l pulses. The receiver frequency is thus

$$f_R = \frac{N_l}{N_y} f^0 = \frac{l}{y} f^0 = \frac{f^0}{\sin \theta_R}.$$

It would seem possible to determine $\sin \theta_R$ directly from Figure 16b: by closing the triangle one seemingly finds

$$\sin \theta_R = \frac{\sqrt{c^2 - v^2}}{c} = \sqrt{1 - \beta^2}.$$

This process is incorrect, however, and it is only a coincidence that the answer obtained happens to be the correct one. If, in Figure 16a, a line is drawn from T to R_1 we again obtain θ_R at R_1 and here one finds

$$\sin \theta_R = \frac{c}{\sqrt{c^2 + v^2}} = \frac{1}{\sqrt{1 + \beta^2}}$$

if this process is employed. In the next chapter we will see that velocities may not be combined relativistically in the usual fashion, either by scalar addition along the same straight line or by vector addition along the lines of a triangle. There, in discussing aberration and the appearance of moving objects we will show that

$$\sin \theta_R = \sqrt{1 - \beta^2}.$$

Taking this on faith until then, we have

$$f_R = \frac{f^0}{\sqrt{1 - \beta^2}}.$$

This is the formula for the transverse Doppler effect. Because of the presence of β^2 rather than β under the radical the transverse Doppler effect is small compared to the longitudinal Doppler effect, which is of first order in β.

When the receiver moves to the right of R_2, say to R_3 (as far from R_2 as R_2 is from R_1), the relativistic relation between f^0 and f_R will remain the same as before, since a change in the sign of v does not affect the value of $\left(\dfrac{v}{c}\right)^2$. This, however, is a result which violates common sense. For finite distances, classically, there would be a decreased (rather than an increased) frequency for the receiver observer R_3 as compared to an observer stationary at R_2 relative to T (i.e., a transmitter observer). The frequency shift at the receiver must change from positive to negative at R_2. Classically, then, the frequency shift for the receiver precisely at R_2 must be zero. Recent experimental results employing the Mössbauer effect have shown that the relativistic prediction is the correct one. It may be tempting to assert that the basic relativistic reason for the difference in frequencies measured by the stationary and moving observers at R_2 is the time dilation for the moving observer, but this is incorrect. The correct result could be obtained by drawing a 3-dimensional space-time diagram similar to the previous 2-dimensional drawing for the communicating travelers.

5. THE PARADOX OF THE TWINS

The famous paradox of the twins, like almost everything else in the theory of special relativity, was first introduced by Einstein himself in his original paper of 1905. Perhaps the most important exception, not introduced by Einstein himself, is the geometric concept of space-time: this was proposed by H. Minkowski in 1908.

Imagine two identical twins on earth: A and B are precisely the same age. Let A remain on earth while B takes a trip into outer space at a constant speed along a straight line. At some point B reverses his direction in a negligible time and then returns to earth along the same path with the same speed. When B returns to earth the twins find that A has aged T years while B has aged $T\sqrt{1 - \beta^2}$ years!

The paradox here is not that their ages are different. In the case of the proper-time intervals versus nonproper-time intervals for Galilean observers the results are symmetrical—a proper-time interval for A is less than the corresponding nonproper-time interval for B, but a proper-time interval for B is less than the corresponding nonproper-time interval for A. The paradox here is that, while their ages differ, the result is not symmetrical. Both A and B agree that B is younger and they also agree by how much he is younger. It is, therefore, possible to determine which twin took the trip. Physically, there is an essential difference between the twins—if an accelerometer with A recorded zero acceleration throughout the entire journey, start to finish, then an accelerometer with B would record an acceleration at some instant. What we are comparing is a Galilean observer with a nonGalilean observer; so the twins are *not* truly identical and it is not correct to compare this case with the one where A is considered to take the journey while B remains at home.

It is possible to eliminate acceleration completely from this problem by introducing a third traveler. This we will do, to remove any doubts about the effects of acceleration on age. The space-time diagram of Figure 17 is an

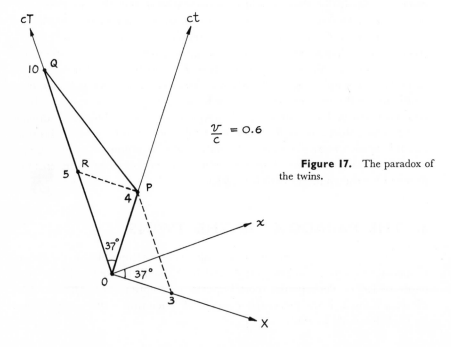

Figure 17. The paradox of the twins.

especially valuable aid in the paradox of the twins. In Figure 17 the (x, ct) axes represent a Galilean observer, moving toward $+X$ relative to twin A on earth. The (X, cT) axes represent twin A, on earth, moving toward $-x$ relative to the (x, ct) observer. For this example we have chosen $\beta = 0.6$, i.e., $\alpha = 37°$ instead of the value $\alpha = 53°$ used in most of the previous diagrams, just to be different. The world-line of the rocket twin, B, is a straight line along the ct axis for the outward journey, representing the sequence of events occurring at $x = 0$. In order to avoid any problems associated with acceleration at the beginning of the journey we assume that twin B had previously reached the steady velocity, v, while approaching the earth. The world-line for twin A is a straight line along the cT axis, representing the sequence of events occurring at a fixed value of X, namely $X = 0$.

Let twin B, continuing on his journey, approach event P. The coordinates of the event P as seen on earth are $X = 3$ light-years and $cT = 5$ light-years (or $T = 5$ years), giving the rocket B the velocity $\dfrac{v}{c} = \dfrac{X}{cT} = \dfrac{3}{5} = 0.6$.

The coordinates of event P as seen on rocket B are $x = 0$ and $ct = 4$ light-years. The proper-time interval on rocket B for the outward trip is 4 years. The nonproper-time interval, on earth, is 5 years for OP. Event P designates the acceleration of the rocket to start it on its homeward journey, represented by the world-line PQ. To avoid any problems associated with acceleration, let us assume that twin B continues at constant velocity on his outward journey. At P, however, a third rocket, C, passes twin B going toward A on earth with constant speed $v = 0.6c$. As C passes B instantaneously, C starts his clock to find the time that elapses until C reaches twin A on earth.

The slope of the world-line of rocket C from event P is determined by the specification that the velocity of C relative to A is $-0.6c$, along the $-X$ direction. As C moves from P to Q, X changes by -3 while cT changes by 5, giving $v = 0.6c$. When rocket C passes A at point Q, both A and C stop their clocks. C continues on his path to avoid any deceleration effect, and communicates his time measurement to A, at his leisure, by radio.

From the graph, A's proper-time interval for the entire journey is OQ: 10 years, while B's proper-time interval for the outward journey is OP: 4 years. C's proper-time interval for the inward journey can be obtained from the magnitude of QR, a nonproper-time interval on earth of $10 - 5 = 5$ years for the inward journey. C's proper-time interval is then $5\sqrt{1 - (0.6)^2}$ or 4 years. The combined proper-time interval for B and C is 8 years.

For an arbitrary choice of v, $t_b{}^0 + t_c{}^0 = t_a{}^0\sqrt{1 - \beta^2}$. The combined proper-time intervals of the two rockets (or the accelerated twin) is less than the proper-time interval of the earth twin. It should be emphasized that this is not a relation between two Galilean observers—it is one among three Galilean observers or, alternatively, between one Galilean and one non-Galilean observer.

The question arises: If, instead of the one twin B who accelerates, there are the two twins, B and C, who do not accelerate, what is the phenomenon that distinguishes A from B and C? To answer this, let us first put arrows on the world-lines of Figure 17: from O to Q, from O to P, from P to Q.

With the arrows pointing away from O and toward Q, the line OQ has the largest proper-time interval between the events O and Q. To apply these considerations to twin B, instead of to twin A, it is necessary to reverse the arrow on PQ. But this is not permissible for ordinary matter since it represents time moving in the negative direction. It is necessary to recon-struct the diagram making OQ short enough so that it is possible to go from Q to P in the sense of increasing time. When this is done, for example by interchanging the world-lines on the ct and cT axes, then the proper-time for twin B is greater than the sum of the proper-times of twins A and C.

The physical principle that permits one of the three nonaccelerating twins to be singled out as having the maximum proper-time interval is simply the fact that time must go in one direction—a direction which is the same for each of the twins. For ordinary matter this direction is in the sense of increasing time only.

The two cases above (twins A and B, one of whom accelerates, and twins A, B, and C, none of whom accelerates) may be treated as special examples of one over-all principle which sharply contrasts the properties of space-time with those of ordinary real space. In the latter, a straight line is the shortest distance between two points. In space-time a straight world-line has the greatest proper-time between two events. (This can be proven, in general, by a diagram employing arbitrary triangles.) Both in real space and in space-time the straight line is an extremum. Since interval is related to proper-time by $s = ct^0$, a straight world-line has a maximum interval between two events.

Because of the many controversies which have been raised in the past concerning this famous paradox we will present one final argument recently given by Feenberg. Suppose a very remote periodic variable star, with frequency f^0, is at rest with respect to twin A on earth. Let B leave the earth at right angles to the direction of the star, go for some distance with speed v, then turn around and come back at the same speed. A will count N cycles between the time B leaves and the time he returns, an elapsed time for A of T_a; the frequency for A will be $f_a = f^0 = N/T_a$. For B the transverse Doppler effect will give a frequency of $f_b = \dfrac{f^0}{\sqrt{1 - \beta^2}}$ both on the outward and on the inward portions of the journey. But $f_b = N/T_b$, since the same number of cycles is counted both by A and by B. Then

$$T_b = \frac{N}{f_b} = \frac{N}{f^0} \sqrt{1 - \beta^2} = T_a \sqrt{1 - \beta^2}.$$

The explanation has been obtained here by the introduction of an optical effect produced by distant matter with respect to which one of the twins, but not the other, is stationary. The two twins then have an essential distinction between them. The optical effect here takes the place of the inertial effect of the accelerometer above.

In a universe consisting only of A and B, with no other matter present, the twin paradox would no longer exist: the twins would be identical and interchangeable. There would then be only the symmetrical time dilation effect; there would be no asymmetrical twin paradox. In such a universe there would be no distinction between Galilean and nonGalilean observers. Most of the confusion about this paradox consists in substituting this case of the empty universe for the case of the real universe.

BIBLIOGRAPHY

The American Association of Physics Teachers has been prolific in publishing articles dealing with relativity. The following articles devoted to time have all appeared in the Association's monthly periodical, the American Journal of Physics:

Boya, L. J.: A Note on Time-Reversal Invariance. *33:* 139, Feb., 1965.
Bradbury, T. C.: Relativistic Theory of the Behavior of Clocks. *28:* 443, May, 1960.
Crowell, A. D.: Observation of a Time Interval by a Single Observer. *29:* 370, June, 1961.
Feenberg, E.: Doppler Effect and Time Dilation. *27:* 190, March, 1959.
Gamba, A.: Time Dilation and Information Theory. *33:* 61, Jan., 1965.
Gold, T.: The Arrow of Time. *30:* 403, June, 1962.
Kowalski, K. L.: Relativistic Reaction Systems and the Asymmetry of Time Scales. *28:* 487, May, 1960.
Kutliroff, D.: Time Dilation Derivation. *31:* 137, Feb., 1963.
Lass, H.: Accelerating Frames of Reference and the Clock Paradox. *31:* 274, Apr., 1963.
Little, E. M.: Two Simpler Relativity Twin Paradoxes. *33:* 747, Sept., 1965.
Lowry, E. S.: The Clock Paradox. *31:* 59, Jan., 1963.
Michels, W. C.: Phase Shifts and the Doppler Effect. *24:* 51, Feb., 1956.
Robinson, J. D., and Feenberg, E.: Time Dilation and Doppler Effect. *25:* 490, Oct., 1957.
Romer, R. H.: Twin Paradox in Special Relativity. *27:* 131, March, 1959.
Scott, G. D.: On Solutions of the Clock Paradox. *27:* 580, Nov., 1959.

Chapter 4 SPACE

I. TRANSVERSE LENGTH

In the previous chapter we have made use of the second basic axiom of relativity—the constancy of the velocity of light in vacuum for all Galilean observers—to derive some consequences concerning time. The results were in accord with the first axiom—the principle of relativity, or the absence of any preferred observer. The first axiom was not actually employed, however, to obtain the results. We will start this chapter by using the first axiom alone to obtain a relation between length measurements made by two Galilean observers.

Consider, then, an observer A moving in a rocket ship with constant velocity v toward observer B, the velocity being along the line of the common x and x' axes. On this line lie the centers of both A and B. Suppose in A's rocket ship there is a rod, two meters long as measured by A, set along the y axis perpendicular to the direction of relative velocity and fastened so that its center is on the x axis. Similarly, observer B has a rod two meters long, as measured by B, set along the y' axis perpendicular to the direction of relative velocity and so fastened that its center is on the x' axis. The question is: When the center of A arrives adjacent to the center of B, what will be the length of B's rod as measured by A and what will be the length of A's rod as measured by B?

It is not proper to assume that the two rods will be equal in length when they are in relative motion just because they were equal in length when at rest with respect to each other. Experimental evidence obtained at low relative velocities is, also, not necessarily relevant for high relative velocities. As we saw in the previous chapter, identical clocks give different time intervals when the clocks are moving relative to each other. We must, to be rigorous, allow for the possibility that Galilean rods will not agree on their length determinations.

How does A actually go about taking a measurement of B's rod? A must note the two distances on his own rod, infinitesimally distant from the two ends of B's rod, corresponding to two events which are simultaneous for A. Similarly, B requires two events which are simultaneous for him—the instants when the ends of A's rod cross his y' axis—so he can measure the distance between the two events. In the present case the two simultaneous events occur for A (when B is adjacent to A) at the same instant as that when the two events are simultaneous for B (when A is adjacent to B). Since the simultaneous events occur at the same instant for both A and B, they must agree about the results of their individual measurements. Either they both say A's rod is longer than B's; or they both say A's rod is smaller than B's; or they both say the two rods are of equal length. If the two events are simultaneous both for A and B it is not possible to have a situation in which A says B's rod is smaller while B says A's rod is smaller.

Two of the three possibilities which are open violate the principle of relativity. If both A and B agree that A's rod is longer than B's then a situation exists which could occur only because (a) one or the other is "really" stationary with respect to the ether while the other is "really" moving, or (b) one or the other is moving in a "preferred" direction with respect to the ether while the other is moving in the opposite direction. A similar case exists if both A and B agree that A's rod is shorter than B's. The third possibility, that A and B each measure the same length for the other's rod, is symmetrical—it is consistent with the first axiom.

We have thus established by logical reasoning that relative motion along one direction does not affect transverse lengths, i.e., lengths perpendicular to this direction. If the motion is along the x and x' axes then $y = y'$ and $z = z'$. Many words have been used to obtain a seemingly trivial and obvious result. In the following section the same procedure will be employed for a slightly different case, with altogether different results.

It is worth noting at this point that the results of the present discussion were implicitly assumed in the imagined experiment on time at the beginning of the previous chapter. There, for the case of a reflected radar pulse in a rocket ship, the proper-time interval for the observer in the rocket ship was

$$\Delta t^0 = \frac{2L}{c}.$$

The nonproper-time interval for the outside observers (stationary with respect to each other) was given as

$$\Delta t = \frac{\left(\dfrac{2L}{c}\right)}{\sqrt{1 - \beta^2}}.$$

Actually, this should have been

$$\Delta t = \frac{\left(\dfrac{2L'}{c}\right)}{\sqrt{1 - \beta^2}},$$

where L' is the length the outside observers would measure for the distance

L measured by the inside observer. Only after showing $L' = L$ is it correct to deduce

$$\Delta t = \frac{\Delta t^0}{\sqrt{1 - \beta^2}} .$$

Since the discussion of the present section does not depend on the previously obtained results, the tacit assumption made in the previous section is justified.

2. THE LORENTZ-FITZGERALD CONTRACTION

Instead of comparing the lengths of two rods which are perpendicular to the direction of motion we will now compare the lengths of two rods which lie

SONAR PULSE

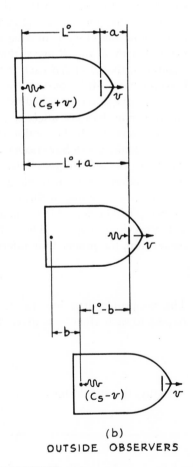

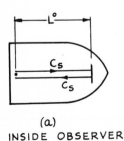

(a)

INSIDE OBSERVER

(b)

OUTSIDE OBSERVERS

Figure 18. Length measurements.

RADAR PULSE

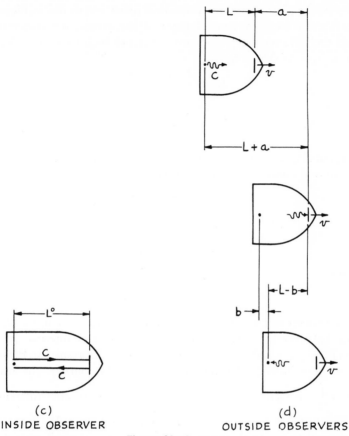

(c)
INSIDE OBSERVER

(d)
OUTSIDE OBSERVERS

Figure 18. *Continued*

parallel to the direction of relative motion. Such rods are called longitudinal rather than transverse. Let us go back to the imagined experiment at the beginning of the previous chapter on time, except that we will modify the conditions: the sonar and radar pulses are now sent to the reflector along the direction of relative travel (between the one observer in the rocket ship and the two stationary observers outside). Taking the case of the sonar pulses first, a short sonar pulse travels a distance L^0 from the transmitter at the rear of the rocket ship to a reflector in the front of the rocket ship and then back, again a distance L^0, to a receiver located at the same point as the transmitter. The proper-time interval at the transmitter-receiver is

$$\Delta t^0 = \frac{2L^0}{c_s}.$$

Figure 18a shows this. For convenience the two rays have been shown displaced from each other.

A nonproper-time interval Δt would be obtained by the two stationary outside observers, one located at the point where transmission occurred and the other at the place where reception took place. As shown in Figure 18b, during Δt_f, the forward time of flight of the pulse from transmitter to reflector, the reflector moved forward a distance such that $a = v \, \Delta t_f$ while $L^0 + a = (c_s + v) \, \Delta t_f$. Thus

$$\Delta t_f = \frac{L^0 + a}{c_s + v} = \frac{a}{v}.$$

Then

$$a = \frac{v}{c_s} L^0 \quad \text{and} \quad \Delta t_f = \frac{L^0}{c_s}.$$

Similarly, during the return flight of the pulse from reflector to receiver, the receiver moved forward a distance b such that

$$\Delta t_r = \frac{L^0 - b}{c_s - v} = \frac{b}{v}.$$

So

$$b = \frac{v}{c_s} L^0 \quad \text{and} \quad \Delta t_r = \frac{L^0}{c_s}.$$

Therefore,

$$\Delta t = \Delta t_f + \Delta t_r = \frac{2L^0}{c_s}.$$

The outside observers measure the same elapsed time as the inside observer. It is seen that reflection occurred midway during this time interval. Although the velocities $c_s + v$ and $c_s - v$ of the sonar pulse with respect to the outside observers were different for the two parts of the journey, the distances $L^0 + a = \left(1 + \dfrac{v}{c_s}\right)L^0$ and $L^0 - b = \left(1 - \dfrac{v}{c_s}\right)L^0$ were also different, and in just such a way as to make the total distance equal to $2L^0$ with an average velocity equal to c_s. In this case, therefore, there is over-all agreement on the results.

Now we consider the case of the radar pulses. In Figure 18c the proper-time interval

$$\Delta t^0 = \frac{2L^0}{c}$$

is obtained for the inside observer. For the outside observers the time of forward flight of the pulses is given in Figure 18d by

$$\Delta t_f = \frac{L + a}{c} = \frac{a}{v}$$

so that

$$a = L\left(\frac{\dfrac{v}{c}}{1 - \dfrac{v}{c}}\right)$$

while

$$L + a = \frac{L}{1 - \dfrac{v}{c}}, \quad \text{and} \quad \Delta t_f = \frac{L}{c - v}.$$

Here we have called the length measured by the outside observers L to allow for the possibility that L differs from L^0. The time of rearward flight of the pulses is given by

$$\Delta t_r = \frac{L - b}{c} = \frac{b}{v}$$

so that

$$b = L \left(\frac{\dfrac{v}{c}}{1 + \dfrac{v}{c}} \right)$$

while

$$L - b = \frac{L}{1 + \dfrac{v}{c}}, \quad \text{and} \quad \Delta t_r = \frac{L}{c + v}.$$

Then

$$\Delta t = \Delta t_f + \Delta t_r = \frac{2\left(\dfrac{L}{c}\right)}{1 - \dfrac{v^2}{c^2}}.$$

However,

$$\Delta t = \frac{\Delta t^0}{\sqrt{1 - \beta^2}} = \frac{2\left(\dfrac{L^0}{c}\right)}{\sqrt{1 - \beta^2}}.$$

Consequently, we obtain the final result

$$L = L^0\sqrt{1 - \beta^2}.$$

In this case the outside observers assert not only that the time interval they measure is larger than that measured by the inside observer but also that reflection did not occur midway in the time interval. The velocity of the radar pulse for the outside observers was c, the same as for the inside observer, on both parts of the journey. The total distance traveled by the radar pulse was $(L + a) + (L - b) = 2L^0/\sqrt{1 - \beta^2}$. Finally, the moving rod had, for them, a length less than that assigned by the inside observer. It is seen that here the two sets of observers obtain different results for everything but the velocity. All this is a direct consequence of the assumption that the velocity of the radar pulse is the same for the two outside observers as for the inside observer, despite the fact they are moving relative to each other.

A length measured by observers with respect to whom it is stationary will be called a proper-length and will be designated L^0. Such a measurement may either be made at two points simultaneously for them or at one point using light pulses, allowing for the time of travel so the events again occurred simultaneously as calculated, not observed.

A length measured by observers with respect to whom it is moving will be called a nonproper-length and will be designated L. The result that L is less than L^0 when the length is longitudinal is called the Lorentz-Fitzgerald contraction. It is the analog of the time dilation of the previous chapter. If the rod had been stationary on earth, the nonproper-time length measured by the rocket observers would have been less than the proper-length measured on earth.

The space-time diagram is well suited for illustrating the Lorentz-Fitzgerald contraction. In Figure 19 a rod of proper-length $L^0 = x_2 - x_1$ is at rest in a rocket ship with coordinate system (x, ct). The two world-lines of the ends of the rod are x_1x_1 and x_2x_2, each parallel to the ct axis. At one instant of time the rod is identified by the rocket observers at AA'. The length AA' is the length of the rod: L^0. The line AA' is parallel to the Ox axis, so A and A' have the same value of ct.

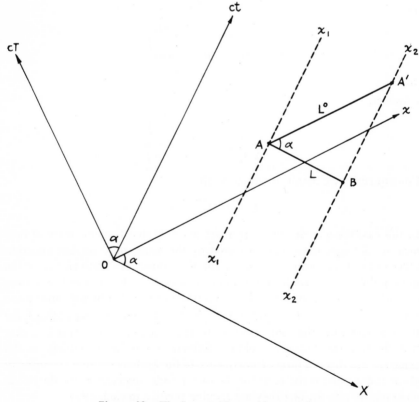

Figure 19. The Lorentz-Fitzgerald contraction.

An observer on the earth, moving toward smaller x relative to the rocket with velocity v, will agree with the rocket observers that x_1x_1 and x_2x_2 are the world-lines of the two ends of the rod. For the earth observer, however, A and A' have different values of cT: they are not simultaneous for the earth observer. The earth observer would pick two events, such as A and B, which *are* simultaneous for him in order to perform a measurement. A and B lie on a line parallel to the OX axis, so they have the same value of cT.

The length, L, of the rod is given by AB for the earth observer. From the diagram $L = L^0 \cos \alpha$. But $\cos \alpha = \sqrt{1 - \beta^2}$; so

$$L = L^0\sqrt{1 - \beta^2}.$$

This is the famous Lorentz-Fitzgerald contraction of longitudinal lengths.

The contraction is seen to depend on the relative nature of simultaneous events. To the rocket observers the nonproper-length of the earth rod measures shorter than the proper-length of the rocket rod. To find the lengths measured by the earth observers it is necessary to perform measurements which are simultaneous for the earth observers. In the diagram this means drawing lines at a constant value of cT: A similar construction then gives the nonproper-length of the rocket rod to be shorter than the proper-length of the earth rod.

Proper-lengths and nonproper-lengths are not the only kind of length measurements. Just as with time, so also with length: an apparent-length measurement may be defined. This occurs when one observer tries, by utilizing light rays, to measure the length of an object which is moving with respect to him. If the object is moving toward him it may be shown that the apparent-length measurement will be $L^0\sqrt{\dfrac{1 - \beta}{1 + \beta}}$, while if the object is moving away from him the apparent-length measurement will be $L^0\sqrt{\dfrac{1 + \beta}{1 - \beta}}$.

The formulas are quite different from the Lorentz-Fitzgerald contraction because the separation between the ends is not measured simultaneously. Both apparent-time and apparent-length measurements are intimately connected with the Doppler effect.

3. IS THE CONTRACTION REAL?

Is the Lorentz-Fitzgerald contraction a real effect or is it merely some trick of measurement? The following imagined experiment may help to make it clear that the effect is a real one. Suppose a rod of proper-length $l_r{}^0$ is traveling with a velocity v toward a barn to the right in real space. The barn has an open door on its left wall which can be closed very quickly. The proper-length of the barn is $l_b{}^0$. From the viewpoint of the rod, the barn has a nonproper-length $l_b{}^0 \sqrt{1 - \beta^2}$. One is tempted to say the rod can be trapped in the barn if $l_r{}^0 < l_b{}^0 \sqrt{1 - \beta^2}$. But from the viewpoint of the barn, the rod has a nonproper-length $l_r{}^0 \sqrt{1 - \beta^2}$, so the condition for capture then appears to be $l_r{}^0 \sqrt{1 - \beta^2} < l_b{}^0$. Consequently, if $l_r{}^0 = l_b{}^0$ it would seem the rod and barn should come to opposite conclusions about the possibility of shutting the barn door and finding the rod inside. Which is correct, the rod or the barn?

We will resolve this paradox by the introduction of deceleration: after the rod has been brought to rest with respect to the barn it can be stated definitely whether the rod is in or out of the barn. For convenience, the deceleration will be assumed to occur instantaneously, as in the paradox of the twins. Now, however, it becomes necessary to specify the meaning of the word instantaneously. Here instantaneously means that all points of the rod simultaneously change their velocity from $v = v$ to $v = 0$ relative to the earth. But, simultaneously for whom—for the rod or for the barn? As we have seen, the two will not agree on simultaneity.

In Figure 20 the deceleration of the rod is simultaneous as measured by the barn observers. We may imagine that a barn mechanism, very close to the rod along its length, suddenly clamps the rod in place, the mechanism

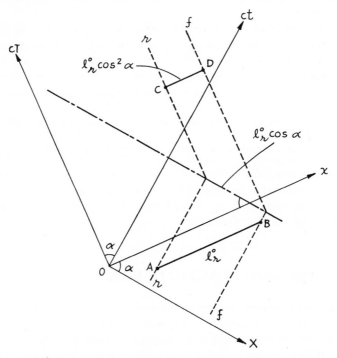

(a) MEASURED BY R OBSERVERS

Figure 20. The rod and the barn (simultaneity for barn).

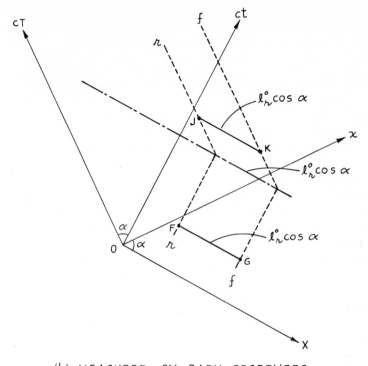

(b) MEASURED BY BARN OBSERVERS

Figure 20. *Continued*

acting as a unit. Figure 20a shows the space-time diagram for this case as measured by R, imagined Galilean observers who move with the rod before deceleration and continue with the same velocity after the rod's deceleration.

AB, of magnitude $l_r{}^0$, represents the position of the rod at one instant, ct, before the deceleration as seen by R. The world-lines of the rod, originally parallel to the ct axis, become, at some instant, simultaneous in this case for the barn observers (X, cT), world-lines parallel to the cT axis: the rod is brought to rest with respect to the barn instead of being at rest with respect to the R observers. After deceleration the R observers (who are continuing the journey with the rod's initial velocity) measure the rod, at one instant for them, at CD. The magnitude of CD, from the diagram, is $l_r{}^0 \cos^2 \alpha$ or $l_r{}^0(1 - \beta^2)$.

Figure 20b shows the space-time diagram for this same case as measured by the barn observers. The barn observers record the same world-lines as do the rocket, R, observers. At one instant for the barn, then, the rod may be at FG. This magnitude is $l_r{}^0 \cos \alpha = l_r{}^0 \sqrt{1 - \beta^2}$. After deceleration the B observers see the rod at JK, say. The magnitude of JK, from the diagram, is also $l_r{}^0 \cos \alpha = l_r{}^0 \sqrt{1 - \beta^2}$.

This information is summarized in the table below:

LENGTH OF ROD

	OBSERVERS R	BARN OBSERVERS
BEFORE DECELERATION	1. l_r^0	2. $l_r^0 \sqrt{1 - \beta^2}$
AFTER DECELERATION	4. $l_r^0(1 - \beta^2)$	3. $l_r^0 \sqrt{1 - \beta^2}$

Deceleration instantaneous for barn observers

(1) is a proper-length. (2) is a nonproper-length related to (1) by the Lorentz-Fitzgerald contraction. Deceleration simultaneously for the barn observers leaves the length of the rod, as measured by the barn, unaffected; this is shown by (3), which is now a proper-length. But the deceleration is not simultaneous for the observers R, and the length of the rod as measured by them is, consequently, affected by the deceleration. The length (4) obtained from the graph is a nonproper-length and is related to (3) by the Lorentz-Fitzgerald contraction. Measured by R the rod has shrunk to a smaller magnitude than that called for by the Lorentz-Fitzgerald contraction.

As for the length of the barn, this stays constant at the value l_b^0 for the barn observers, both before and after deceleration of the rod. For observers R it stays constant at the value $l_b^0\sqrt{1 - \beta^2}$ both before and after the deceleration of the rod. This is shown in the following table:

LENGTH OF BARN

	OBSERVERS R	BARN OBSERVERS
BEFORE DECELERATION	$l_b^0\sqrt{1 - \beta^2}$	l_b^0
AFTER DECELERATION	$l_b^0\sqrt{1 - \beta^2}$	l_b^0

Deceleration instantaneous for barn observers

For the rod to fit in the barn, observers R require that

$$l_r^0(1 - \beta^2) < l_b^0 \sqrt{1 - \beta^2}$$

while the barn observers require that

$$l_r^0 \sqrt{1 - \beta^2} < l_b^0.$$

Both sets of observers agree: the proper-length of the barn must be larger than the Lorentz-Fitzgerald contracted length of the rod. This conclusion would be unaffected if the deceleration were gradual instead of abrupt, provided only that the instantaneous acceleration of all points of the rod was the same, simultaneously, for the barn observers. On the graph the world-lines of the ends of the rod would be curves, spaced $l_r{}^0 \cos \alpha$ apart at any value of cT, instead of the straight lines near the previous abrupt deceleration points.

For this case, therefore, the barn observers measure the Lorentz-Fitzgerald contraction of the rod as a real physical phenomenon. But observers permanently attached to the rod record (1) and (3) and do not agree that the deceleration was instantaneous. They measure the Lorentz-Fitzgerald contraction of the barn as precisely cancelled out by their own deceleration because, for them, the front of the rod was decelerated before the rear, thereby decreasing the length by a factor which happens to be equal to the Lorentz-Fitzgerald contraction factor.

Figure 21 considers another possibility—the deceleration of the rod is instantaneous and simultaneous as measured by the rod observers (also, by the R observers). The clamping mechanism is now attached to the rod; it grabs the barn, acting as a unit, and stops the rod instantaneously as seen by the rod. In Figure 21a the situation is shown as measured by R, while Figure 21b shows this case as measured by the barn. It is instructive to compare this case with the graphs of Figure 20. The following table is

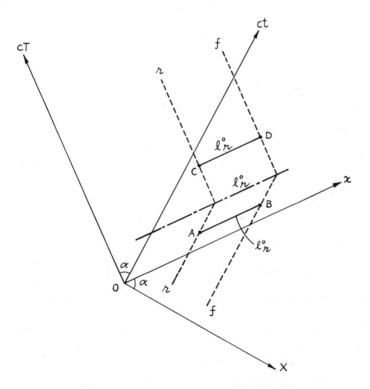

(a) MEASURED BY R OBSERVERS

Figure 21. The rod and the barn (simultaneity for R observers).

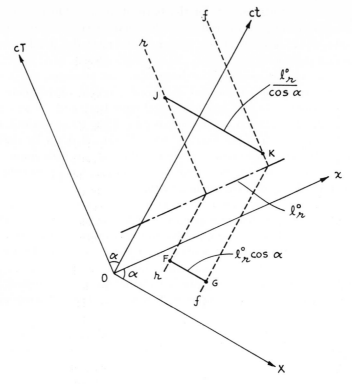

(b) MEASURED BY BARN OBSERVERS

Figure 21. *Continued*

obtained in the present case:

LENGTH OF ROD

	OBSERVERS R	BARN OBSERVERS
BEFORE DECELERATION	1. l_r^0	2. $l_r^0 \sqrt{1 - \beta^2}$
AFTER DECELERATION	4. l_r^0	3. $\dfrac{l_r^0}{\sqrt{1 - \beta^2}}$

Deceleration instantaneous for rod (and R) observers

(1) and (2) are analogous to the previous case, but now (4) has the same value as (1).

The length of the barn in the present case, precisely as before, stays constant. The values are given by the table for the barn in the previous case.

For the rod to fit in the barn in this case both the R observers and the barn observers agree that it is necessary that

$$l_r^0 < l_b^0 \sqrt{1 - \beta^2}.$$

Here the Lorentz-Fitzgerald contracted length of the barn must be larger than the proper-length of the rod. Again this conclusion is unaffected if the deceleration is gradual, but this time the instantaneous acceleration of all points of the rod must be the same simultaneously for either the rod or R observers.

For this case, then, the barn observers measure different points of the rod as decelerated at different instants. They measure the Lorentz-Fitzgerald contracted length of the rod as increased by a factor of $\dfrac{1}{1 - \beta^2}$ because for them the rear of the rod was decelerated first, thereby stretching the rod. Observers permanently attached to the rod measure both their own length and the length of the barn as increased by a factor of $\dfrac{1}{\sqrt{1 - \beta^2}}$ because of the deceleration.

The two cases treated above yield different, nonsymmetrical results. The reason for this is that the two cases are not similar. If the rod clamping mechanism suddenly accelerated the barn while leaving the rod velocity unaffected, a result symmetrical to the first case would be obtained.

There are many special cases which could be treated in this manner. For our purpose, however, the first case is significant. If the barn mechanism grabs the rod and brings it to a halt without moving the barn, then the barn observers verify that their Lorentz-Fitzgerald contracted measure of the rod in flight is correct.

4. THE SHAPE OF MOVING OBJECTS

The Lorentz-Fitzgerald contraction is obtained by the position measurements of two points of a moving object made, simultaneously for them, by two detection devices which are stationary with respect to each other. If the measurements are optical then, to avoid an incorrect result, the light photons must *leave* the two points of the object at the same time, as measured by the observers: they must leave simultaneously.

In seeing or photographing a moving object nonstereoscopically, on the other hand, it is necessary that photons from various parts of the object *arrive* at one point simultaneously (at the same instant for the eye or camera located at that point); otherwise, the motion of the object would produce a blurred image. Since the various points of the object are generally at different distances from the eye, the simultaneously arriving photons could not all have left the object simultaneously for the viewer.

It is clear that the process of length measurement is different from the process of seeing. Amazingly, this distinction was not noticed until 1959, when it was first pointed out by James Terrell. One of the famous popular expositions of relativity, for example, assumed a world in which the speed of light was 10 miles per hour and then described the effect that the Lorentz-Fitzgerald contraction had on the appearance of pedestrians, cyclists, etc. This misconception was shared by all the workers in the field of relativity and persisted so long only because of the lack of experimental evidence. Actually, in order to determine how very rapidly moving objects would appear to the eye or to a camera it is necessary to make a separate calculation. It is not valid to assume that the Lorentz-Fitzgerald contraction is visible simply because it is measurable.

The computation is greatly simplified if it is assumed that the object is either small or far away, i.e., that the solid angle subtended at the eye by the object is a small one. Then the various light rays from different parts of the object to the eye are essentially parallel. Suppose that the object is a cube, each length being of proper-length d^0. In Figure 22 this object moves with velocity v toward positive x along a line displaced from the eye of the observer by a distance D such that $d^0 \ll D$. The z axis is upward toward the reader from the plane of the paper.

How will this object appear when seen (not: observed) in a direction that makes an angle θ_R, at the eye, with the $+x$ direction? As an example,

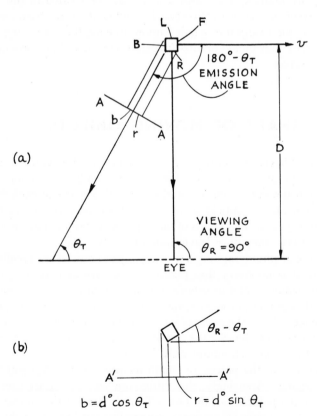

Figure 22. The appearance of moving objects.

first consider $\theta_R = 90°$. The object must have been at the position shown in Figure 22a when the light was emitted if the direction actually traveled by the light is perpendicular to the x axis. Thus, the cube will actually be at some position to the right of the position shown when the light is received at the eye. Assuming the object gives off light in all directions, only those rays given off at some angle $180° - \theta_T$ with the $+x$ direction will reach the eye (because the velocity of the source, $+v$ with respect to the eye, is equivalent to a velocity of the eye, $-v$ with respect to the source). The velocity of the source does not modify the velocity of the light; the velocity of the observer changes the apparent direction, but not the speed, of the light. It is now necessary to obtain a relation between θ_T and θ_R.

The angle θ_R corresponds to the angle made at the windshield of a moving car by falling snowflakes when the angle made by the direction of the snowflakes with the earth is θ_T. In this analogy Figure 22a would correspond to a wind blowing snow to the left; the velocity of a car to the left would make the snowflakes appear to drop vertically. A more familiar case, perhaps, would be the one with $180° - \theta_T = 90°$: the snow is actually dropping vertically. To a car moving toward the left, however, the snowflakes would appear to be falling with a velocity component directed horizontally to the right—toward the windshield.

We will here anticipate the results of the subsequent section on aberration, which does not depend on the present calculation, and write the relation between θ_R and θ_T:

$$\tan \frac{\theta_T}{2} = \sqrt{\frac{1 - \beta}{1 + \beta}} \tan \frac{\theta_R}{2}.$$

(When $\theta_R = 90°$, $\sin \theta_T = \sqrt{1 - \beta^2}$ and $\cos \theta_T = \beta$; but at other values of θ_R these simpler equations do not hold). This relation determines the appearance of the cube, as follows.

The line AA in Figure 22a, shows a wave front, perpendicular to the direction of propagation. Along the line AA we have

$$r = d^0 \sin \theta_T = \sqrt{1 - \beta^2}\, d^0,$$
$$b = d^0 \cos \theta_T = \beta d^0.$$

Here r and b are the apparent widths of the right and back sides, respectively, on the line AA. In the direction perpendicular to the plane of the page the apparent height equals the actual height, d^0. In Figure 22b the wave front $A'A'$ is shown horizontal, perpendicular to the ray—the direction of propagation of the light that reaches the eye. The only effect of the eye's velocity relative to the object is to change the direction of the wave front from AA to $A'A'$, leaving the distances b and r unaltered. In this case it is seen that the right side of the cube, of longitudinal length d^0, appears reduced by the Lorentz-Fitzgerald contraction factor. The back side of the cube, of transverse length d^0, also appears reduced, but by a factor v/c. The other transverse length, the depth, appears unaltered. The entire appearance can be ascribed to an apparent counterclockwise rotation of the cube about the z axis through an angle equal to $90° - \theta_T$ or $\theta_R - \theta_T$.

If the viewing angle is changed from $90°$ to some other value of θ_R the longitudinal length will still appear contracted to $d^0 \sin \theta_T$, now different from the Lorentz-Fitzgerald contraction factor. This does not affect the reality of the Lorentz-Fitzgerald contraction, which is defined by measurement—not by viewing. At any viewing angle θ_R the cube appears rotated CCW by $(\theta_R - \theta_T)$ degrees. The longitudinal length appears to the eye as $d^0 \sin \theta_T$ while the transverse length in the plane of the figure appears as $d^0 \cos \theta_T$.

Figure 23 shows an unusual effect which arises at velocities approaching that of light. Here $v/c = 0.5$; on the abscissa $\theta_R = 180°$ corresponds to the

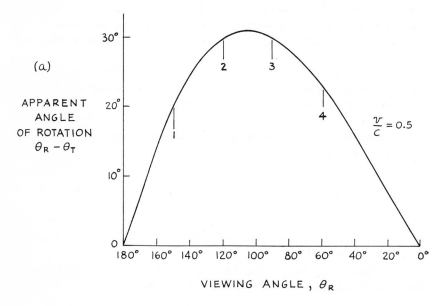

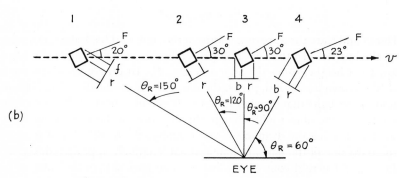

Figure 23. Apparent rotation of a moving cube.

case when the object is at the extreme left while $\theta_R = 0°$ gives the case when the object is at the extreme right. Figure 23a is a graph of the apparent angle of rotation at different viewing angles, determined from the equation given above. When the moving object is near the extreme left the angle of rotation is very small and the view of the approaching cube would essentially be of one face—the front. When θ_R is 150°, as at 1, the apparent angle of rotation is 20°. Now there are two faces seen—the front and right, as designated with respect to the motion of the cube. This is shown in Figure 23b. At 2, where $\theta_R = 120°$, the cube is still approaching the viewer. The apparent rotation of the cube, 30°, is now great enough so that only the right face is visible.

From this viewing angle onward, even though the cube is still approaching the viewer, the back face of the cube is visible while the front face is not. At 3, where $\theta_R = 90°$, the eye sees the right face contracted by the Lorentz-Fitzgerald factor and also the back face, contracted by a different factor; the apparent rotation of the cube is again 30°. At 4 the right and back faces remain visible, in a direction corresponding to that of a receding cube, but with lengths multiplied by different factors. Finally, near the extreme right the apparent angle of rotation is again very small and only the back face of the cube is seen. For other values of β similar results are obtained, the effect being accentuated as v approaches c.

When the relation between θ_T and θ_R is obtained classically rather than relativistically one obtains similar, but more complicated, results. The contraction factors for the two sides which are visible are then not as simply related to each other as they are above and it is not possible to ascribe the resultant view to an apparent rotation of the cube. In that case the cube is not only rotated; it is also distorted.

If the moving object subtends a large solid angle at the eye, either because it is larger or closer, the calculation above does not apply. It has been shown that for a sphere the circumference will remain a circle to the viewer, regardless of the solid angle; for large enough solid angles, however, there will be visual distortion of the relative positions of objects within the boundary.

In addition to the apparent rotation of the moving body the appearance is also affected by apparent changes in the color. Both the longitudinal and transverse Doppler effects enter here to change the received frequencies and wavelengths from the transmitted proper-values.

BIBLIOGRAPHY

Penrose, R.: The Apparent Shape of a Relativistically Moving Sphere. Proc. Camb. Phil. Soc. *55:* 137, Jan., 1959.
Terrell, J.: Invisibility of the Lorentz-Contraction. Phys. Rev. *116:* 1041, Nov. 15, 1959.
Weisskopf, V. F.: The Visual Appearance of Rapidly Moving Objects. Physics Today *13:* 24, Sept., 1960.

The American Journal of Physics is the source for the following articles on various topics concerning relativistic length:

Boas, M. L.: Apparent Shapes of Large Objects at Relativistic Speeds. *29:* 283, May, 1961.

Epstein, L.: A Classical Analog for Relativistic Contraction. *31:* 913, Dec., 1963.

Rindler, W.: Length Contraction Paradox. *29:* 365, June, 1961; Erratum *29:* 859, Dec., 1961.

Sears, F. W.: Length of a Moving Rod. *33:* 266, Apr., 1965.

Scott, G. D., and Viner, M. R.: The Geometrical Appearance of Large Objects Moving at Relativistic Speeds. *33:* 534, July, 1965.

Shaw, R.: Length Contraction Paradox. *30:* 72, Jan., 1962.

Sherwin, C. W.: Regarding the Observation of the Lorentz-Contraction on a Pulsed Radar System. *29:* 67, Feb., 1961.

Weinstein, R.: Observation of Length by a Single Observer. *28:* 607, Oct., 1960.

Wells, W. H.: Length Contraction Paradox. *29:* 858, Dec., 1961.

Chapter 5 THE LORENTZ TRANS-FORMATION

I. DERIVATION

The Brehme diagram of Figure 24 leads very simply to the relations connecting the (x, t) coordinates of an event for one observer with the (X, T) coordinates of the same event for a second Galilean observer. Directly from the diagram

$$x + (\sin \alpha)ct = (\cos \alpha)X,$$

$$(\sin \alpha)x + ct = (\cos \alpha)cT.$$

Since $\sin \alpha = \dfrac{v}{c}$ and $\cos \alpha = \sqrt{1 - \dfrac{v^2}{c^2}}$, this yields the famous Lorentz transformation:

$$
\begin{cases}
X = \dfrac{x + vt}{\sqrt{1 - \left(\dfrac{v}{c}\right)^2}} \\[4ex]
Y = y \\[1ex]
Z = z \\[3ex]
T = \dfrac{t + \dfrac{vx}{c^2}}{\sqrt{1 - \left(\dfrac{v}{c}\right)^2}}
\end{cases}
\quad \text{or} \quad
\begin{cases}
X = \dfrac{x + \left(\dfrac{v}{c}\right)ct}{\sqrt{1 - \left(\dfrac{v}{c}\right)^2}} \\[4ex]
Y = y \\[1ex]
Z = z \\[3ex]
cT = \dfrac{\left(\dfrac{v}{c}\right)x + ct}{\sqrt{1 - \left(\dfrac{v}{c}\right)^2}}
\end{cases}
$$

The same result would be obtained from a Loedel diagram.

The inverse relations may be derived by solving the equations above or, directly, by interchanging capitalized and uncapitalized variables and then

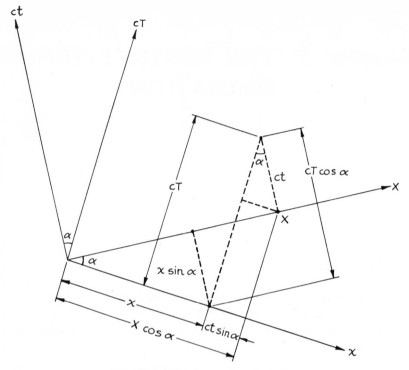

Figure 24. The Lorentz transformation.

replacing v by $-v$. In the limit when v/c approaches zero, the Lorentz transformation becomes the Galilean transformation:

$$\begin{cases} X = x + vt, \\ Y = y, \\ Z = z, \\ T = t. \end{cases}$$

The consequences of the Lorentz transformation which violate common sense occur when v is approximately equal to c. When v is very much less than c the Galilean transformation, with its common sense physical behavior, becomes very closely the same as the Lorentz transformation. From the equations for the Lorentz transformation it is seen that the velocity of light in vacuum c plays a very basic role: it enters explicitly into the fundamental kinematic equations. Further, it is seen that c represents an upper limit for the velocity v; when $v = c$ two of the expressions become infinite, while for $v > c$ they become imaginary. This is also seen directly from the space-time diagrams where $\sin \alpha = \dfrac{v}{c}$; for $v = c$ the space and time axes of these diagrams coincide, while for $v > c$ no real α exists.

The Lorentz transformation is the basic set of equations for special relativity. It was obtained here from either one of the two space-time diagrams, which is equivalent to saying: from the invariance of the interval, with the added assumptions of homogeneous and isotropic space plus homogeneous time. Historically, of course, the Lorentz transformation came first. In fact, H. A. Lorentz introduced the transformation one year before relativity was proposed by Einstein, though this was then unknown to Einstein. Many years later, in 1932, an experiment by Kennedy and Thorndike disproved the Lorentz viewpoint, which was based on the existence of the ether. By then, it had already become clear many years before that Einstein had pointed out the real significance of the transformation. Though Lorentz had introduced the transformation from considerations based on the existence of the ether, Einstein obtained the same transformation in a derivation rejecting the ether but assuming the constant value of c for all Galilean observers.

2. CONSTANT-INTERVAL SURFACES

Suppose an interval between two events, O and E, has the value s_a for observer A; it then has the same value $s_b = s_a$ for observer B. Let us compare the values of the coordinates of the event E assigned by observers other than A and B; observers who move at all possible values of velocity relative to A and B, along the same direction and with the same space-time origin. The event O, of course, will have the coordinates $(0, 0)$ for all observers.

In Figure 25a a horizontal axis, H, and a vertical axis, W, have been added to the Brehme diagram. They are introduced as aids in the construction of various curves plotted against standard orthogonal axes. They may also, however, be considered the axes for a pair of observers who are moving with respect to each other with a relative velocity that is infinitesimal. This pair constitutes a fundamental reference pair since the extension to three spatial axes does not require the singling out of any one direction. It is particularly easy to plot curves on their axes. World-line diagrams with respect to such axes have been used extensively to describe various scattering processes of elementary particles—they are called Feynman diagrams. For our purpose, however, we merely need to consider the H-W axes as aids in the construction of various curves plotted against standard orthogonal axes.

The equation of the invariant interval for one observer is $c^2t^2 - x^2 = s^2$. This equation represents a curve when plotted against the (x, ct) axes. We wish to determine the equation for this curve when it is referred to the orthogonal axes H and W. From Figure 25b:

$$x = H \cos \frac{\alpha}{2} - W \sin \frac{\alpha}{2}.$$

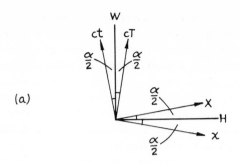

(a)

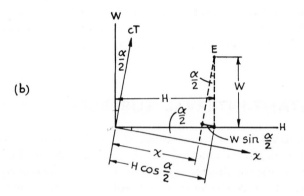

(b)

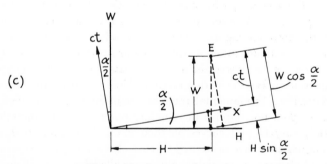

(c)

Figure 25. Invariant intervals.

Similarly, from Figure 25c:

$$ct = W \cos \frac{\alpha}{2} - H \sin \frac{\alpha}{2}.$$

This gives $c^2t^2 - x^2 = H^2\left(\sin^2 \frac{\alpha}{2} - \cos^2 \frac{\alpha}{2}\right) + W^2\left(\cos^2 \frac{\alpha}{2} - \sin^2 \frac{\alpha}{2}\right)$ or $s^2 = (W^2 - H^2) \cos \alpha$. The desired expression is, then,

$$W^2 - H^2 = \frac{s^2}{\sqrt{1 - \beta^2}}.$$

If we set

$$K^2 = \frac{s^2}{\sqrt{1 - \beta^2}}$$

we obtain the equation of a hyperbola,

$$W^2 - H^2 = K^2,$$

referred to the H and W axes.

The locus of all events with a given interval s for one pair of observers (x, ct) and (X, cT), moving relative to each other with velocity v, is the hyperbola $W^2 - H^2 = K^2$ referred to orthogonal axes H and W. Figure 26a shows

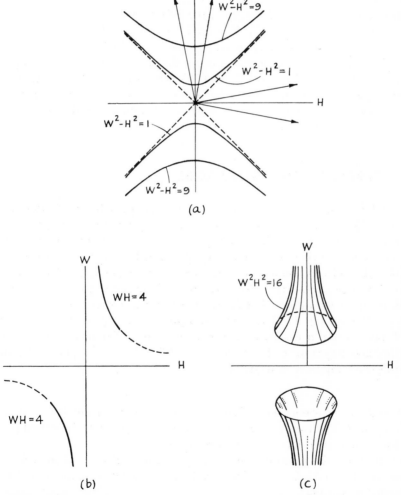

(a)

(b)   (c)

Figure 26. Time-like constant-interval curves; time-like given-event curve and surface.

two such hyperbolas, each consisting of two sections, for the cases $K^2 = 1$ and $K^2 = 9$. One such curve also represents the locus of all events for some other interval, s', as measured by another pair of observers moving with velocity v' with respect to each other. The actual space-time axes for this second pair of observers have been omitted from the diagram to avoid confusion. It is only necessary that

$$K^2 = \frac{s'^2}{\sqrt{1 - \dfrac{v'^2}{c^2}}}.$$

Consequently, a single hyperbola referred to H and W actually represents an infinite number of curves—each the locus of all events having a given interval—with a different interval for a different pair of observers. One particular curve is picked out, from the infinity of overlapping curves that satisfy the equation with given K, as soon as either s or v is specified. There is a continuum of such curves, for all possible $+s^2$, filling the entire region of the space-time diagram above and below the origin between the two world-lines of light making angles of $45°$ and $135°$ with $+H$. The remaining region of the space-time diagram, to the left and to the right of the origin between the two world-lines, corresponds to a similar continuum for all possible $-s^2$, i.e., space-like intervals.

3. GIVEN-EVENT SURFACES

Let us focus our attention on a point of one such hyperbola, fixed with respect to the H and W axes. There are infinitely many space-time axes on which the coordinates of this point may be read, and the point thus represents infinitely many events for different observers, each event being referred to a different set of axes. Suppose we select one set of axes, so that we have a given event for a given observer. What will be the locus of this particular event in (H, W) space for all possible Galilean observers who coincide with each other at $x = 0$ when $t = 0$? The path that a point of the curve $W^2 - H^2 = K^2$ will take so that it designates the same event for different observers is the orthogonal trajectory to the curve $W^2 - H^2 = K^2$. The equation for this orthogonal trajectory, a hyperbola, is

$$WH = \lambda$$

where λ is a constant. Figure 26*b* shows the two sections of $WH = 4$, the solid parts being those pertinent to time-like intervals while the dotted parts refer to imaginary (i.e., space-like) intervals.

If λ is positive then the hyperbola representing a given event for different observers lies in the first and third quadrants; if negative, in the second and fourth. By writing

$$W^2H^2 = \lambda^2,$$

where λ is real, all four parts can be combined into one equation. This is useful if, as in Figure 26c, we wish to bring in one of the other two axes, say the y axis, changing the 2-dimensional curve to a 3-dimensional surface of two sheets. The surface of Figure 26c represents a single event as seen by the various possible Galilean observers, taking into account x, y, and ct. One observer may have small x and y but a large ct, another a different combination, etc. If one wished to bring z into the picture it would be necessary to imagine a 4-dimensional surface.

Let us extend the Brehme diagram from one space axis to two space axes. Then, instead of the equation $W^2 - H^2 = \dfrac{c^2t^2 - x^2}{\cos \alpha} = \dfrac{s^2}{\cos \alpha}$ obtained for the one-spatial axis case above, one would have for the case of two spatial axes $W^2 - H^2 = \dfrac{c^2t^2 - x^2}{\cos \alpha} = \dfrac{s^2 + y^2}{\cos \alpha}$. The equation, written as

$$W^2 - \left\{H^2 + \left(\frac{y}{\sqrt{\cos \alpha}}\right)^2\right\} = \left(\frac{s}{\sqrt{\cos \alpha}}\right)^2,$$

shows that this is not a surface of revolution because of the $\dfrac{1}{\sqrt{\cos \alpha}}$ factor multiplying y.

If the W, H axes refer, instead, to Loedel diagrams the equations are slightly different. Here

$$\bar{x} \cos \alpha = \bar{H} \cos \frac{\alpha}{2} - \bar{W} \sin \frac{\alpha}{2}$$

and

$$c\bar{t} \cos \alpha = -\bar{H} \sin \frac{\alpha}{2} + \bar{W} \cos \frac{\alpha}{2}.$$

These give

$$\bar{W}^2 - \bar{H}^2 = s^2 \cos \alpha$$

in the case of one spatial axis and

$$\bar{W}^2 - \left\{\bar{H}^2 + (\sqrt{\cos \alpha}\, y)^2\right\} = (\sqrt{\cos \alpha}\, s)^2$$

in the case of two spatial axes. This surface is also not a surface of revolution.

The Brehme surfaces are such that a cut perpendicular to the ct or cT axes for large enough values of ct or cT, approaches a circle; this is similarly true for the Loedel surfaces with cuts parallel to the xy plane or to the XY plane for large enough values of $c\bar{t}$ or $c\bar{T}$. The surfaces then approach the surface of the light cone. This is elliptical in a cross section perpendicular to the W axis, the major and minor axes reversing themselves in going from a Loedel to a Brehme diagram.

In the cases of both the Brehme and the Loedel diagrams the use of the same scale for the three spatial axes and the one time axis leads to rather complicated 4-dimensional figures for the constant-interval surfaces (and also the given-event surfaces): they are not surfaces of revolution. In the corresponding case of the Minkowski diagram one obtains hyperboloids of revolution about the ct axis in either 3- or 4-dimensional space-time. For one of the two Minkowski observers, but not the other, all four axes may have the same scale. It would seem that in 3- or 4-space the Minkowski diagrams would be easier to follow. Actually, this is not a serious hindrance; it is discussed further in the last section of this chapter.

In 2-dimensional space-time, on the other hand, the Minkowski diagram is at a disadvantage compared to the Brehme and Loedel diagrams. While each observer, in the Minkowski diagram, may use the same scale for his own space and time axes this scale must differ from that employed by the other observer. It appears, therefore, that in 2-dimensional space-time it is preferable to use Loedel or Brehme diagrams. In 4-dimensional space-time the analytic approach is easiest for calculation; although here also, as Professor Synge has pointed out with many fruitful results, the geometric approach is very suggestive of relationships which would otherwise remain hidden.

The interval, s, between the two events, O and E, of Figure 27 is real.

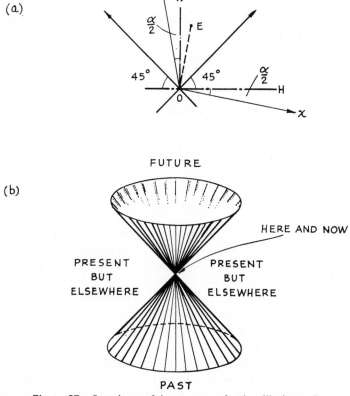

Figure 27. Invariance of time sequence for time-like intervals.

As we have seen, such an interval is called time-like. Part of the reason for this name is that ct predominates over x: $ct > x$. There is a deeper reason, however. (1) In the Brehme diagram of Figure 27a we see that it is always possible to find a pair of axes (x, ct) such that O and E occur at the same place for this observer. Thus, draw OE; then lay off the x axis perpendicular to OE (O and E then have the same x coordinate); measure the angle $\frac{\alpha}{2}$ between the x axis and the horizontal and make the ct axis obtuse with respect to the vertical by this same angle. (x, ct) are the desired axes. So long as O is at the origin and E is within the two world-lines for light this is feasible. (2) For such events, however, no coordinate system can be found for which O and E are simultaneous. OE is within $45°$ of the vertical; if O and E are to be simultaneous then OE must be perpendicular to the ct axis; the ct axis must then be within $45°$ of the horizontal; but this would make α greater than $90°$, which is impossible; so events O and E cannot be made simultaneous. (3) The events cannot be made to reverse their sequence in time on any conceivable set of axes. Any event E in the region above the origin and between the two world-lines occurs after O for the time axis of any observer. If E is below the origin it occurs before O for any observer.

The relative sequence of events in time is, consequently, an invariant for all observers with time-like intervals between O and E. But the relative spatial sequence of such events (for time-like intervals between O and E) is not an invariant, since we can always find an observer for whom O and E occur at the same place. This is the basic reason such intervals are called time-like. They preserve the sequence of events in time for different observers.

If the origin in Figure 27b is called HERE AND NOW, the upper region between the light world-lines becomes the FUTURE, the lower region the PAST. Any event which lies in these regions—FUTURE or PAST—has a real, time-like interval between it and the origin. If there are two such events, however, this is not necessarily true for the interval between themselves; that depends on whether the world-line connecting them makes less than an angle of $45°$ with the vertical. Between any one such event and an event at the origin, the spatial separation is less than the distance traversed by light in the temporal separation between the two events. These two events can, therefore, be related by cause and effect, although this is not necessary. Also, if two events occur in a single body then, since the velocity of the body is less than the velocity of light with respect to any observer, the interval between the events must be time-like.

What of the region in the space-time diagram to the right and left of the origin and outside the above region between the two light world-lines? Any event in this region has an interval, between it and an event at the origin, which is imaginary, and such an interval is called space-like. Figure 28a shows, for such events, the family of hyperbolas in which each curve gives different events of a definite interval for one pair of observers. In Figure 28b a family of hyperbolas, orthogonal to the first family, has each member

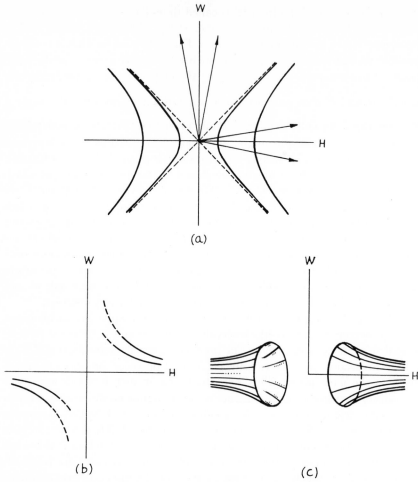

Figure 28. Space-like constant-interval curves; space-like given-event curves and surface.

representing a given event as measured by different observers. Similarly, Figure 28c is an extension of the latter family by the inclusion of the y-axis.

This region of the space-time diagram of Figure 27b may be labeled PRESENT BUT ELSEWHERE. An event in this region cannot be related by cause-and-effect to an event at O: the spatial separation is larger than the distance that can be covered by the fastest velocity possible. If one event O occurs to a body then another event E, to the same body, cannot occur if E is in this region. Of course, O could occur for one body while E occurred for another.

By choosing the proper set of axes, any event in this region may be made to occur simultaneously with the event O. This can be seen from a construction similar to the one made for time-like intervals, and the result here is analogous to the one there. Another set of axes may be chosen in which E occurs after O; similarly, a set can be found for which E occurs before O. The future and the past have no firm significance, relative to O, for events in this region.

The two world-lines of light, $x = \pm ct$, corresponding to an interval of zero, constitute the boundary between the region of time-like real intervals and the region of space-like imaginary intervals. If another dimension, say y, is included with x and ct then the two world-lines become a 2-dimensional surface—two cones about the same axis, oppositely directed, with the same apex. The 1-dimensional world-lines $x = \pm ct$ are the intercepts of this 2-dimensional cone with the (x, ct) plane. Similarly, we may consider the 2-dimensional cone to be extended to an (x, y, z, ct) hypercone. The cone is the intercept of the hypercone with the (x, y, ct) volume. The term lightcone is used indiscriminately for the cone, the hypercone, and the pair of intersecting lines.

4. VELOCITY TRANSFORMATION

Just as the relationship between the coordinates of a given event measured by different observers was determined from the space-time diagram, so it is possible to compare the slope of a given straight world-line for two different sets of axes. This gives the relation between the velocity of a body as measured by A and the velocity of that body as measured by B. It is simpler, however, to obtain the results in this case algebraically. From the Lorentz transformation:

$$\Delta x = x_2 - x_1 = \frac{(X_2 - vT_2) - (X_1 - vT_1)}{\sqrt{1 - \beta^2}} = \frac{\Delta X - v\Delta T}{\sqrt{1 - \beta^2}},$$

$$\Delta y = y_2 - y_1 = Y_2 - Y_1 = \Delta Y, \qquad \Delta z = \Delta Z, \qquad \Delta t = \frac{\Delta T - v\Delta X/c^2}{\sqrt{1 - \beta^2}}.$$

Dividing the first three equations by the last and setting

$$u_x = \frac{\Delta x}{\Delta t}, \quad u_y = \frac{\Delta y}{\Delta t}, \quad u_z = \frac{\Delta z}{\Delta t}, \quad U_X = \frac{\Delta X}{\Delta T}, \quad U_Y = \frac{\Delta Y}{\Delta T}, \quad U_Z = \frac{\Delta Z}{\Delta T}$$

gives

$$\begin{cases} u_x = \dfrac{U_X - v}{1 - \dfrac{vU_X}{c^2}}, \\[4ex] u_y = \dfrac{\sqrt{1 - \beta^2}\, U_Y}{1 - \dfrac{vU_X}{c^2}}, \\[4ex] u_z = \dfrac{\sqrt{1 - \beta^2}\, U_Z}{1 - \dfrac{vU_X}{c^2}}. \end{cases}$$

To find the inverse transformation it is only necessary to change the sign before v and interchange capitalized and uncapitalized velocities:

$$\begin{cases} U_X = \dfrac{u_x + v}{1 + \dfrac{vu_x}{c^2}}, \\[3ex] U_Y = \dfrac{\sqrt{1 - \beta^2}u_y}{1 + \dfrac{vu_x}{c^2}}, \\[3ex] U_Z = \dfrac{\sqrt{1 - \beta^2}u_z}{1 + \dfrac{vu_x}{c^2}}. \end{cases}$$

The appearance of the velocity transformation equations may be made simpler by employing velocities normalized to the speed of light. Thus, let

$$f = \frac{u_x}{c}, \quad g = \frac{u_y}{c}, \quad h = \frac{u_z}{c} \quad \text{and} \quad F = \frac{U_X}{c}, \quad G = \frac{U_Y}{c}, \quad H = \frac{U_Z}{c}.$$

Then

$$\begin{cases} f = \dfrac{F - \beta}{1 - \beta F}, \\[3ex] g = \dfrac{\sqrt{1 - \beta^2}G}{1 - \beta F}, \\[3ex] h = \dfrac{\sqrt{1 - \beta^2}H}{1 - \beta F} \end{cases} \quad \text{and} \quad \begin{cases} F = \dfrac{f + \beta}{1 + \beta f}, \\[3ex] G = \dfrac{\sqrt{1 - \beta^2}g}{1 + \beta f}. \\[3ex] H = \dfrac{\sqrt{1 - \beta^2}h}{1 + \beta f} \end{cases}$$

The equation for F may also be written

$$\tanh^{-1} F = \tanh^{-1} f + \tanh^{-1} \beta.$$

Appendix 1 gives nomographs which permit quick solution of the velocity transformation equations.

These velocity transformation equations go over, for $v \ll c$, into the classical formulas

$$u_x = U_X - v, \qquad u_y = U_Y, \qquad u_z = U_Z.$$

One complicating and unfortunate consequence of the transformation equations is that the vector combination of velocities which is valid when $\dfrac{v}{c} \ll 1$, $\mathbf{v}_{ab} + \mathbf{v}_{bc} = \mathbf{v}_{ac}$, is not true in the general case of arbitrary velocity. In discussing the shape of moving objects, for example, it was not permitted to combine a vector velocity for the light emitted with the vector velocity of the observer to obtain the resultant velocity of the light with respect to the observer.

If $U_X = c$ then $u_x = c$ also; if $U_X < c$ then $u_x < c$ also. The combination of any two velocities, each of them less than c, gives a resultant velocity also less than c. The velocity, c, is an upper limit to any velocity. The significance of c is thus much more than the quantity representing the velocity of electromagnetic waves in vacuum. It is an upper limit to velocity imposed by nature on all objects or signals. It is also a speed which has the same value for all Galilean observers.

It should be mentioned in passing that it is, nevertheless, possible to devise conditions in which the velocity of light is exceeded: a plane wave approaching a shore has a velocity for the point of intersection of the wave front with the shoreline which depends on the angle between the wave front and the shore. When this angle approaches zero then the velocity of the point of intersection approaches infinity. Again, when energy propagates down a wave guide it is necessary to distinguish between group velocity and wave velocity. The former is never larger than c, the latter is never less than c. Finally, the de Broglie waves that represent a moving particle have a velocity which is greater than the velocity of light in vacuum. In all cases when the velocity is greater than c it is found that the velocity is a mathematical construction rather than a physical entity. No energy is transported at this speed and no material body moves at that speed.

5. LIGHT IN MOVING MEDIA

A number of physical phenomena have their basis in the formulas for velocity transformation, among them the velocity of light in moving media, e.g., Fizeau's experiment in flowing water. Consider a body in which the velocity of light is u when the body is at rest with respect to an observer. The index of refraction is defined by $n = \dfrac{c}{u}$. Now let the body move to the right relative to an observer. What is the velocity of light in the body, relative to the observer? From the equations above, $U = \dfrac{u + v}{1 + \dfrac{uv}{c^2}}$. With $u = \dfrac{c}{n}$ this becomes $U = \dfrac{\dfrac{c}{n} + v}{1 + \left(\dfrac{c}{n}\right)\dfrac{v}{c^2}}$. If this is expanded in a power series of $\dfrac{v}{c}$:

$$U = \frac{c}{n} + v\left(1 - \frac{1}{n^2}\right).$$

This is in agreement with the experiment but is contrary to the prediction

$$U = \frac{c}{n} + v$$

which is obtained by using the Galilean, rather than the Lorentz, transformation. In order to account for the extra term obtained experimentally it was necessary to postulate, in the classical version, a dragging along of the ether by the moving body. The quantity in the parenthesis in the second term on the right was called the ether drag coefficient. Other experiments, as we have mentioned, contradicted the ether drag theory.

The results of the Fizeau experiment, which were not in agreement with predictions of the ether theory, constituted a strong motivating factor for Einstein in his development of relativity theory. This experiment, therefore, has great historical importance.

6. ABERRATION

The formulas for the aberration of light have already been utilized in the previous chapter in the section on the shape of moving objects. It is only necessary to apply the equations of velocity transformation by setting

$$U_X = -U \cos \theta_R, \quad U_Y = -U \sin \theta_R, \quad U_Z = 0;$$

$$u_x = -u \cos \theta_T, \quad u_y = -u \sin \theta_T, \quad u_z = 0.$$

Here U is the speed of a particle moving left and down in the XY plane and θ_R is the direction of the oncoming particle, measured from the $+X$ axis, for one Galilean observer; u and θ_T are the corresponding quantities for a second Galilean observer, right-moving relative to the first with speed v. Dividing the second equation of the velocity transformation by the first gives $\dfrac{U_Y}{U_X}$; but this equals $\tan \theta_R$; so $\tan \theta_R = \dfrac{\sqrt{1 - \beta^2}\,(-u \sin \theta_T)}{(-u \cos \theta_T) + v}$.

If the particle is a photon, traveling with velocity c, then $u = c$ and $\tan \theta_R = \dfrac{\sqrt{1 - \beta^2} \sin \theta_T}{\cos \theta_T - \beta}$. A more symmetrical form can be obtained from this by trigonometric manipulation:

$$\tan\left(\frac{\theta_T}{2}\right) = \sqrt{\frac{1 - \beta}{1 + \beta}} \tan\left(\frac{\theta_R}{2}\right).$$

Here θ_R is the viewing angle for the receiver, and $180° - \theta_T$ is the emission angle at the transmitter, as shown in Figure 22 (page 62).

To apply this equation to the aberration of a star we note first that the velocity of the earth in its orbit, 30 km/sec, is small enough so that a power expansion of the radical in powers of β need only retain the first power of β. Then $\sqrt{\dfrac{1 - \beta}{1 + \beta}} \approx 1 - \beta$. Let $\theta_T = \theta_R + \Delta\theta$; so $\tan \Delta\theta \approx \Delta\theta$ when $\Delta\theta$ is small. But

$$\tan\left(\frac{\theta_T}{2}\right) = \tan\left(\frac{\theta_R}{2} + \frac{\Delta\theta}{2}\right) = \frac{\tan\left(\dfrac{\theta_R}{2}\right) + \dfrac{\Delta\theta}{2}}{1 - \dfrac{\Delta\theta}{2} \tan\left(\dfrac{\theta_R}{2}\right)} \approx \tan\left(\frac{\theta_R}{2}\right) + \frac{\Delta\theta}{2} \sec^2\left(\frac{\theta_R}{2}\right).$$

Comparing this with $\tan\left(\dfrac{\theta_T}{2}\right) \approx \tan\left(\dfrac{\theta_R}{2}\right) - \beta \tan\left(\dfrac{\theta_R}{2}\right)$ gives

$$-\beta \tan\left(\frac{\theta_R}{2}\right) = \frac{\Delta\theta}{2} \sec^2\left(\frac{\theta_R}{2}\right)$$

so that

$$\Delta\theta = -\beta \sin \theta_R.$$

This is the condition at one point in the orbit. Half a year later the earth's velocity is reversed in direction and the equation becomes $\Delta\theta = \beta \sin \theta_R$. Then the direction of the viewing telescope has to be changed between the two extremes above. For a star at the zenith the annual motion of the telescope is a cone of half-angle $\Delta\theta = \beta$. Numerically this has the value 10^{-4} radian or 20.5″. This is in agreement with experiment and also with classical theory.

7. ROTATION SYMMETRY

We have chosen to take the direction of the x and X axes as the one along which the two observers have their relative velocity. This, of course, is not the only possible choice—we could equally well have taken the relative velocity to lie in any other direction. If the lightcone had been a surface of revolution for the Loedel and Brehme diagrams we could be indifferent to the actual choice made. Since this is not so, different directions relative to the chosen one acquire different significance.

The extension of the Minkowski diagram from one space dimension to two space dimensions gives an orthogonal set of axes (x, y, ct), all having the same scale, for one observer. The lightcone here is 2-dimensional, symmetrically generated as a surface of revolution about the time axis. There is no distinction between the x direction, along which the relative motion between the two observers occurs, and the y direction. For the other Minkowski observer the lightcone is also a surface of revolution, the same surface as for the first observer. The second observer has a different scale for his (X, cT) axes than the first observer has for his (x, ct) axes; but the Y and y axes have the same scales. It follows that the second observer must employ a scale for his Y axis which differs from the scale used for his (X, cT) axes. If the second observer had the same scale for all his axes then his lightcone would not be a surface of revolution.

The situation that exists for the Loedel and Brehme diagrams is similar to that for this second Minkowski observer, except that it now applies to both observers. In the case of the Brehme diagram one may take the unit length along the two transverse space axes smaller, by the factor $\sqrt{\cos \alpha}$, than the unit lengths along the longitudinal axis and along the time axis. The lightcone is then a surface of revolution about the imagined vertical axis. For the Loedel diagram the unit length along the two transverse axes must be larger, by the factor $\dfrac{1}{\sqrt{\cos \alpha}}$, to give a symmetrical lightcone.

This asymmetry (either of the lightcone or of the scales) for both observers could be a distinct hindrance in some situations. If one does not know, e.g., which is the direction of relative velocity one could not align the axes correctly; such a case would occur in general relativity. There is another alternative, however, which makes the use of Loedel or Brehme axes for such a case essentially the same as for the orthogonal Minkowski observer. Let us consider two Galilean observers who move relative to each other with infinitesimal velocity. The Brehme or Loedel diagrams for these two observers have orthogonal axes (similar to the orthogonal Minkowski axes) so the world-line of any other object or observer can be plotted relative to them for an arbitrary alignment of the space axes. The lightcone is now a surface of revolution regardless of how the axes are directed.

The use of these two observers, moving with infinitesimal relative velocity, as a reference pair is also useful in special relativity for the case in which the velocity is a continuously changing function of time. Then the Minkowski diagram gives one orthogonal set of axes, which maintain their original direction and scale, and a nonorthogonal set of axes whose direction and scale, relative to the first set, both vary with time and space. Here the Loedel and Brehme diagrams give both sets of nonorthogonal axes fluctuating in direction relative to each other. Although the scales do not vary, we have a continuously changing reference diagram, varying from instant to instant and from one point in space to another. Here too, however, the two observers moving at infinitesimal relative speed may be used to good advantage as a reference set. Either reference observer (or both) may be identified with a particle; another particle, with variable velocity relative to the first, then traces out a world-line on a Brehme or Loedel diagram which has orthogonal axes. This gives us an invariant set of axes against which to measure or draw events.

It could be argued that since it is necessary to employ these orthogonal axes in some cases it might be just as well to use them in all cases—to abandon the Loedel or Brehme diagrams in favor of the Minkowski diagram. Our rejection of this course is based on two factors: (1) The Minkowski diagram is more complicated. Either with Cartesian measurements and a scale factor between observers or with the hyperbolas and the Minkowski metric, this diagram is not so simple as the Loedel diagram, which requires no scale factor and no hyperbolas. (2) The Minkowski diagram treats asymmetrically a situation which is, physically, completely symmetric. There is no possibility of finding any criterion which distinguishes between the two Galilean observers.

It would appear possible to assert that dealing only with the orthogonal axes of the Minkowski diagram, as is customary, is in actuality also treating events relative to a pair of infinitesimal-velocity observers. All the different types of space-time diagrams here become identical and there is no justification for labeling such a diagram with any one type.

BIBLIOGRAPHY

The following articles have all appeared in the American Journal of Physics:

Berenda, C. W.: Temporal Reversal of Events in Restricted Relativity. *28:* 799, Dec., 1960.
Bilanuik, O. M. P., Deshpande, V. K., and Sudarshan, E. C. G.: "Meta Relativity." *30:* 718, Oct., 1962.
Brehme, R. W.: A Geometric Representation of Lorentz Frames for Linearly Accelerated Motion. *31:* 517, July, 1963.
Daubin, S. C.: Geometrical Demonstration of Velocity Transformation in Special Relativity. *31:* 792, Oct., 1963.
Davis, W. R., Katzin, G. H., and York, J. W., Jr.: Note on a Decomposition of the Lorentz Transformation. *32:* 167, Feb., 1964.
Durbin, K. A.: A Reply to A. V. Masket. *33:* 510, June, 1965.
Edwards, W. F.: Special Relativity in Anisotropic Space. *31:* 482, July, 1963.
Erber, T., and Malhist, R. J.: Transformation of Acceleration in Special Relativity. *27:* 607, Nov., 1959.
Evett, A. A., and Fried, D. C.: Speed of Light in Flowing Dispersive Liquids. *28:* 733, Nov., 1960.
Jones, R. T.: Extending the Lorentz Transformation by Characteristic Coordinates. *28:* 109, Feb., 1960.
Jones, R. T.: Conformal Coordinates Associated with Uniformly Accelerated Motion. *29:* 124, Feb., 1961.
Marsh, L. M.: Relativistic Accelerated Systems. *33:* 934, Nov., 1965.
Masket, A. V.: Relativity of Simultaneity, Length, and Time. *33:* 509, June, 1965.
Mast, C. B.: "Spherical" Coordinates in Special Relativity. *33:* 281, Apr., 1965.
Nadeau, G.: The Lorentz-Einstein Transformation Obtained by a Vector Method. *30:* 602, Aug., 1962.
Romain, J. E.: Lorentz Transformation in the Undergraduate Curriculum. *31:* 870, Nov., 1963.
Romain, J. E.: Remarks on a Coordinate Transformation to an Accelerated Frame of Reference. *32:* 279, Apr., 1964.
Schwartz, H. M.: Axiomatic Deduction of the General Lorentz Transformation. *30:* 697, Oct., 1962.
Schwartz, H. M.: An Extension of Euler's Theorem to Minkowski Space. *31:* 864, Nov., 1963.
Schwartz, H. M.: A Further Note on an Extension of Euler's Theorem to Minkowski Space. *33:* 376, May, 1965.
Sokoloff, J.: Lorentz Transformation in the Undergraduate Curriculum. *31:* 444, June, 1963.
Weinstock, R.: Derivation of the Lorentz-Transformation Equations Without a Linearity Assumption. *32:* 260, Apr., 1964.
Weinstock, R.: New Approach to Special Relativity. *33:* 640, Aug., 1965.

Chapter 6 $E = mc^2$

I. MASS AND MOMENTUM

Because they are so broad in their application the various conservation laws are generally considered among the most fundamental laws of nature. The laws of conservation of energy, of momentum, of angular momentum, of charge, and of mass are well known to freshman physics students. It may come as something of a shock, then, to find that the velocity transformation law of the previous chapter, based on the Lorentz (rather than the Galilean) transformation, has as an immediate consequence the fact that the law of conservation of mass and the law of conservation of momentum cannot both be valid if momentum and mass are defined in the usual manner.

To see how this follows, let us examine a head-on collision between two identical particles. It is convenient to distinguish between elastic and inelastic collisions; in the former, the total kinetic energy of the system is the same before and after the collision. If the two identical particles were two lumps of putty or two globules of mercury the collision would be an inelastic one, the smaller kinetic energy after the collision being accounted for by an increase in the internal energy of the system caused by surface tension, binding forces, etc. This is the case we wish to consider here.

Figure 29 shows the two particles before collision, each with the same mass, m. One is moving to the right with velocity, v, relative to an observer, A; the other is moving to the left with the same velocity. This is the situation before the collision. Suppose we assume that after the collision both particles have coalesced into one larger particle, of mass $2m$, which is at rest with respect to observer A. The mass is conserved in the collision—it is $2m$ both before and after that event. The momentum is also conserved: it is $m(+v)+m(-v)=0$ before, and $2m(0)=0$ after, collision. The kinetic energy is not conserved: it is $\dfrac{m}{2}(v)^2 + \dfrac{m}{2}(-v)^2 = mv^2$ before, and $2m(0)^2 = 0$ after, the collision. Assuming that the total energy is conserved, then the quantity mv^2 of kinetic energy is converted into mv^2 of internal energy of some sort.

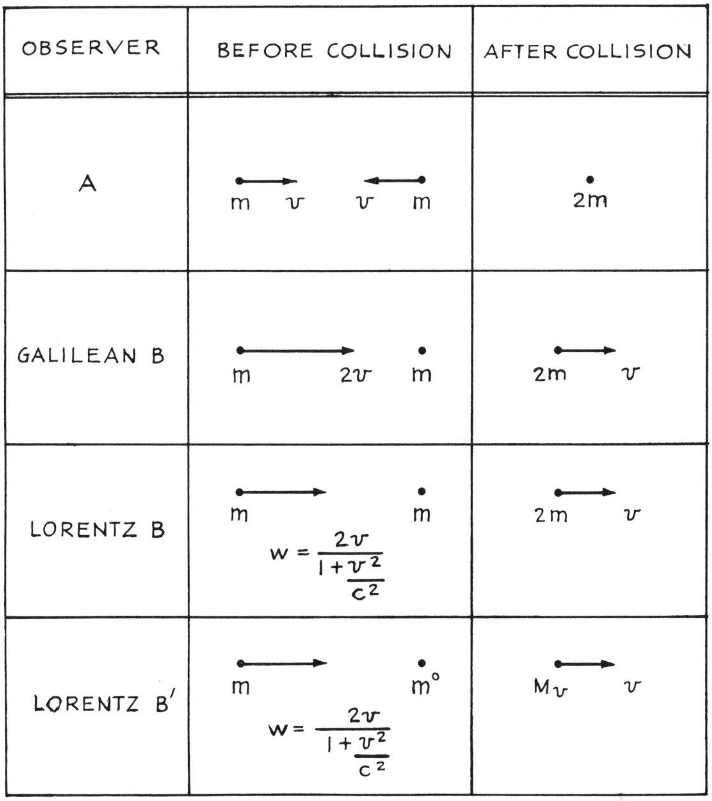

OBSERVER	BEFORE COLLISION	AFTER COLLISION
A	m v v m	2m
GALILEAN B	m $2v$ m	2m v
LORENTZ B	m m $w = \dfrac{2v}{1+\dfrac{v^2}{c^2}}$	2m v
LORENTZ B$'$	m m° $w = \dfrac{2v}{1+\dfrac{v^2}{c^2}}$	Mv v

Figure 29. Mass and momentum.

How would this process be described by a different observer, B, who was also moving to the left with speed v relative to observer A? If B employed the Galilean transformation of velocities, then one particle before collision would have velocity $2v$, the other would be at rest; after the collision the coalesced particle would have the velocity v. Again the mass is conserved, with the value $2m$ both before and after the collision; the momentum is also conserved, this time with the value $2mv$; the kinetic energy is not conserved: of the original $\dfrac{m}{2}(2v)^2 + 0 = 2mv^2$, the quantity mv^2 is again converted into internal energy, leaving $(1/2)(2m)v^2 = mv^2$ as the kinetic energy after the collision.

If B employed the Lorentz transformation, however, the particle velocities would not be those obtained above. After the collision the velocity of the coalesced particle will again be v; before the collision the velocity of one particle will be zero, the velocity of the other $w = \dfrac{2v}{1+\dfrac{v^2}{c^2}}$. Mass is again conserved with the value $2m$; but the momentum is not conserved, being $\dfrac{2mv}{1 + \dfrac{v^2}{c^2}}$ before, and $2mv$ after, the collision. The relativistic considerations of kinematics—space and time—thus have their effects also in dynamics.

Einstein found that both the law of conservation of mass and the law of conservation of momentum could be retained if the mass were to be considered a variable, dependent on the velocity. Thus, suppose that the mass of either particle when it is at rest with respect to an observer is m^0 while the mass is m_v when it is moving with speed v relative to that observer. We wish to find the explicit variation of m_v with velocity.

Figure 29 shows that the Lorentz observer B' (who is equivalent to the Lorentz observer B in velocity calculations but who is different from him in employing variable mass) will express conservation of mass and conservation of momentum by

$$m_w + m^0 = M_v$$

and

$$m_w w = M_v v.$$

Then, $m_w = \dfrac{v}{w} M_v$ and $M_v = \dfrac{m^0}{1 - \dfrac{v}{w}} = \dfrac{2m^0}{1 - \dfrac{v^2}{c^2}}$. The nonrest-mass or moving-mass, M_v, is not equal to the sum of the constituent rest-masses: $M_v \neq 2m^0$. We now have

$$m_w = \frac{v}{w}\left(\frac{2m^0}{1 - \beta^2}\right) = \frac{1 + \beta^2}{2}\left(\frac{2m^0}{1 - \beta^2}\right) = \frac{m^0}{\left(\dfrac{1 - \beta^2}{1 + \beta^2}\right)} = \frac{m^0}{\sqrt{1 - \left(\dfrac{w}{c}\right)^2}}.$$

But v is an arbitrary velocity; so w is arbitrary also. Consequently,

$$m_v = \frac{m^0}{\sqrt{1 - \beta^2}}$$

gives the moving-mass of a particle with rest-mass, m^0, which is moving with velocity v relative to the observer.

It is worth noting that M_v, the combined mass after the collision, can be written as

$$M_v = \frac{\left(\dfrac{2m^0}{\sqrt{1 - \beta^2}}\right)}{\sqrt{1 - \beta^2}}.$$

This would indicate that the rest-mass of the coalesced particle is $\dfrac{2m^0}{\sqrt{1 - \beta^2}}$.

This is in accord with the view that a Lorentz observer A would have of the symmetrical situation in the first line of Figure 29: conservation of mass requires

$$\frac{(m^0)}{\sqrt{1 - \beta^2}} + \frac{(m^0)}{\sqrt{1 - \beta^2}} = \frac{\left(\dfrac{2m^0}{\sqrt{1 - \beta^2}}\right)}{\sqrt{1 - 0^2}} \, .$$

With this equation for mass, $m = \dfrac{m^0}{\sqrt{1 - \beta^2}}$, it is possible to retain the definition of momentum as the product of mass and velocity:

$$p = mv = \frac{m^0 v}{\sqrt{1 - \left(\dfrac{v}{c}\right)^2}} \, .$$

This, of course, differs from the nonrelativistic definition $p = m^0 v$. However, m differs from m^0 only negligibly except when v is comparable to c. For $v = c$, m becomes infinite (except if $m^0 = 0$); for $\dfrac{v}{c} > 1$, m becomes an imaginary quantity. Physically, this means that for material particles (i.e., $m^0 \neq 0$) the velocity of light in vacuum acts as an upper bound which cannot be attained. For nonmaterial particles ($m^0 = 0$) such as photons (and neutrinos, probably), the moving-mass can become finite and real only if $v = c$, in which case $m = \dfrac{0}{0}$. The evaluation of this indeterminate case is made in the next section, on page 91.

The same formula for the variation of mass with velocity would have been obtained from consideration of an elastic collision. The equation is quite general and applies not only to collisions, elastic or inelastic, but to all cases of moving-mass. It is well, perhaps, to point out explicitly the fact that the variation of mass with velocity is a direct consequence of (1) the constant velocity of c for different Galilean observers, expressed via the Lorentz transformation and (2) the principle of relativity, expressed through the validity of the laws of conservation of moving-mass and conservation of momentum for all Galilean observers.

2. MASS AND ENERGY

Since the variation of mass with velocity has made it necessary to change the definition of momentum from $m^0 v$ to $\dfrac{m^0 v}{\sqrt{1 - \dfrac{v^2}{c^2}}}$ it is not surprising to find that a different relationship must also now prevail between mass and energy. Classically, the energy of a free particle (i.e., one not subject to any forces) is given by the expression $\frac{1}{2}mv^2$. It is tempting to generalize this at once by going to the formula $\dfrac{1}{2}\left(\dfrac{m^0}{\sqrt{1-\dfrac{v^2}{c^2}}}\right)v^2$, but the result would be incorrect. We will now proceed to find the correct expression from basic considerations. The formula that results is probably the most famous consequence of the entire theory. Because of the fame of the resultant formula we will derive it in two separate ways; the first is an imagined experiment of Einstein's.

Think of a closed box, as shown in Figure 30a, in which a transmitter at a emits a short pulse of radiation to a receiver b. During the very brief emission process there is a mechanical recoil to the left by the transmitter, and the box to which it is attached, caused by the radiation pressure of the

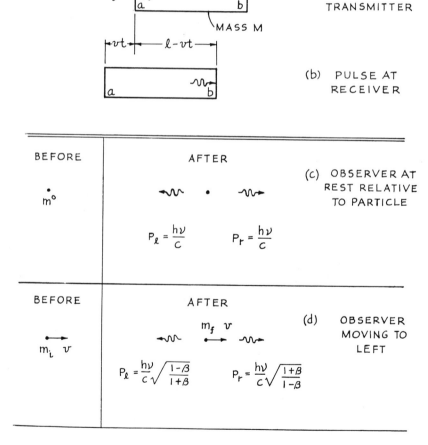

Figure 30. Mass and energy.

emitted pulse. The box would tend to move to the left during the time it takes the pulse to go from a to b. When the pulse reaches b, as in Figure 30b, an equal impulse to the right would be imparted by the radiation to the receiver, bringing the box to rest at some position to the left of its original position. With no interaction between box and environment, the mass of the box and contents would discontinuously have been displaced to the left while a pulse of energy traveled from the left wall to the right wall. Because of Newton's first law, however, the center of mass of the box and contents must remain at the same point if there are no external forces and the box was originally at rest. Consequently, it is necessary to consider that the transfer of the pulse of energy from left to right was accompanied by the transfer of equivalent mass, m, from left to right as well.

Absorbed radiation of energy E is accompanied (in classical theory, in quantum theory, and in experiment) by a radiation momentum $\dfrac{E}{c}$. For example, from quantum theory $E = h\nu$ and $\lambda = \dfrac{h}{p}$. Since $\lambda\nu = c$ this gives $\dfrac{h}{p}\left(\dfrac{E}{h}\right) = c$ or $p = \dfrac{E}{c}$. The recoil momentum, Mv, transferred to the box at emission is now $Mv = \dfrac{E}{c}$, where M is the mass of the box and v is its velocity.

During the time, t, that the pulse travels to the receiver, as measured by a stationary outside observer, the box moves to the left a distance vt. The pulse must go a distance $l - vt$ at velocity c: $t = \dfrac{l - vt}{c}$. Then $t = \dfrac{\dfrac{l}{c}}{1 + \dfrac{v}{c}}$ and $l - vt = \dfrac{l}{1 + \dfrac{v}{c}}$.

The transfer of the pulse of energy to the right for the distance $l - vt$ is, as we saw above, equivalent to the transfer of mass m over the distance $l - vt$. This must be balanced by the motion of the box, of mass M, through the distance vt to the left:

$$M(vt) = m(l - vt) \quad \text{or} \quad (Mv)t = m(l - vt).$$

So

$$\left(\frac{E}{c}\right)\left[\left(\frac{l}{c}\right)\middle/\left(1 + \frac{v}{c}\right)\right] = m\left[l\middle/\left(1 + \frac{v}{c}\right)\right].$$

Then,

$$E = mc^2.$$

The transfer of the pulse of energy E is, therefore, equivalent to the transfer of a mass m given by the above equation. Because c itself is a very large number, c^2 is an extremely large number. Consequently, for a value of E

that is typical of ordinary processes, the equivalent value of m is extremely small; for a value of m that is typical of ordinary processes, the equivalent value of E is extremely large.

Because of the equivalence of mass and energy we should refer hereafter only to the law of conservation of mass-energy, rather than to the conservation of mass or to the conservation of energy. Of course, when only one type of interchange is involved, the resulting equation may be equivalent only to the conservation of mass, or only to the conservation of energy.

For the second derivation of this formula (a derivation of P. Langevin), consider the transformation, as in Figure 30c, of a particle with zero charge into a different particle plus two oppositely directed photons of the same frequency. To an observer for whom the original particle is instantaneously at rest, the momentum before the transformation is zero and the momentum after the transformation is $\dfrac{hv}{c} - \dfrac{hv}{c} = 0$, where h is Planck's constant and v is the frequency. For this observer, the particle after the transformation is at rest; so that, for all other observers also, the particle's velocity is not affected by the radiation.

To an observer moving with velocity v to the left relative to the first observer the process seems different. The two photons will no longer have the same frequency but, as shown in the discussion of the Doppler effect, will have different frequencies: $v_r = v\sqrt{\dfrac{1 + \beta}{1 - \beta}}$ and $v_l = v\sqrt{\dfrac{1 - \beta}{1 + \beta}}$. A trivial difference actually exists here from the previously considered case of the Doppler effect. There, whether the observer was approaching the source or receding from it, the photons were directed from the source toward the observer. Here, if the observer is moving toward the left and approaching the source, only the right-going photon, of frequency v_r, will be directed toward the observer. The left-going photon will never reach this observer since its velocity is greater than the observer's velocity. If this observer, however, is considered to have instruments, fixed in relation to him and sufficiently far to the left, then the left-going photon will be directed toward the instruments and yield the frequency v_l. *All equipment and observers stationary relative to an observer are considered to be the same observer.*

The photon to the right will have momentum $\dfrac{hv}{c}\sqrt{\dfrac{1 + \beta}{1 - \beta}}$, the one to the left will have momentum $\dfrac{hv}{c}\sqrt{\dfrac{1 - \beta}{1 + \beta}}$. The initial mass of the particle, m_i, gives an initial particle momentum $m_i v$; while the final mass, m_f, will give a final momentum $m_f v$. From conservation of momentum

$$m_i v = m_f v + \frac{hv}{c}\left(\sqrt{\frac{1 + \beta}{1 - \beta}} - \sqrt{\frac{1 - \beta}{1 + \beta}}\right).$$ Then $\Delta m = m_i - m_f$ gives

$$\Delta m = \frac{hv}{vc}\left(\frac{2v/c}{\sqrt{1 - \beta^2}}\right).$$

If we assume conservation of energy then the initial particle energy, E_i, is equal to the sum of the final particle energy, E_f, and the individual energies of the photons: $E_i = E_f + h\nu\left(\sqrt{\dfrac{1+\beta}{1-\beta}} + \sqrt{\dfrac{1-\beta}{1+\beta}}\right)$. With $\Delta E = E_i - E_f$ this gives $\Delta E = h\nu\left(\dfrac{2}{\sqrt{1-\beta^2}}\right)$. Comparing the two expressions gives $\Delta E = (\Delta m)c^2$.

The law of conservation of energy remains valid in this example—the energy of the photons comes from the decrease in the energy of the particle. So, also, the law of conservation of momentum applies. The law of conservation of mass does not apply—m_i and m_f are not the same, even though the particle has the same velocity both initially and finally—unless one includes an equivalent moving-mass $m = \dfrac{E}{c^2}$ for each photon. This is true even though the rest-mass of the photon is zero. The left-going photon has energy $E = cp = h\nu\sqrt{\dfrac{1-\beta}{1+\beta}}$ or a mass $\dfrac{E}{c^2} = \dfrac{h\nu}{c^2}\sqrt{\dfrac{1-\beta}{1+\beta}}$. The right-going photon has a mass $\dfrac{h\nu}{c^2}\sqrt{\dfrac{1+\beta}{1-\beta}}$. The sum of these is $\dfrac{2h\nu}{c^2\sqrt{1-\beta^2}}$, which is just $\Delta m = m_i - m_f$. This is the indeterminate case evaluation mentioned on page 87.

To maintain the conservation laws it is necessary to consider mass and energy as two different manifestations of a single entity: mass-energy. The masses of particles must be considered in the energy balance; the energy of radiation must be considered in the mass balance. The formula gives the rate of exchange, so to speak, between two interchangeable different currencies—energy and mass.

Some further examples will now serve to bring out the importance of these considerations. Let a particle of rest-mass M^0 decay spontaneously into a system of two particles, with rest-masses m^0 and μ^0. To an observer for whom M^0 is at rest the law of conservation of mass-energy gives

$$M^0 = \frac{m^0}{\sqrt{1 - v_1^2/c^2}} + \frac{\mu^0}{\sqrt{1 - v_2^2/c^2}},$$

where v_1 and v_2 are the velocities of the decay particles. Now, v_1 and v_2 cannot both be zero, for then there would be no distinction between the mother mass and the daughter masses. We cannot have, in fact, $v_1 = 0$ and $v_2 \neq 0$ (or vice versa) since this would violate conservation of momentum. Consequently,

$$M^0 > (m^0 + \mu^0)$$

is a necessary condition for spontaneous disintegration. If $M^0 \leq (m^0 + \mu^0)$ the particle is stable against this one disintegration and it requires the addition of energy E to permit the transformation. In that case, the law of conservation of mass-energy gives

$$M^0 + \frac{E}{c^2} = \frac{m^0}{\sqrt{1 - v_1^2/c^2}} + \frac{\mu^0}{\sqrt{1 - v_2^2/c^2}}.$$

The larger the value of E supplied, the greater will be the sum of the moving-masses of the two resultant particles, i.e., the greater the velocities v_1 and v_2. The smallest value of E that is sufficient to initiate the disintegration, called the binding energy, E_b, must correspond to velocities that differ infinitesimally from zero. The kinetic energies of the products then approach zero, or

$$M^0 + \frac{E_b}{c^2} = m^0 + \mu^0.$$

The binding energy, E_b, of a hydrogen atom (a proton and an electron) is 13.6 electron-volts. Since $1 \text{ eV} = 1.6 \times 10^{-19}$ joule, we have E_b equals 2.18×10^{-18} joule; so $\frac{E_b}{c^2}$ corresponds to a mass of 2.42×10^{-35} kg. But the rest-mass of the hydrogen atom is $M^0 = 1.67 \times 10^{-27}$ kg. The binding energy term is negligibly small compared to this, roughly one part in 10^8. Neglecting this small term gives the ordinary law of conservation of mass: $M^0 = m^0 + \mu^0$. This is valid for all chemical reactions, where E_b is of the order of magnitude given here.

Similarly, $M^0 c^2 + E = mc^2 + \mu c^2$. If we set $mc^2 = m^0 c^2 + K_m$, and $\mu c^2 = \mu^0 c^2 + K_\mu$, where K_m and K_μ are kinetic energies of the individual particles, then $M^0 c^2 + E = m^0 c^2 + K_m + \mu^0 c^2 + K_\mu$. Subtracting $M^0 c^2 + E_b = m^0 c^2 + \mu^0 c^2$ gives $E - E_b = K_m + K_\mu$: the ordinary law of conservation of energy.

In nuclear reactions E_b has a value millions or billions of times as large as the values typical of chemical reactions. $\frac{E_b}{c^2}$ is then no longer negligible compared to M^0 and the ordinary law of conservation of mass, $M^0 = m^0 + \mu^0$, is no longer valid. However, the relativistic law of conservation of mass-energy, $M^0 + \frac{E}{c^2} = m + \mu$, still holds true here also.

3. MOMENTUM AND ENERGY

A particle of rest-mass m^0 moving with velocity v relative to an observer has, as we have seen above, a momentum $p = \dfrac{m^0 v}{\sqrt{1 - v^2/c^2}}$ and an energy $E = \dfrac{m^0 c^2}{\sqrt{1 - v^2/c^2}}$ for this observer. For a different observer these values will be different. But from the two quantities p and E it is possible to form the quantity

$$E^2 - c^2 p^2 = (m^0 c^2)^2,$$

which has the same value for all observers. cp and E play roles here that are similar to the roles played by x and ct, respectively, while the rest-energy corresponds to the interval. A graph of this equation is given in Appendix 1.

Just as the Lorentz transformation $x' = \dfrac{x - (v/c)ct}{\sqrt{1 - v^2/c^2}}$, $y' = y$, $z' = z$, $ct' = \dfrac{-(v/c)x + ct}{\sqrt{1 - v^2/c^2}}$ followed from the invariance of the interval, the transformation of the momentum and energy components follows immediately from the invariance of the rest-energy:

$$
\begin{cases}
cp_x' = \dfrac{cp_x - \left(\dfrac{v}{c}\right)E}{\sqrt{1 - \dfrac{v^2}{c^2}}}, \\[3ex]
cp_y' = cp_y, \\[1ex]
cp_z' = cp_z, \\[2ex]
E' = \dfrac{-\left(\dfrac{v}{c}\right)cp + E}{\sqrt{1 - \dfrac{v^2}{c^2}}}
\end{cases}
$$

Momentum and energy are the components or coordinates of one quantity, momentum-energy, just as space and time are the components or coordinates of space-time.

It is instructive to draw a momentum-energy diagram, similar to the space-time diagram but with cp and E as the axes, as in Figure 31. Here cp and E give the momentum and energy of a particle; cp' and E' apply to the same particle for another observer. For a given type of particle, with rest mass m^0, there is a given rest-energy $E^0 = m^0 c^2$ such that $E^2 - c^2 p^2 = (E^0)^2$. Just as with the H, W axes of the x-ct diagram it is possible to represent this equation by a curve plotted on the H, W axes here: $W^2 - H^2 = \dfrac{(E^0)^2}{\sqrt{1 - \beta^2}}$.

The hyperbola of two sections in Figure 31 represents all the combinations of p and E that are possible for a given type of particle of rest-mass m^0, either for the observer with the (cp, E) axes or for the observer with the (cp', E') axes. Since $(E^0)^2$ cannot be negative for real E^0 the curve is time-like, or energy-like: it can only appear in the cone above and below the origin, not in the regions to the left and to the right. For a given observer it is possible to place the particle such that $cp = 0$ but not possible to have $E = 0$ (unless

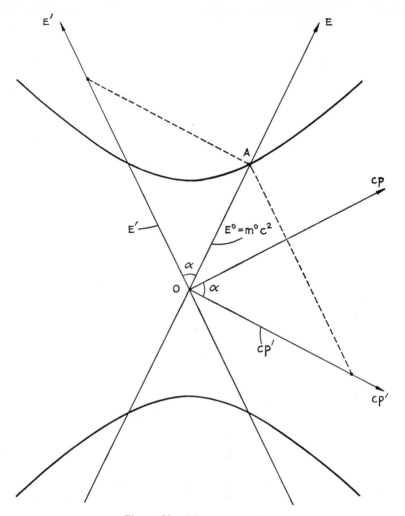

Figure 31. Momentum and energy.

$m^0 = 0$, when the two sections of the hyperbola become the two straight lines through the origin at 45° and 135°).

To find the relation between the cp-E and the cp'-E' observers consider a particle at A in Figure 31. There $cp = 0$ (using a Loedel-type diagram) so the particle is attached to the system of the observer who has the inner set of axes, (cp, E). The equation $E^2 - c^2p^2 = (E^0)^2$ then gives $E^2 = (E^0)^2$ or $E = \pm E^0$. The + refers to the upper section of the hyperbola, for particles with positive rest-mass; the − refers to the lower section of the hyperbola, for particles with negative rest-mass, such as a positron or an electron hole in a lattice. The value of cp' is $\dfrac{cm^0v}{\sqrt{1 - v^2/c^2}}$. Then Figure 31 gives, by the

Pythagorean theorem, $E' = \dfrac{m^0 c^2}{\sqrt{1 - v^2/c^2}}$. Consequently $\sin \alpha = \dfrac{v}{c}$. Just as in the case of the x-ct Loedel diagram, the observer of the inner (cp, E) axes is moving to the right with velocity v relative to the observer of the outer (cp', E') axes.

For a given pair of observers let the hyperbola of Figure 31 represent electrons with all possible values of velocity. Protons with various velocities would have a different hyperbola for these same observers. For a different set of observers, however, the previous curve for the electrons, considered against the H-W axes, could become the curve for the protons. In fact, for different observers the curve for the electrons becomes any member of the family of hyperbolas filling the upper region inside the lightcone with a value of $v \geq 0$ in $W^2 - H^2 = \dfrac{(E^0)^2}{\sqrt{1 - \dfrac{v^2}{c^2}}}$.

If we consider a given electron on the hyperbola of electrons for one pair of observers, then this electron generates another hyperbola, orthogonal to the first, when we consider all other pairs of observers. The situation is similar to the previous case with intervals; but it is simpler here in that only one value of rest-energy is permissible for a given particle, while any value of interval is permissible for an event. The section of the hyperbola $H^2 W^2 = \lambda^2$ inside the lightcone and above the hyperbola $W^2 - H^2 = (E^0)^2$ gives all the possible combinations of p and E which a given electron may have for different observers. To the extent permitted by this curve it is possible to change the momentum and energy for a given particle by employing other observers. In the same way, it was possible to change space and time coordinates for a given event by going to other observers.

The relation $E^2 - c^2 p^2 = (m^0 c^2)^2$ provides enough information so that, with the laws of conservation of momentum and conservation of mass-energy, the energies of the decay products in the example of the previous section are uniquely determined. As before, $M^0 c^2 = m c^2 + \mu c^2 = E_m + E_\mu$. However $E_m{}^2 - c^2 p_m{}^2 = (m^0)^2 c^4 = E_\mu{}^2 - c^2 p_\mu{}^2 = (\mu^0)^2 c^4$; in addition, from momentum conservation $0 = p_m + p_\mu$ so $c^2 p_m{}^2 = c^2 p_\mu{}^2$; then $E_m{}^2 - (m^0)^2 c^4 = E_\mu{}^2 - (\mu^0)^2 c^4$. The two equations for E_m and E_μ give:

$$E_\mu = \frac{c^2}{2 M^0} [(M^0)^2 + (\mu^0)^2 - (m^0)^2],$$

$$E_m = \frac{c^2}{2 M^0} [(M^0)^2 - (\mu^0)^2 + (m^0)^2].$$

These results may also be obtained from the E-cp diagram but it is more simply done algebraically. This, unfortunately, is even more true when more than one dimension is involved in the process.

4. KINETIC ENERGY

The energy of a particle at rest is m^0c^2 and the energy of the particle when moving is mc^2. The difference between these two is the kinetic energy

$$K = (m - m^0)c^2 = m^0c^2\left(\frac{1}{\sqrt{1 - \beta^2}} - 1\right).$$

This, rather than $\frac{1}{2}\left(\frac{m^0}{\sqrt{1 - \beta^2}}\right)v^2$, is the proper relativistic generalization of the $\frac{1}{2}m^0v^2$ classical formula for kinetic energy. When $v \ll c$ an expansion by the binomial theorem gives

$$K = m^0c^2\left[\left(1 + \frac{v^2}{2c^2} + \cdots\right) - 1\right] = \frac{m^0}{2}v^2\left(1 + \frac{3}{4}\frac{v^2}{c^2} + \cdots\right).$$

For slow speeds this formula is approximated by the ordinary expression $K = \frac{m^0}{2}v^2$. The incorrect formula above would give

$$K = \frac{m^0}{2}v^2\left(1 + \frac{1}{2}\frac{v^2}{c^2} + \cdots\right).$$

With the formulas now available it is instructive to solve several problems involving energy interchange between particles and photons. In the *photoelectric effect* a photon striking matter releases an electron, the energy of the photon being completely absorbed; the photon vanishes. Let us see why this is not possible for the collision between a photon and a free electron. Conservation of mass-energy gives $E_v + m^0c^2 = mc^2$ or $hv = (m - m^0)c^2 = K$. Here E_v is the photon energy in the system where the electron was originally at rest; after absorbing the photon, the electron is presumed to have velocity v. Conservation of momentum gives $\frac{hv}{c} = mv$, so $mv = (m - m^0)c$. Inserting $m = \frac{m^0}{\sqrt{1 - \beta^2}}$ and solving for β gives $\beta = 0, 1$. Neither of these results is acceptable physically. Consequently, a free electron cannot completely absorb a photon. A classical computation using $K = \frac{1}{2}mv^2$ gives only $v = 0$ as the solution, unacceptable as before.

When the collision occurs between a photon and an atom, however, it is quite possible to convert a bound electron to a free electron while conserving both mass-energy and momentum. The mass-energy equation becomes $hv + M^0c^2 = mc^2 + \mu c^2$. Here M^0 = rest-mass of the atom, m = moving-mass of the free electron, and μ = moving-mass of the ion produced by the ejection of the electron. With K_e and K_i as the kinetic energies of the electron and ion, respectively, this equation may also be written $hv = (m^0 + \mu^0 - M^0)c^2 + K_e + K_i$. It may be shown (Problems 12, 13, 14 for Chapter 6) that, because the mass of any ion is thousands of times as large as that of an electron, $K_i \ll K_e$. Also $E_b = (m^0 + \mu^0 - M^0)c^2$ is the binding energy of the electron in the atom; then, very nearly, $h\nu = E_b + K_e$. The ion energy may be neglected, therefore, in the equation showing the energy balance. The momentum of the ion can be significant, however, even though its energy is negligible compared to the electron's energy. This is considered in Problems 12 to 14.

Although it is not possible for a free electron to absorb all the energy of an impinging photon, it is quite possible for a free electron to absorb a fraction of a photon's energy, the difference in energy going off as a scattered photon. This is the *Compton effect*. Let the incident photon of frequency ν and wavelength λ move to the right along the x axis, toward an originally stationary electron; and let the scattered photon (ν' and λ') make an angle θ with the x axis, while the scattered electron (p and E) moves along a direction making an angle $-\phi$ with the x axis. Then

$$\begin{cases} h\nu + m^0c^2 = h\nu' + E, \\[2mm] \dfrac{h\nu}{c} = p\cos\phi + \dfrac{h\nu'}{c}\cos\theta, \\[2mm] 0 = -p\sin\phi + \dfrac{h\nu'}{c}\sin\theta. \end{cases}$$

These may be solved to give

$$\Delta\lambda = \lambda' - \lambda = \frac{h}{m^0c}(1 - \cos\theta).$$

The combination $\dfrac{h}{m^0c}$ is called the Compton wavelength and has the value 0.024 Å. For $\theta = 0$ or π the scattering is readily shown on the E-cp diagram, but for other values of θ a three-dimensional graph is required; this is not easily drawn.

The shift in wavelength for visible light ($\sim$5000 Å) is negligible, but for x-rays ($\sim$1 Å to 0.001 Å) the effect may be quite large. When the wavelength of the scattered wave is essentially that of the incident wave the process is called Thomson scattering; when there is an appreciable percentage shift in wavelength the process is called Compton scattering. There is no sharp borderline between the two types. The bound electrons within an atom also scatter incident photons. Here the scattering is called Rayleigh scattering for low energy photons such as visible light—a classical, nonrelativistic phenomenon. The scattered light is coherent with the incident light but the formula for scattered intensity is different from Thomson scattering. For high energy photons the scattering from bound electrons also becomes Compton scattering. Again, there is no sharp limit for the transition.

As a final example illustrating both the application of the relativistic kinetic energy expression and the exchange of energy between mass and radiation we consider the process of *pair production*—the creation of matter from electromagnetic radiation. To form a single particle of nonvanishing rest-mass from a photon requires a photon whose energy is at least the equivalent of the rest-mass of the particle. An electron or a positron would each require the least energetic photon. However, if either one or the other particle, alone, were created there would be a violation of the law of conservation of charge. Therefore, it is necessary to produce a pair of particles from the photon—one electron and one positron (the latter being the antiparticle of the former)—with the same mass magnitude but opposite charge.

Conservation of mass-energy gives, if the process takes place without interacting with other particles,

$$h\nu = m_+c^2 + m_-c^2 = 2m^0c^2 + K_+ + K_-,$$

where the $+$ subscripts refer to positrons, the $-$ subscripts to electrons, and a 0 superscript to either. If the kinetic energies of the resultant particles are zero, then the least energetic incident photon is required, with an energy equal to $2m^0c^2 = 2(9.1 \times 10^{-31} \text{ kg})\left(3 \times 10^8 \frac{\text{m}}{\text{sec}}\right)^2 = 1.64 \times 10^{-13}$ joule. Since 1 electron-volt $= 1.6 \times 10^{-19}$ joule, this gives 1.02×10^6 eV or 1.02 MeV: the rest-mass of an electron is 0.51 MeV. By comparison, the proton's rest-mass is 938 MeV or 0.938 BeV—almost a billion electron-volts. In chemical processes the binding energies, as we saw previously, are of the order of 1 electron-volt.

In the previous section we considered a hyperbola of two branches in (cp, E), or momentum-energy, space. The top branch, with positive energy, was said to apply for electrons; the bottom branch, with negative energy, applied for positrons. $E = mc^2$, so if m is negative then E is negative; at low velocities a negative mass would mean that a force in one direction would produce an acceleration in the opposite direction. This is actually observed experimentally; common examples occur with electron holes in many solids: in the Hall effect, in diode junctions, etc.

In the present section it might seem we are considering the positron mass as positive, but this is only apparently so. What we actually have is the following: the energy, $h\nu$, is utilized to lift an ordinary electron of positive rest-mass, (m^0), from a negative energy level, $E = -(m^0)c^2$, where it is unobservable, to a positive energy level, $E = +(m^0)c^2$, where it becomes observable. For the observable electron $E = m^0c^2$ applies, with all quantities positive; the equation is not applied to the unobservable electron. The electron has its energy increased, however, from $-m^0c^2$ to $+m^0c^2$; conservation of mass-energy gives $h\nu = 2m^0c^2$. The vacancy, left by the uplift of the ordinary electron, is the observable positron of negative mass and negative energy. For it $E = (-m^0)c^2$ with the positron energy negative and the positron rest-mass negative.

We now show that it is not possible for a single, isolated photon (i.e., one remote from an electron or a nucleon) to create an electron-positron pair.

This is so because it is not possible to conserve both mass-energy and momentum in such a process. The situation is somewhat similar to the case of the photon and the isolated electron in the photoelectric effect. We have

$$hv = m_+c^2 + m_-c^2 = \sqrt{(m^0c^2)^2 + c^2p_+^2} + \sqrt{(m^0c^2)^2 + c^2p_-^2}$$

from conservation of mass-energy, where $+$ subscripts again refer to the positron. So

$$(hv)^2 = 2(m^0c^2)^2 + c^2p_+^2 + c^2p_-^2 + 2\sqrt{[(m^0c^2)^2 + c^2p_+^2][(m^0c^2)^2 + c^2p_-^2]}.$$

From conservation of momentum, if the electron and positron go off in the same direction as that of the incident photon, then $\dfrac{hv}{c} = p_+ + p_-$. If this condition is not satisfied then the electron and positron go off symmetrically about the initial direction of the photon, each with the same component of momentum along this direction but with opposite components of momentum perpendicular to this direction. In that case $\dfrac{hv}{c} < (p_+ + p_-)$. In general,

$$(hv)^2 \le c^2p_+^2 + c^2p_-^2 + 2c^2p_+p_- .$$

Comparing the two expressions gives

$$2(m^0c^2)^2 + 2\sqrt{[(m^0c^2)^2 + c^2p_+^2][(m^0c^2)^2 + c^2p_-^2]} \le 2c^2p_+p_- .$$

This equation cannot be satisfied if we restrict ourselves to real quantities.

Pair production is, consequently, not possible in free space. However, as in the case of the photoelectric effect, this process is possible in the vicinity of a nucleus or an atom. The nucleus acquires negligible energy because of its preponderant mass but obtains sufficient momentum to balance the books, so to speak, for the conservation of momentum. As in the previous cases in this chapter, the algebraic solutions are simpler than the geometric ones when several dimensions are involved.

Suppose a particle of rest-mass m^0 moves with momentum p_x, kinetic energy K_x, and energy E_x toward $+x$ for an (x, ct) observer. Let this observer move with velocity v toward the right relative to an (X, cT) observer. Also, let p_v, K_v, and E_v be the corresponding quantities for this particle relative to the (X, cT) observer if the particle were at rest relative to the (x, ct) observer. The quantities p_X, K_X, and E_X representing the total values relative to the (X, cT) observer have been shown, by Pathria, to be represented by the following symmetric equations, which are nomographed in Appendix 1:

$$\begin{cases} \sinh^{-1}\left(\dfrac{p_X}{m^0c}\right) = \sinh^{-1}\left(\dfrac{p_x}{m^0c}\right) + \sinh^{-1}\left(\dfrac{p_v}{m^0c}\right), \\[2mm] \cosh^{-1}\left(\dfrac{E_X}{m^0c^2}\right) = \cosh^{-1}\left(\dfrac{E_x}{m^0c^2}\right) + \cosh^{-1}\left(\dfrac{E_v}{m^0c^2}\right), \\[2mm] \sinh^{-1}\sqrt{\dfrac{K_X}{2m^0c^2}} = \sinh^{-1}\sqrt{\dfrac{K_x}{2m^0c^2}} + \sinh^{-1}\sqrt{\dfrac{K_v}{2m^0c^2}} . \end{cases}$$

We conclude this section with the remark that relativity, itself, offers no connection between the *x-ct* graph and the *cp-E* graph. A particle, say an electron, may be represented by a one-dimensional line in the former and by a zero-dimensional point in the latter for a given pair of observers. But quantum theory does offer a connection—the indeterminancy principle. Written as $\Delta x \, \Delta(cp_x) > c\hbar$, $\Delta y \, \Delta(cp_y) > c\hbar$, $\Delta z \, \Delta(cp_z) > c\hbar$, $\Delta(ct) \, \Delta E > c\hbar$, where the Δ's are uncertainties in the respective measured quantities, it is seen to offer a restriction on the resolution with which corresponding axes of the two graphs may be utilized. The situation is one in which there is an uncontrollable jiggling of the two sets of axes relative to each other. The *x* axis and the cp_x axis are connected in such a way that the more firmly one is fixed the more violent is the shaking of the other. The *y* and cp_y axes behave similarly. There is no coupling, however, between jiggling along different "directions"—an indeterminancy Δx imposes no restriction on Δp_y, on Δp_z, on ΔE, or on Δt.

5. FORCE AND ACCELERATION

In Newton's mechanics the concept of force, like that of mass, plays a central role. In Einstein's mechanics the equations rarely mention force but this is, for the most part, a matter of convenience. We will obtain several necessary consequences by applying, in an elementary way, the outlook of relativity to the concept of force.

Consider the case of a tensile testing machine pulling one end of a steel rod with an infinitesimal velocity while the other is held in a massive clamp. Let the subscript inf refer to this case; the superscript zero refers to the almost identical rest-case. It is found that when the applied tensile force per unit cross sectional area, $\dfrac{F_{\text{inf}}}{A_{\text{inf}}} \approx \dfrac{F^0}{A^0}$, reaches a critical value the rod is torn into two parts, so that a value of proper-tensile-strength may be applied to the steel. Assume the rod lies along the *x* axis, so that its cross section is in the *yz* plane. Suppose we then consider the test from the viewpoint of an observer moving with a finite velocity *v* along the *x* axis. To this observer the cross section of the rod is the same as that above. If the nonproper-tensile-strength, *F/A*, is taken (like the proper-tensile-strength, F^0/A^0) as characteristic of the material when the stretching due to the force occurs at an infinitesimal rate, i.e., if $\dfrac{F}{A} = \dfrac{F^0}{A^0}$, then the critical force has the same value for both observers. With this assumption a force component F_x parallel to the direction of relative motion has the same value for all Galilean observers: $F_x = F^0_x$.

If the rod is put along the *y* axis while the relative velocity is again along the *x* axis then the cross section of the rod, in the *xz* plane, will measure $A = A^0\sqrt{1 - \beta^2}$ for the moving observer since the *x* dimension shrinks by the Lorentz factor while the *y* dimension is unchanged. To give the same characteristic tensile strength it is now required that $F = F^0\sqrt{1 - \beta^2}$. The same result would have been obtained along the z axis. Summarizing:

$$\begin{cases} F_x = F^0{}_x, \\ F_y = \sqrt{1 - \beta^2}\, F^0{}_y, \\ F_z = \sqrt{1 - \beta^2}\, F^0{}_z. \end{cases}$$

It is well to point out here that these are not the most general transformation equations for force. The latter are considerably more complicated and may be found, e.g., in Tolman's book. In the present case we are considering the transformation between a proper-force and a nonproper-force. This will be sufficient for our purpose.

Force and energy are related concepts: a force that moves an object a distance x along the direction of the force does work $W = Fx$, where work is the mechanical expenditure of energy. Let an observer have a proper-force $F^0{}_x$ acting in the x direction on a body which is stationary relative to him. Then the force $F^0{}_x$ does no work. ($F^0{}_x$ is not the total force in the x direction. There are other forces giving a component $-F^0{}_x$ in this direction. The total x component force is zero; the x component of acceleration is zero; and the x component of velocity is also zero for this proper-observer.) A second observer, moving with speed v relative to the first one along the $-x$ direction, will measure some finite displacement, $X = vT$, of the body along the line of action of the nonproper-force F_X. For him the force F_X does the work $W = F_X X$ (F_X and v are in the same sense along X). The X components of total force and acceleration are also zero for the nonproper-observer; the X component of velocity is not zero. But there can be no physical difference between these proper- and nonproper-observers: they differ only in being separate and distinct Galilean observers. The finite difference in the work, W, is consequently more mathematical than physical. It is a bookkeeping operation.

Now suppose we alter conditions for the first observer by considering the previously stationary body to move in the x direction with an infinitesimal velocity u_{inf}. For this observer there is work produced at an infinitesimal rate; we will call him the very-slow-observer and designate the work W_{inf}. Here

$$W_{inf} = (F^0{}_x)(x^0) = (F^0{}_x)(u_{inf}t^0),$$

where the time is essentially a proper-time, t^0. What is the work produced for the second observer in this case?

With respect to the second observer the body is now moving with velocity U where, if $\beta = \dfrac{v}{c}$ as before,

$$U = \frac{u_{inf} + v}{1 + \dfrac{u_{inf}v}{c^2}} = v\left[\frac{1 + \left(\dfrac{u_{inf}}{v}\right)}{1 + \beta^2\left(\dfrac{u_{inf}}{v}\right)}\right] \approx v\left[1 + (1 - \beta^2)\left(\dfrac{u_{inf}}{v}\right)\right].$$

The work done in a nonproper-time interval T for this observer is

$$W' = (F_X)(X) = F_X(UT) = F_X v \left[1 + (1 - \beta^2) \left(\frac{u_{\text{inf}}}{v} \right) \right] T$$

$$= F_X v T + [F^0{}_x](1 - \beta^2) u_{\text{inf}} \left[\frac{t^0}{\sqrt{1 - \beta^2}} \right]$$

$$= W + \sqrt{1 - \beta^2}\, W_{\text{inf}}.$$

The finite work component W is, just as before, a transformation quantity and will here be ignored. The physical portion of the work measured by the second observer is the infinitesimal component $W'_{\text{inf}} = W' - W$ or $\sqrt{1 - \beta^2}\, W_{\text{inf}}$. This is the work in which we are interested. It may be obtained directly from $W' = F_X X$ by setting $X = \sqrt{1 - \beta^2}\, x^0$. We will make use of this in the next chapter when we discuss the potential difference (work per unit charge) produced in a moving conductor.

When the proper-force acts perpendicular to the direction of relative velocity we have

$$W_{\text{inf}} = (F^0{}_y)(y^0) = F^0{}_y(v_{\text{inf}} t^0) ;$$

$$W'_{\text{inf}} = (F_Y)(Y) = F_Y(VT)$$

$$= F_Y \left[\frac{\sqrt{1 - \beta^2}\, v_{\text{inf}}}{1 + 0} \right] T = (\sqrt{1 - \beta^2}\, F^0{}_y)(\sqrt{1 - \beta^2}\, v_{\text{inf}}) \left(\frac{t^0}{\sqrt{1 - \beta^2}} \right),$$

$$W'_{\text{inf}} = \sqrt{1 - \beta^2}\, W_{\text{inf}} ;$$

and similarly for a proper-force along the z direction. The result is the same in all cases: independent of the relative direction of force and velocity, the work performed for the moving-observer is

$$W'_{\text{inf}} = \sqrt{1 - \beta^2}\, W_{\text{inf}}.$$

The work for the moving-observer differs from that for the rest-observer by the factor $\sqrt{1 - \beta^2}$. Note that the equation $W = \sqrt{1 - \beta^2}\, W^0$ for the work is quite different from the equation $E = \dfrac{E^0}{\sqrt{1 - \beta^2}}$ obtained in the previous chapter for the total energy.

In Newtonian mechanics $F = ma$ or, indifferently, force is the rate of change of momentum. If the mass is a constant the two statements are equivalent, since $p = mv$ and acceleration is the rate of change of velocity. When the mass becomes a function of velocity, however, the two statements are no longer synonymous and it becomes necessary to pick one alternative. One way to do this is to equate the work $W = Fl$ to the change in the kinetic energy of a particle $(m - m^0)c^2$. We shall here merely give the answer that this procedure yields the result of the second alternative above. With this approach, force is defined as the rate of change of momentum, relativistically as well as classically.

Using $\mathbf{p} = \dfrac{m^0}{\sqrt{1 - \beta^2}} \mathbf{v}$, where the velocity $\mathbf{v}$ has the components v_x, v_y, and v_z, the rate of change of $\mathbf{p}$ with respect to the time may be calculated to give

$$\mathbf{F} = \left[\frac{m^0}{\sqrt{1 - \beta^2}}\right]\mathbf{a} + \left\{\left[\frac{m^0}{(1 - \beta^2)^{3/2}}\right]\frac{va_v}{c^2}\right\}\mathbf{v},$$

where a_v is the component of the acceleration parallel to the velocity. Here $\mathbf{v}$ represents the velocity of a particle with respect to a given observer. The force vector does not point in the same direction, in general, as the acceleration vector because the last term in the equation above gives a component along the velocity vector: $\mathbf{F} = \mathbf{F}_a + \mathbf{F}_v$.

In Figure 32 the velocity has been taken along the x axis, with the

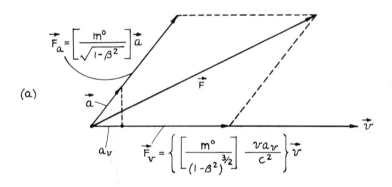

(a)

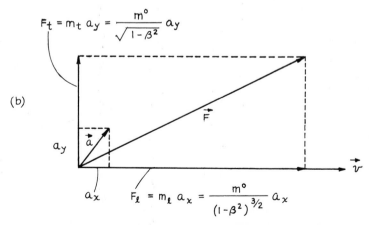

(b)

Figure 32. Force and acceleration.

acceleration having x and y components. Then the equation above becomes

$$F_x = \frac{m^0}{\sqrt{1-\beta^2}} a_x + \frac{m^0\beta^2}{(1-\beta^2)^{3/2}} a_x = \left[\frac{m^0}{(1-\beta^2)^{3/2}}\right] a_x \equiv m_l a_x,$$

$$F_y = \left[\frac{m^0}{\sqrt{1-\beta^2}}\right] a_y \equiv m_t a_y.$$

When the acceleration also has a z component we obtain

$$F_z = \left[\frac{m^0}{\sqrt{1-\beta^2}}\right] a_z = m_t a_z.$$

If we insist on employing $F = ma$, then the effective mass for acceleration perpendicular to the velocity is different from that for acceleration parallel to the velocity. m_l is called the longitudinal mass while m_t is the transverse mass. Figure 32 shows these two equivalent ways of giving the relationship among **F**, **a**, and **v**.

Neither the acceleration nor the force, as given above, are fundamental quantities in relativity. The reason why this is so will be discussed in the next chapter.

BIBLIOGRAPHY

Orear, J., Rosenfeld, A. H., and Schluter, R. A.: Nuclear Physics: A Course Given by Enrico Fermi. Revised edition. Chicago, University of Chicago Press, 1950 (paperback).

The following have all appeared in the American Journal of Physics:

Bertozzi, W.: Speed and Kinetic Energy of Relativistic Electrons. *32:* 551, July, 1964.
Cha, M. H., and Simons, D. G.: Geometrical Method for Relativistic Particle Kinematics. *31:* 280, Apr., 1963.
Crawford, F. S.: Mnemonic Device for Relativistic Particle Kinematics. *26:* 376, Sept., 1958.
Dewdney, J. W.: Relativistic Relations Among Mass, Velocity, Momentum, and Kinetic Energy. *28:* 562, Sept., 1960.
Ehlers, J., Rindler, W., and Penrose, R.: Energy Conservation as the Basis of Relativistic Mechanics, II. *33:* 995, Dec., 1965.
Feenberg, E.: Inertia of Energy. *28:* 564, Sept., 1960.
Hart, R. R.: Relativistic Rigid Bodies and the Uncertainty Principle. *33:* 1006, Dec., 1965.
Kantor, W.: Inertia of Energy. *22:* 528, Nov., 1954.
Pathria, R. K.: On Transformations in Relativistic Mechanics. *24:* 411, Aug., 1956.
Penrose, R., and Rindler, W.: Energy Conservation as the Basis of Relativistic Mechanics. *33:* 55, Jan., 1965.
Pomeranz, K. B.: The Equations of Motion for Relativistic Particles and Systems with a Variable Rest Mass. *32:* 955, Dec., 1964.
Reff, I.: Rest Mass of a Free Particle. *28:* 745, Nov., 1960.
Rhee, J. W.: Relativistic Rocket Motion. *33:* 587, July, 1965.
Robinson, B. L.: Collisions of Relativistic Particles. *29:* 369, June, 1961.
Sears, F. W.: Some Applications of the Brehme Diagram. *31:* 269, Apr., 1963.
Sears, F. W.: Two Notes on Special Relativity. *32:* 59, Jan., 1964.

The following articles from the American Journal of Physics relate to a paradox which is closely connected to the one of the rod and the barn discussed in connection with the reality of the Lorentz-Fitzgerald contraction:

Dewan, E. M.: Stress Effects due to Lorentz Contraction. *31:* 383, May, 1963.

Dewan, E., and Beran, M.: Note on Stress Effects due to Relativistic Contraction. *27:* 517, Oct., 1959.

Evett, A. A., and Wangsness, R. K.: Note on the Separation of Relativistically Moving Rockets. *28:* 566, Sept., 1960.

Nawrocki, P. J.: Stress Effects due to Relativistic Contraction. *30:* 771, Oct., 1962.

Romain, J. E.: A Geometrical Approach to Relativistic Paradoxes. *31:* 576, Aug., 1963.

Chapter 7 ELECTRICITY AND MAGNETISM

I. CHARGE AND CURRENT

The effect of relativity on mechanics, as we have seen, was revolutionary. On electricity and magnetism the influence was rather a broadening of viewpoint. It is interesting to note, however, that although the effects treated here so far have all dealt with mechanics, Einstein's original 1905 paper was titled "On the Electrodynamics of Moving Bodies."

A collection of electric charges which is at rest with respect to an observer produces, for that observer, an electric field **E** throughout all space. The electric force that this observer will measure on a small test charge q at some point, whether the test charge is fixed or moving, will be $\mathbf{F} = q\mathbf{E}$ where the field is evaluated at the test point.

When the electric charges which produce the field are not stationary but move with respect to the observer, it is found experimentally that, while the electric field is still present, an additional force is produced on a moving test charge. This force is attributed to a magnetic field **B**, created throughout all space by the moving charges. Although **B** is produced by charges moving relative to the observer, the field itself is defined as fixed in space relative to the observer. In general, this field can vary in time but we will consider only time-constant magnetic fields. The magnetic force that is measured is given by $\mathbf{F} = q\mathbf{v} \times \mathbf{B}$ in the MKSA system of units. Here $\mathbf{v} \times \mathbf{B}$ is the vector product, giving a vector of magnitude $vB \sin \theta$, where θ is the smaller angle between **v** and **B**; the resultant vector is in the direction of advance of a right-hand screw when **v** is turned into **B**.

The combined total force, electric and magnetic, consists of one part which is due to the mere presence of the field-producing charges and a second part which is due to the motion of these field-producing charges relative to the observer. A nonvanishing magnetic force, however, requires not only motion of the field-producing charges relative to the observer but also motion of the test charge, itself, relative to the observer. In addition, the latter motion will produce a maximum magnetic force only when it is perpendicular to the magnetic field, **B**, created by the motion of the field-producing charges; when the test charge velocity is parallel to the field, **B**, created by the velocities of the field-producing charges then no magnetic force is produced on the test charge. The magnetic force is seen to be relatively complicated compared to the electric force. The total force is called the Lorentz force and is given by $\mathbf{F} = q[\mathbf{E} + (\mathbf{v} \times \mathbf{B})]$. This equation may be considered a definition both for **E** and for **B**. We repeat: **E** and **B** are defined as fixed relative to the observer.

Moving charges are not the only means by which a magnetic field **B** may be created. Permanent magnets, for example, also produce magnetic fields. This type of magnetic field is produced predominantly by the spin magnetic moment of the individual electrons within the magnet. We will restrict ourselves to the magnetic fields produced by moving charges.

If the charge which produces the magnetic field **B** has a volume density ρ coulomb/meter^3 at a given point in space and also a velocity **v** meters per second, then it is said to constitute a current density $\mathbf{j} = \rho\mathbf{v}$ ampere/meter^2, where 1 ampere = 1 coulomb/second and **j** gives the rate of flow of charge across a unit area perpendicular to **v**. Sometimes the charge is distributed on a surface, with a surface charge density σ coulomb/meter^2 and a velocity restricted to the surface; then $\mathbf{j}_l = \sigma\mathbf{v}$ ampere/meter gives a linear current density—a flow per unit length across a line in the surface and perpendicular to **v**. Another case occurs when the charge is distributed along a line with a linear density λ coulomb/meter and a velocity restricted to the line. Here $\mathbf{I} = \lambda\mathbf{v}$ ampere gives the total current passing a point in the line.

Let an observer, A, measure a volume charge density ρ^0 in a region of space stationary with respect to him. A will then measure a total charge, $Q = \rho^0(l^0)^3$ coulomb, within a cube of side l^0. Since the charge is stationary for A there is no current. For this observer an electric, but no magnetic, field is produced. Suppose another observer, B, is moving with velocity $-\mathbf{v}$ relative to the first and perpendicular to one face of the cube. To B the charge is moving with velocity **v** so both electric and magnetic fields are produced for him.

The first question to arise is—do A and B each measure the same total charge Q? It cannot be assumed that the charge is invariant; in the analogous case of mass there is no invariance, the value of mass being dependent upon the velocity of the mass relative to the observer. It turns out that for charge, however, there is excellent experimental evidence that the charge is, indeed, invariant: both A and B will measure the same value of Q regardless of the value of **v**. One such piece of evidence is provided by the electrical neutrality of both He and H_2. Each of these contain two electrons and two protons, but the motions of the particles are quite different in the helium atom than in the hydrogen molecule.

Although the total charge is the same for A and B, this is not true of the charge density. For B the volume has two sides measuring l^0 and one side measuring $\sqrt{1-\beta^2}\, l^0$, so the volume is $\sqrt{1-\beta^2}\,(l^0)^3$ rather than $(l^0)^3$. Consequently, the charge density for B is $\rho = \dfrac{\rho^0}{\sqrt{1-\beta^2}}$. The current measured by B will be $\mathbf{I} = Q\mathbf{v}$ and the current density will be $\mathbf{j} = \rho\mathbf{v}$ or $\dfrac{\rho^0\mathbf{v}}{\sqrt{1-\beta^2}}$ with components $j_x = \dfrac{\rho^0 v_x}{\sqrt{1-\beta^2}}$, $j_y = \dfrac{\rho^0 v_y}{\sqrt{1-\beta^2}}$, $j_z = \dfrac{\rho^0 v_z}{\sqrt{1-\beta^2}}$.

A current $\mathbf{I}$ which is obtained by relative motion, alone, between charge and observer—without the necessity for an electric field—is called a convection current. The beam current in a TV picture tube (in the drift space between the electron gun and the phosphor screen) is just such a convection current. Such currents, of course, do not satisfy Ohm's law. This law, $V = IR$ with the resistance R a constant, holds for many ordinary materials and applies to conduction currents, currents which do require an electric field intensity to produce them.

It is possible to form an invariant quantity, one which has the same value for all observers, from the four factors above:

$$c^2\rho^2 - (j_x{}^2 + j_y{}^2 + j_z{}^2) = c^2(\rho^0)^2.$$

This is precisely analogous to the way x, y, z, ct formed the invariant quantity called the interval. Here $c\rho^0$ plays the role of the interval. ρ^0 is called the proper-charge density while ρ is a nonproper-charge density. The space-time diagrams may thus be taken over, letting $x \rightarrow j_x$, $y \rightarrow j_y$, $z \rightarrow j_z$, $ct \rightarrow c\rho$, to give a current density–charge density diagram. As with space-time, $\mathbf{j}$ and ρ are not independent quantities but are the components of one entity. Subject to the constraints of the current density–charge density diagram the individual components will have different relative proportions for different Galilean observers.

If we had started with a straight line charge density λ^0 (instead of ρ^0) then, by similar reasoning, an observer moving with velocity $-\mathbf{v}$ along the line would measure a linear density $\lambda = \dfrac{\lambda^0}{\sqrt{1-\beta^2}}$ and a current $\mathbf{I} = \dfrac{\lambda^0\mathbf{v}}{\sqrt{1-\beta^2}}$.

2. PARALLEL BEAMS

Imagine two infinitely long parallel beams of electrons produced by an electron gun, separated by a distance D and traveling with constant velocity $\mathbf{v}$ along the positive x direction in a space free of external fields. Although it can be imagined, this situation is not physically realizable because the fields set up by one beam produce a Lorentz force on the second beam which is perpendicular to the latter, causing the beams to repel each other. To avoid this we will substitute two infinitely long parallel conductors, one $D/2$ above and the other $D/2$ below the x axis, stationary with respect to an observer A.

The two metallic conductors originally contained equal and opposite charge densities of negative electrons and positive ions, with some of the former (approximately one electron per atom of the material) free to move about within the metal but with none of either type free to leave the surface. An external linear charge density λ^0, however, is assumed to have been added to each conductor, with the charges stationary referred to A. With respect to another observer B, moving with velocity $-\mathbf{v}$ relative to A, we would then have two parallel charged beams moving to the right. If λ^0 is positive, two currents also flow to the right; if λ^0 is negative, the equivalent currents flow to the left.

A will measure an electric field intensity E_a at one conductor produced by the charges of the second conductor. E_a is directed away from the latter if λ^0 is positive while it is directed toward the latter if λ^0 is negative. The value of E_a, derived from Coulomb's law, is $E_a = \dfrac{\lambda^0}{2\pi\varepsilon_0 D}$ where ε_0 is a constant (the permittivity) associated with the free space in which the conductors are embedded. The force per unit length on the first conductor produced by the entire second conductor is then

$$F_a = \frac{(\lambda^0)^2}{2\pi\varepsilon_0 D}$$

and will be directed away from the latter regardless of whether λ^0 is positive for both conductors or negative for both conductors.

B will measure a nonproper-charge density $\lambda = \dfrac{\lambda^0}{\sqrt{1-\beta^2}}$ for each conductor. His corresponding value of electric field intensity will be $E_b = \dfrac{\lambda}{2\pi\varepsilon_0 D}$ although, unlike the case for A, it is not correct to derive the value of E for observer B from Coulomb's law. When a charge is moving relative to an observer, the value of E is no longer given by Coulomb's law. The latter law is spherically symmetric; the value of the field at a given distance from the charge is independent of the direction. The actual law when the charges are moving approaches Coulomb's law for small velocities but, as $v \to c$, concentrates E more and more in a trasverse plane; the distribution becomes pancake shaped instead of spherical. However, if the exact law is integrated to give the value of E produced by infinitely many charges, uniformly distributed on a straight line and all moving with the same constant velocity, then the same result is obtained as that found by assuming Coulomb's law. (See Problems 3, 4, 5 and 6 for Chapter 7.)

The repulsive electrical force per unit length will be given by

$$F_{\text{elec}} = \frac{\lambda^2}{2\pi\varepsilon_0 D} = \frac{(\lambda^0)^2}{2\pi\varepsilon_0 D(1-\beta^2)}.$$

B will also measure two parallel currents, $I = \lambda v$. A magnetic flux density $\mathbf{B}$ is produced at one conductor by the current in the other. The value of $\mathbf{B}$, derived from Ampere's law, is $\mathbf{B} = \dfrac{\mu_0 I}{2\pi D}\,\hat{\boldsymbol{\phi}}$ where μ_0 is the permeability of free space and $\hat{\boldsymbol{\phi}}$ is a unit vector in the ϕ direction. $\mathbf{B}$ at a conductor is perpendicular to the plane of the two conductors. This produces an attractive magnetic force per unit length of one conductor (caused by the entire second conductor) whose magnitude is

$$F_{\text{mag}} = \frac{\mu_0 I^2}{2\pi D} = \frac{\mu_0 \lambda^2 v^2}{2\pi D} .$$

This expression may be multiplied, top and bottom, by ε_0; then substituting

$$\varepsilon_0 \mu_0 = \frac{1}{c^2},$$

an expression derived from Maxwell's equations, there results

$$F_{\text{mag}} = \frac{v^2}{c^2} F_{\text{elec}},$$

where F_{mag} is opposite in direction to F_{elec}.

The total repulsive force per unit length of one conductor, as measured by B, that is produced by the entire second conductor is given by $F_{\text{elec}} + F_{\text{mag}}$:

$$F_b = (1 - \beta^2)F_{\text{elec}} = (1 - \beta^2)\frac{(\lambda^0)^2}{2\pi\varepsilon_0 D(1 - \beta^2)} = \frac{(\lambda^0)^2}{2\pi\varepsilon_0 D} .$$

This is precisely the same value calculated by A, although A records only an electric field while B records both an electric and a magnetic field. It is worth noting that it is not necessary to assume Ampere's law in order to obtain the force per unit length for B, as we have done here. Coulomb's law and the Lorentz transformation, alone, are sufficient to calculate the result. (See Problem 12 for Chapter 7.)

However, although A and B agree as to the value of the force per unit length, they are actually talking of different unit lengths. A given length of the conductor, between two marks stationary for A, will measure L^0 for A and $L^0\sqrt{1 - \beta^2}$ for B because of the Lorentz contraction. Consequently, on a given length of conductor the total repulsive force, F, measured by B will be equal to $F^0\sqrt{1 - \beta^2}$, where F^0 is the total repulsive force measured by A. Since the forces here are perpendicular to the direction of relative motion of the two observers, this result agrees with the transformation of forces obtained in the previous chapter.

For A, stationary relative to the beam charges, the force on a length L^0 of beam #1 caused by the entire length of beam #2 is $\dfrac{(\lambda^0)^2 L^0}{2\pi\varepsilon_0 D}$: a finite quantity. For B, relative to whom the beam charges move with velocity $\mathbf{v}$, the force on the same length is $\dfrac{(\lambda^0)^2 L^0\sqrt{1 - \beta^2}}{2\pi\varepsilon_0 D}$, a quantity which approaches zero as $\beta \to 1$. This effect is of great benefit in the design of high energy beam accelerators since the defocusing repulsive force between different parts of the beam becomes less and less important as $v \to c$. It then becomes that much less difficult to achieve higher current densities.

The example given here serves to show that the concepts of electric field and magnetic field are not absolute but are only relative. One observer may say there is a magnetic field, another may not. They also disagree on the value of the electric field. Nevertheless, they agree in their measures of force per unit length.

3. PARALLEL CONDUCTORS

In the previous section we considered the forces between two parallel convection currents. In this section we will treat parallel conduction currents, considering only ideal conductors; in Appendix 3 we consider the case of real conductors. Ideal conductors have no resistance and no fields exist inside them, all current flow being restricted to the surface. The conduction current, which is produced by a battery or some other source of electrical energy acting in a closed circuit, is limited to some finite value by the presence of a resistor somewhere in the circuit.

Consider two long, parallel ideal wires, a and c. Subsequently we will introduce a third ideal wire, b, but for the present this is unnecessary. Very far to the left a battery and a switch are connected in series with the conductors; the potential difference of the battery is V, the wire a being connected to the plus terminal. Very far to the right a resistor R is connected between the two conductors, completing the circuit when the switch is closed at time $t = 0$. The two ideal wires constitute a transmission line; the line has a characteristic impedance which is here a pure resistance, R_o, determined by the diameter and spacing of the conductors. R_o is the initial instantaneous resistance seen by the battery at the moment when the switch is closed; this is true regardless of the value of the terminating resistor R.

When the switch is closed both a voltage wave, V, and a current wave, $I_o = \dfrac{V}{R_o}$, start traveling down the line to the right. At a point P on wire a, distant l from the left end, the current will be zero from $t = 0$ to $t = \dfrac{l}{c}$ since the wave travels with a speed that is essentially that of light in vacuum (the presence of air reduces this a trifle). At $t = \dfrac{l}{c}$ the current at P will change from 0 to I_o, toward the right; this actually occurs during some finite time interval but we may treat the duration of this interval as negligibly small. The voltage wave is exactly transverse to the wires for ideal conductors, the lines of force extending from a to c in a plane perpendicular to the wires. The current wave to the right in a is produced by electrons flowing to the left; in c the wave moving to the right produces a current to the left which actually consists of electrons moving to the right. The electrons do not move with the speed of the wave. Rather, they move on the surface of the conductors with a very slow speed called the drift velocity. (For a real conductor such as copper the drift velocity of the electrons in the interior of the metal is of the order of 0.03 cm/sec—only 10^{-12} as great as the speed of the wave.)

We will idealize the situation by considering both the free electrons and the ions of the ideal conductors to be stationary in the absence of a field, with a mean axial separation of L^0 for each type. The positive linear proper-charge density will be $\lambda_p = \lambda$, the negative linear proper-charge density will be $\lambda_n = -\lambda$, and the net linear charge density will be zero. Transient changes are required to accomplish the transition from the initial current, $I_o = \dfrac{V}{R_o}$, to the final steady-state current, $I = \dfrac{V}{R}$, determined by the value of the terminating resistor. The transient changes actually last for an infinitely long time but they get smaller and smaller quite rapidly so that, for practical purposes, the steady-state condition is attained in a fraction of a second. When steady-state conditions have been established, i.e., when the transient changes have become so small that we may ignore them, the electrons will all have a common drift velocity, to the left in wire a and to the right in wire c. For an observer, A, stationary with respect to the ions and the wires, what are the new values of mean axial separation between the electrons? Or, put another way, what will be the value of the negative linear nonproper-charge density?

The question posed here is the crux of our problem. Its answer is by no means obvious. We will show that for ideal conductors the new values are not the same as the old values, L^0 and λ_n; for real conductors, on the other hand, the new values are the same as the old ones in the interior but differ from the old values on the surface. The relativistic method we will employ is suited only for ideal conductors; for nonideal conductors this method is quite impractical and we will use other, nonrelativistic, arguments. Since we will obtain, for the ideal case, a change in λ_n but not in λ_p it follows that for this case the wires become charged for the stationary observer, A. For the lossy or nonideal wires we will see that the conductors are uncharged internally; on the surface there will still be a charge which, however, now varies with position along the wire.

Consider a Galilean observer, B, moving to the left relative to A with velocity $\mathbf{v}$, the same as the drift velocity acquired by the electrons in a after the voltage wave has been established by the passage of the first wave. The space-time diagram of Figure 33a illustrates a case in which an instantaneous acceleration is given to two adjacent electrons simultaneously, as seen by A: the new spacing is the same as the old spacing L^0. If, instead of sharp kinks in the world-lines of the electrons, the curves were smooth—corresponding to gradual instead of sudden acceleration—then the results could be obtained with finite forces. The conclusions would be unchanged, however, provided

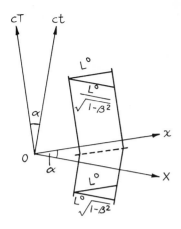

(a)   INSTANTANEOUS FOR A

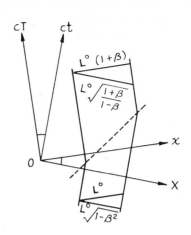

(b)   DETERMINED BY RIGHT-MOVING
ELECTROMAGNETIC WAVE

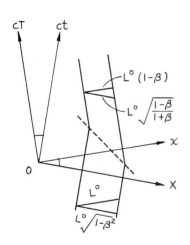

(c)   DETERMINED BY LEFT-MOVING
ELECTROMAGNETIC WAVE

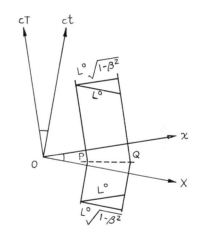

(d)   IN A SYMMETRICAL FASHION FOR
A AND B (I OF 2 POSSIBILITIES)

Figure 33.   Space-time diagrams for change in electron velocity.

the curves had the same separation for A at all times; that is, provided the two electrons had accelerations which were identical functions of time for A.

In this figure only the value of L^0 before the transition is assumed; the other values shown are calculated from the geometry. Of course, this figure cannot apply to our case for it corresponds to a wave which is propagated with infinite velocity. This, however, does not preclude the possibility that the same answer—identical spacing, L^0, before and after—can be obtained by means other than a wave of infinite velocity.

Figure 33*b* gives the space-time diagram for the electron spacing when the transition in velocity to the left in *a* is determined by an electromagnetic wave moving to the right: the dotted line at 45° with the horizontal is the world-line of the wave with velocity *c*. Again assuming only L^0 for *A* before the transition, one obtains the other values shown in the figure directly from the geometry. Since the total charge between any two given points is the same for all observers, the following table of negative linear charge density is obtained from density $= \dfrac{\text{charge}}{\text{separation}}$:

	OBSERVER *B* (moving left)	OBSERVER *A* (moving right)
BEFORE ACCELERATION	$\dfrac{1}{\sqrt{1-\beta^2}}\,\lambda_n$	λ_n
AFTER ACCELERATION	$\sqrt{\dfrac{1-\beta}{1+\beta}}\,\lambda_n$	$\left(\dfrac{1}{1+\beta}\right)\lambda_n$

In similar fashion Figure 33*c* depicts the situation when the transition in velocity to the left is determined by an electromagnetic wave moving to the left. This would occur, e.g., if a battery were connected with its negative terminal to wire *a* and its positive terminal to wire *c*, both at the right end of the transmission line. This case is pertinent to the one we are actually considering if we have a wave reflected from the terminating resistor, *R*, at the far right end. From the lengths in this figure we obtain the following table of negative linear charge density:

	OBSERVER *B* (moving left)	OBSERVER *A* (moving right)
BEFORE ACCELERATION	$\dfrac{1}{\sqrt{1-\beta^2}}\,\lambda_n$	λ_n
AFTER ACCELERATION	$\sqrt{\dfrac{1+\beta}{1-\beta}}\,\lambda_n$	$\left(\dfrac{1}{1-\beta}\right)\lambda_n$

A simple analogy suggests itself: a locomotive and a string of cars, all connected by couplers. When the train is at rest the distance between couplers is L^0. If all parts of the train were rigid bodies then, even while the locomotive was accelerating, the coupler separation would remain L^0. With actual couplers, however, when a locomotive at the left moves to the left then a mechanical wave moves to the right, accelerating the most-left car first and the most-right car last; the distance between the couplers in this case is increased. If a locomotive at the right end were to push the train to the left, a mechanical wave would travel down the train to the left, decreasing the distance between couplers.

It is interesting to consider the following symmetric case. For A the density is increased by some factor, while for B the density is decreased by the same factor.

	OBSERVER B (moving left)	OBSERVER A (moving right)
BEFORE ACCELERATION	$\dfrac{1}{\sqrt{1 - \beta^2}} \lambda_n$	λ_n
AFTER ACCELERATION	λ_n	$\dfrac{1}{\sqrt{1 - \beta^2}} \lambda_n$

This table represents two possibilities, one of which is shown in Figure 33d: the transition in velocities here is determined by the wave corresponding to the horizontal line PQ. Whether the wave moves left or right (it is left for A, right for B), it corresponds to a speed which is greater than c, namely $u = \dfrac{1}{1 - \sqrt{1 - \beta^2}} v$. That $u > c$ is seen at once from the fact that the slope of PQ with respect to the horizontal corresponds to an angle less than 45°. This possibility is, then, physically inadmissable. The other possibility, not shown, corresponds to a vertical line PQ, representing a left-moving wave with velocity $w = \dfrac{1}{1 + \sqrt{1 - \beta^2}} v$. This velocity is also $w = \dfrac{c^2}{u}$; it is never larger than c. It possesses the property of reversing the relative left-right position of any two electrons. It is ruled out in the present case by the fact that $w = \frac{1}{2} v$ for $\beta \sim 10^{-12}$. This is a very slow wave, whereas we know the velocity of the actual wave is approximately c.

Let us return to Figure 33b for the case of one wave traveling to the right. If the line is infinitely long, or if it is terminated in a resistance equal to the characteristic resistance, then the initial conditions set up by this wave are also the steady-state conditions and no further changes are necessary: there are no reflected waves. In general, however, $R \neq R_o$ and transient changes are required to bridge the gap between the initial-state and the steady-state. A reflected wave of voltage and current starts down the line, from the right end toward the left; when it gets to the left end another reflected wave starts toward the right. This will happen regardless of whether or not the left end of the line is terminated with a characteristic impedance in series with the battery, etc. Depending on whether or not $R = R_o$, there will either be one wave or an infinite number of waves. These reflected waves produce the transient changes required to alter conditions from the initial values, set up by the first wave, to the steady-state conditions determined by the value of the terminating resistor, R.

The initial current wave from the left imposes the current value $I_o = \dfrac{V}{R_o}$;

everywhere on the transmission line, to the right in a and to the left in c. The electrons on the surface of a move to the left with constant speed v, according to our assumption; those on c move right with the same speed. We must then have

$$I_o = \frac{\lambda_n v}{1 + \beta}$$

for observer A, stationary relative to the wires.

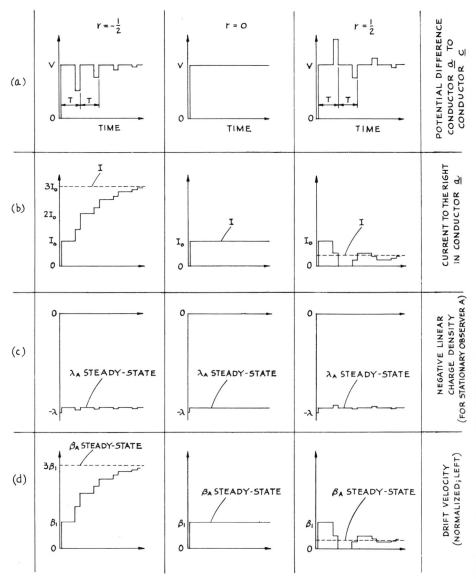

Figure 34. Transient behavior for parallel conductors.

When reflected waves are also present the steady-state current $I = \dfrac{V}{R}$ must be given by a corresponding expression: $I = \lambda_{ss} v_{ss}$. The question then immediately arises: Is λ_{ss} equal to $\lambda_n/(1 + \beta)$ also? Perhaps, instead, v_{ss} equals v; it is also possible that neither equality holds.

Appendix 2 contains the derivation of the steady-state values of charge density and electron velocity when the terminating resistance is not equal to the characteristic impedance, so that there are an infinite number of reflected waves. The results, summarized in Figure 34, show that the steady-state negative linear charge density for stationary observer A, approached by the infinite sequence of waves, is identically the same as the initial value established by the first wave.

We are now prepared to determine the force between two parallel ideal conducting wires. Consider a second 2-wire circuit, with conductor b parallel to conductors a and c of the first 2-wire circuit. Let the return wire of this second circuit be the same conductor, c, that already exists in the first circuit. We further assume that the conductor diameters are small compared to their separation. Assume also that the same switch and battery activates this circuit. Then similar conditions exist at the corresponding points in wires a and b at all times. After steady-state conditions have been established, what force exists on conductor b caused by conductor a? The following table supplies the answer. Here, from Appendix 2, $f = \beta_1/(1 + \beta_1)$ where β_1 is the normalized drift velocity after the first wave. Also from Appendix 2, $I_o = cf\lambda$.

	OBSERVER A (stationary relative to wires)		
	$+$	$-$	net
CHARGE DENSITY	λ	$-(1 - f)\lambda$	$f\lambda$
CURRENT	0	$(1 - f)\lambda v$	$(1 - f)\lambda v = I$
ELECTRIC FORCE per unit length of b due to all of a		$-\dfrac{f^2\lambda^2}{2\pi\varepsilon_0 D} = -\dfrac{\mu_0 c^2 f^2\lambda^2}{2\pi D} = -\dfrac{\mu_0}{2\pi D}I_o^2$	
MAGNETIC FORCE per unit length of b due to all of a		$\dfrac{\mu_0}{2\pi D}(1 - f)^2\lambda^2 v^2 = \dfrac{\mu_0}{2\pi D}I^2$	
TOTAL FORCE per unit length of b due to all of a		$\dfrac{\mu_0}{2\pi D}(I^2 - I_o^2)$	

The final answer for the force, obtained relativistically, differs from the value usually given, $\dfrac{\mu_0 I^2}{2\pi D}$, by the presence of the term $-\dfrac{\mu_0 I_o^2}{2\pi D}$. Furthermore, this is true even for extremely small drift velocities. There arises, then, the necessity for explaining the discrepancy on a classical basis. The explanation is not difficult to find.

Consider a battery, V, and switch connected in series to a pair of parallel wires, a and c, each of diameter d and separated by a distance s, with the wires open-circuited at the far end. When the switch is closed the wires become charged, one $+$ and one $-$, with linear charge density given by

$\lambda = CV$; here $C = \dfrac{\pi\varepsilon_0}{\cosh^{-1}(s/d)}$ is the capacitance per unit length between

conductors a and c. If the same switch and battery are also connected to another open-circuited pair, b and c, then b acquires the same linear charge density as a, and conductors a and b will repel each other. This is, indeed, the principle of operation of the gold-leaf electroscope.

If we calculate the force of repulsion per unit length of b caused by all of

a ($D = $ separation between a and b) we get $F'_{\text{rep}} = \dfrac{1}{2\pi\varepsilon_0 D}\left[\dfrac{\pi\varepsilon_0 V}{\cosh^{-1}(s/d)}\right]^2$.

The table gives $F''_{\text{rep}} = \dfrac{\mu_0 I_o{}^2}{2\pi D}$. But $I_o = \dfrac{V}{R_o}$, where

$$R_o = \frac{1}{\pi}\sqrt{\frac{\mu_0}{\varepsilon_0}}\,\cosh^{-1}(s/d)$$

is the characteristic impedance for a–c and for b–c. Substituting this and

$\mu_0 = \dfrac{1}{\varepsilon_0 c^2}$ we see that $F'_{\text{rep}} = F''_{\text{rep}}$. The $I_o{}^2$ term in the force expression in the

table gives the electrostatic repulsion between a and b. It may be ignored only when $R \ll R_o$. For infinitely long parallel ideal conductors, the case usually considered, $R = R_o$ and the total force is zero. This is true regardless of the spacing between conductors.

It is now necessary to modify our original assumption that the drift velocities in a and c are equal in magnitude, even though this led to the correct expression for the linear charge density. In a the negative linear charge density is, for $R = R_o$,

$$\frac{\lambda_n}{1 + \beta_a}\,;$$

the current in a is

$$I_a = \frac{\lambda_n v_a}{1 + \beta_a}\,.$$

In c, where the electromagnetic wave and electron drift velocities are both in the same (right) direction, the situation is similar to that illustrated in Fig. 33c for left-moving wave and drift velocities. The density is increased to the value

$$\frac{\lambda_n}{1 - \beta_c}$$

and the current is

$$I_c = \frac{\lambda_n v_c}{1 - \beta_c}.$$

In the steady-state we must have $I_a = I_c$. This gives

$$\beta_c = \frac{\beta_a}{1 + 2\beta_a}.$$

If $\beta_a = 10^{-12}$ the difference between the two drift velocities is negligible; but if it were possible to make $\beta_a \approx 1$ then there would be an appreciable difference.

The modification of the original assumption is undoubtedly necessary because of interactions between the particles; this was neglected at the start. We wish to repeat our statement at the beginning of this section: this treatment applies only to ideal conductors. The case of real conductors is treated in Appendix 3; it is altogether different from the present case.

The difference between the drift velocities in the two conductors, a and c, is a somewhat unusual phenomenon. It is called for here by the necessity to obtain a net positive charge on a and a net negative charge on c. Without this difference there could be no difference between the density of the moving electrons in a and the corresponding density in c. One would then have to postulate that some electrons were moving, while others were stationary, in each conductor. In a there would be required a deficiency of stationary electrons, in c an excess of stationary electrons. But, under a given force, why should some electrons move while others remain stationary?

The difference in the two drift velocities also serves another function. It provides for conservation of charge. In a there is now a net excess of positive charge, per unit length of conductor, given by

$$\lambda - \frac{\lambda}{1 + \beta_a} = \lambda\left(\frac{\beta_a}{1 + \beta_a}\right).$$

In c there is a net excess of negative charge, per unit length of conductor, given by

$$\frac{\lambda}{1 - \beta_c} - \lambda = \lambda\left(\frac{\beta_c}{1 - \beta_c}\right)$$

$$= \lambda\left[\frac{\beta_a/(1 + 2\beta_a)}{1 - \beta_a/(1 + 2\beta_a)}\right]$$

$$= \lambda\left(\frac{\beta_a}{1 + \beta_a}\right).$$

4. FIELD TRANSFORMATIONS

It is possible to obtain by fairly simple means the quantitative expressions determining the values of **E** and **B** for one Galilean observer when the values are known for another. In Figure 35a an observer O has a test electron, at rest relative to him, located at his origin. Observers A and A' move relative to O with velocities to the left of $\dfrac{v}{c} = \alpha$ and $\dfrac{u}{c} = \delta$, respectively. The normalized velocity of the electron is α to the right for A and δ to the right for B. A's velocity with respect to A' is $\dfrac{V}{c} = \beta$. The force on the electron measured by O is $\mathbf{F}_o$, produced by fields $\mathbf{E}_o$ and $\mathbf{B}_o$; for A' the values are $\mathbf{F}'$, $\mathbf{E}'$, $\mathbf{B}'$; for A they are $\mathbf{F}$, $\mathbf{E}$, $\mathbf{B}$. Thus $v = \dfrac{u + V}{1 + \dfrac{uV}{c^2}}$ or $\alpha = \dfrac{\delta + \beta}{1 + \delta\beta}$.

Since all velocities are taken along the x axis, the expressions for the

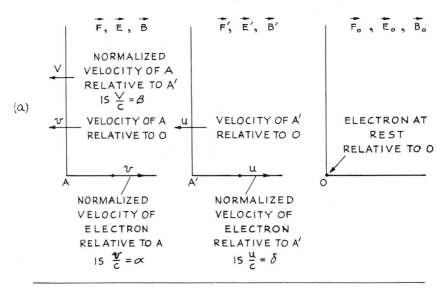

(a)

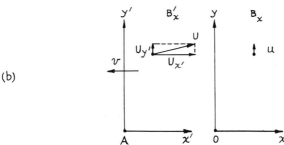

(b)

Figure 35. Transformation of fields.

Lorentz force are

$$\begin{cases} F_x = eE_x \\ F_y = e(E_y - vB_z) , \\ F_z = e(E_z + vB_y) \end{cases} \quad \begin{cases} F'_x = eE'_x \\ F'_y = e(E'_y - uB'_z) , \\ F'_z = e(E'_z + uB'_y) \end{cases} \quad \begin{cases} F_{ox} = eE_{ox} \\ F_{oy} = eE_{oy} . \\ F_{oz} = eE_{oz} \end{cases}$$

The equations for the transformation of force give

$$\begin{cases} F_x = F_{ox} \\ F_y = F_{oy}\sqrt{1 - \alpha^2} \quad \text{and} \\ F_z = F_{oz}\sqrt{1 - \alpha^2} \end{cases} \quad \begin{cases} F'_x = F_{ox} \\ F'_y = F_{oy}\sqrt{1 - \delta^2} . \\ F'_z = F_{oz}\sqrt{1 - \delta^2} \end{cases}$$

Then

$$\begin{cases} E_x = E_{ox} \\ E_y - \alpha c B_z = E_{oy}\sqrt{1 - \alpha^2} \quad \text{and} \\ E_z + \alpha c B_y = E_{oz}\sqrt{1 - \alpha^2} \end{cases} \quad \begin{cases} E'_x = E_{ox} \\ E'_y - \delta c B'_z = E_{oy}\sqrt{1 - \delta^2} . \\ E'_z + \delta c B'_y = E_{oz}\sqrt{1 - \delta^2} \end{cases}$$

We see at once that $E_x = E'_x$.

From $\alpha = \dfrac{\delta + \beta}{1 + \delta\beta}$ we obtain $\dfrac{1}{\sqrt{1 - \alpha^2}} = \dfrac{1 + \beta\delta}{\sqrt{(1 - \delta^2)(1 - \beta^2)}}$. Now

$$\frac{E_y - \alpha c B_z}{\sqrt{1 - \alpha^2}} = E_{oy}; \quad \text{also} \quad \frac{E'_y - \delta c B'_z}{\sqrt{1 - \delta^2}} = E_{oy}.$$

Then

$$\left[E_y - \left(\frac{\delta + \beta}{1 + \delta\beta}\right)cB_z\right] \cdot \left[\frac{1 + \beta\delta}{\sqrt{(1 - \delta^2)(1 - \beta^2)}}\right] = \frac{E'_y - \delta c B'_z}{\sqrt{1 - \delta^2}}$$

after equating the two expressions for E_{oy} and substituting the expressions for α and $\dfrac{1}{\sqrt{1 - \alpha^2}}$. So $\dfrac{E_y(1 + \beta\delta) - (\delta + \beta)cB_z}{\sqrt{1 - \beta^2}} = E'_y - \delta c B'_z$.

Now suppose we let u become an infinitesimal; that is, we have $u \to 0$ and $\delta \to 0$. Then in the last equation we can equate those terms which do not contain δ; and we can also equate those terms which do contain δ.

$$\frac{E_y - \beta c B_z}{\sqrt{1 - \beta^2}} = E'_y \quad \text{and} \quad \delta\left(\frac{\beta E_y - cB_z}{\sqrt{1 - \beta^2}}\right) = \delta(-cB'_z).$$

So

$$\begin{cases} E'_y = \dfrac{E_y - \dfrac{V}{c}(cB_z)}{\sqrt{1 - \beta^2}} , \\[4mm] (cB'_z) = \dfrac{-\dfrac{V}{c}E_y + (cB_z)}{\sqrt{1 - \beta^2}} . \end{cases}$$

Similarly, by equating the two expressions for E_{oz} after substituting for α and $\dfrac{1}{\sqrt{1 - \alpha^2}}$:

$$\left[E_z + \left(\frac{\delta + \beta}{1 + \delta\beta} \right)cB_y \right] \cdot \left[\frac{1 + \beta\delta}{\sqrt{(1 - \delta^2)(1 - \beta^2)}} \right] = \frac{E'_z + \delta cB'_y}{\sqrt{1 - \delta^2}}.$$

Again letting $\delta \to 0$ and equating terms, left and right, which do not contain δ and repeating with those which do, we obtain

$$\begin{cases} E'_z = \dfrac{E_z + \dfrac{V}{c}(cB_y)}{\sqrt{1 - \beta^2}}, \\[4ex] (cB'_y) = \dfrac{\dfrac{V}{c}E_z + (cB_y)}{\sqrt{1 - \beta^2}}. \end{cases}$$

Of the 6 field components for A' we now have equations giving 5 of them in terms of 5 of the field components for A. None of these equations involve either B_x or B'_x. Since the charge of the electron (assumed stationary for the O observer) no longer enters the equations, the latter are quite general and apply to any two Galilian observers moving relative to each other in the x direction with velocity V.

To obtain the transformation equations for B_x and B'_x consider the situation of Figure 35b. We require a separate derivation to obtain a very simple result. Here we have an electron moving relative to O with velocity components $(0, u, 0)$, where u is an infinitesimal, in a magnetic field $(B_x, 0, 0)$. Then $\mathbf{F} = e[\mathbf{E} + (\mathbf{u} \times \mathbf{B})]$ gives the force on the electron measured by O as $F_z = -euB_x$.

A moves to the left with velocity v relative to O. Relative to A the electron velocity is (note that v means the same as above but β does not):

$$U_{x'} = \frac{u_x + v}{1 + \dfrac{vu_x}{c^2}} = v, \qquad U_{y'} = \frac{\sqrt{1 - \beta^2}\, u_y}{1 + \dfrac{vu_x}{c^2}} = \sqrt{1 - \beta^2}\, u,$$

$$U_{z'} = \frac{\sqrt{1 - \beta^2}\, u_z}{1 + \dfrac{vu_x}{c^2}} = 0$$

or $(v, \sqrt{1 - \beta^2}\, u, 0)$, where $\beta = \dfrac{v}{c}$. Since $B_y = B_z = E_x = E_y = E_z = 0$, the transformation equations above give $B'_y = B'_z = E'_x = E'_y = E'_z = 0$; thereby leaving only B'_x. The force measured on the electron by A is $\mathbf{F}' = e[\mathbf{E}' + (\mathbf{U} \times \mathbf{B}')]$ or $F'_z = -e\sqrt{1 - \beta^2}\, uB'_x$.

The force F_z is a proper-force since the electron moves only at an infinitesimal rate relative to O. The force F'_z is a nonproper-force since the electron velocity, U, relative to A is finite. Then $F'_z = \sqrt{1 - \beta^2} F_z$ and $B'_x = B_x$.

The field transformation equations for a primed observer, moving with velocity v toward positive x with respect to an unprimed observer, may now be written (notice the switch in position between cB'_z and cB'_y):

$$\begin{cases} E'_x = E_x \\[2mm] E'_y = \dfrac{E_y - \beta(cB_z)}{\sqrt{1 - \beta^2}} \\[4mm] E'_z = \dfrac{E_z + \beta(cB_y)}{\sqrt{1 - \beta^2}} \end{cases} \quad \text{and} \quad \begin{cases} cB'_x = cB_x \\[2mm] cB'_z = \dfrac{-\beta E_y + (cB_z)}{\sqrt{1 - \beta^2}} \\[4mm] cB'_y = \dfrac{\beta E_z + (cB_y)}{\sqrt{1 - \beta^2}} \end{cases}.$$

From these it is seen that

$$(E'_y)^2 - c^2(B'_z)^2 = E_y{}^2 - c^2 B_z{}^2$$

and

$$(E'_z)^2 - c^2(B'_y)^2 = E_z{}^2 - c^2 B_y{}^2.$$

Consequently, with $E^2 = E_x{}^2 + E_y{}^2 + E_z{}^2$ and $B^2 = B_x{}^2 + B_y{}^2 + B_z{}^2$, we have

$$E^2 - c^2 B^2 = (E')^2 - c^2(B')^2.$$

The components E_y and cB_z are seen to transform like X and cT in the space-time diagram. Similarly, E_z and cB_y transform like x and ct. A diagram may thus be drawn with $X \rightarrow E_y$, $cT \rightarrow cB_z$, $x \rightarrow E'_y$, $ct \rightarrow cB'_z$. E_z and cB_y would also be connected graphically in this fashion, with $x \rightarrow E_z$, $ct \rightarrow cB_y$, $X \rightarrow E'_z$, $cT \rightarrow cB'_y$.

An interesting effect may be noticed from these equations for $\dfrac{v}{c} \ll 1$.

The denominators are then all very nearly equal to unity. In the numerators when v/c multiplies an electric field this term becomes negligible compared to the other term, which contains a magnetic field; but when v/c multiplies a magnetic field term then this term does not become negligible compared to the electric field term. Accordingly, we have $E'_y \approx E_y - vB_z$, $B'_z \approx B_z$, $E'_z \approx E_z + vB_y$, $B'_y \approx B_y$. There is an analogous effect in space-time, where the position coordinates of two observers moving relative to each other at low relative velocity differ by a term vt which may be large; but the time coordinates are essentially equal.

5. INDUCED VOLTAGE

The dimensions of $\mathbf{E}$, the electric field intensity, are those of force per unit charge. The unit for $\mathbf{E}$ is, correspondingly, 1 Newton/Coulomb or 1 N/C. Since force is work per unit distance (when force and displacement are along the same direction), $1\ N = \dfrac{1\ \text{Joule}}{1\ \text{meter}} = 1\dfrac{J}{m}$. Then $1\ N/C = 1\ (J/m)/C$ or $1\ (J/C)/m$. The unit 1 Joule/Coulomb is also called 1 Volt, by definition. A completely equivalent name for the unit of **E** is, therefore, 1 V/m.

If the component of **E** taken along some displacement is multiplied by the displacement, the resultant quantity is called the emf, the potential difference, or the voltage. Historically, the designation emf arose from a contraction of "electromotive force"; however, it is seen that emf or voltage is measured in J/C and represents work per unit charge. Since the application of the term "force" to a quantity which is actually not a force is incorrect and misleading, we will try to avoid this term. In this section it is possible to use the term induced voltage instead of induced emf.

This is by way of introducing the well known fact that when a wire made of conducting metal is moved in a magnetic field it is possible to obtain in the wire a flow of current produced by an induced voltage, i.e., a potential difference induced in the wire by the motion of the wire relative to the field. The wire provides the means for establishing the effect: it supplies the electrons whose flow constitute the current. The basic cause of the current flow is the induced voltage, which exists quite independently in space even if the wire is not there. The induced voltage is a phenomenon of great economic importance for on it depends the generation of electricity in dynamos, the source of virtually all our electric power. The mechanism by which this voltage is induced is a subject on which much misinformation exists. Relativity has a simple, clarifying message on this point.

Suppose we have a magnetic field along the z direction, uniform in space and constant in time, produced by a combination of a large, uniform, magnetic north pole below the $z = 0$ plane and a similar south pole above this plane. Let a conductor point in the y direction at the $z = 0$ plane and assume that the two uniform magnetic poles (with their plane faces parallel to the xy plane) are moved with speed v in the $-x$ direction. Question: Is there an induced voltage in the wire? Answer: No. Although the poles are moving relative to the wire, the magnetic field (defined here as a constant function of space and time) is indistinguishable in this case, relative to an observer on the wire, from the field when the poles are stationary. There is a magnetic field but no electric field at the wire. With no **E** there is no potential difference. Any stationary electron in the wire will experience the force $e[\mathbf{E} + (\mathbf{v} \times \mathbf{B})] = e[0 + (0 \times \mathbf{B})] = 0$. Consequently, no current flows in the wire.

Any difficulty in accepting this answer comes from assuming, implicitly, that the lines of **B** are rigidly attached to the magnetic poles, so that the conductor cuts lines of magnetic flux when the poles are moved. This is incorrect. The field **B** is defined here relative to an observer who is stationary with respect to the conductor; the definition of the field is not with respect to the poles. If the field is unvarying in space and the poles are broad planes there is no relative motion between field and wire here.

Now suppose the poles (and field) to be stationary relative to an observer but let the wire move toward $+x$ with speed v. Will there be an induced voltage in the conductor now? Answer: Yes. The field transformation equations of the previous section give the (primed) fields for an observer moving along with the conductor:

$$\begin{cases} E'_x = E_x = 0 \\ E'_y = \dfrac{E_y - vB_z}{\sqrt{1 - \beta^2}} \approx -vB_z \\ E'_z = \dfrac{E_z + vB_y}{\sqrt{1 - \beta^2}} = 0 \end{cases} , \qquad \begin{cases} B'_x = B_x = 0 \\ B'_z = \dfrac{0 + B_z}{\sqrt{1 - \beta^2}} \approx B_z \\ B'_y = \dfrac{\dfrac{v}{c}E_z + cB_y}{\sqrt{1 - \beta^2}} = 0 \end{cases} .$$

In comparing this case with the previous one, there is no contradiction with the principle of relativity if one considers relative motion between an observer attached to the wire and an observer fixed relative to the field.

The magnetic field for the moving observer is virtually the same as that, B_z, for the stationary observer with $v/c \ll 1$. The former, however, will have an electric field, $E'_y = -vB_z$, while the stationary observer has none. If the length of wire in the field is l, the emf will be $-vB_z l$; with a circuit resistance R, the current for the moving observer will be given as $vB_z l/R$ by Ohm's law. Since this current in the moving wire is perpendicular to the velocity of the wire, the current for the stationary observer will have the same value.

The explanation that relativity offers, then, for the origin of the induced (motional) voltage in a wire moving in a time-unvarying field is merely the transformation of fields between observers moving relative to each other. There is no reference to cutting lines of flux. The clarity of this answer will perhaps be better appreciated if the single conductor above, of length l in the y direction and moving in the x direction, is replaced by a long thin metal rod. Let the rod be both directed along and moving along the x axis; the width in the z direction is negligible but the width along the y direction is l. This rod can be thought of as a very large number of conductors, similar to the one above, side by side along the x axis. Stationary sliding contacts along the edges of the conductor, a distance l apart, will carry any current that exists to an external circuit while allowing the rod to move with velocity v: each element of the rod acts like the conductor above and has a motional voltage induced in it. The many elements of the rod in parallel lower the resistance to the flow of current in the closed circuit, giving the same induced voltage but a larger current than in the corresponding case of the single conductor moving with the same velocity. This induced voltage and current flow are usually explained on a flux-cutting basis; but then, how does one explain the absence of the induced voltage when the rod is held stationary and the poles are moved?

The example above is the linear analog of the Faraday disc, also called the homopolar generator: a metal disc in the xy plane revolves at a constant rate about the z axis through its center. A uniform magnetic field points in the z direction. Between a brush on the axis and one at the rim of the disc a unidirectional potential difference is generated (without the commutators of conventional d-c generators). If, instead of the disc revolving, the field-producing magnets are caused to revolve about the z axis, then no induced voltage is produced between the brushes. A flux-cutting explanation here is not possible.

An excellent example of the difference in outlook between the classical and relativistic views is provided by the following case: Let observer A have the field B_z produced by stationary magnet faces in parallel xy planes. If the magnets move very fast relative to him toward $+x$, then A still measures B_z when the magnetic field is absolutely uniform. What about observer A', standing on one of the magnet faces—what are the fields for him? Classically, A' would have the same field, B_z, whether or not the magnet moves relative to A—he is at one spot on the magnet. Relativistically, A' measures B_z only when A' is stationary relative to A; but, when A' and the magnet move relative to A, then A' will have

$$B'_z = \frac{B_z}{\sqrt{1 - \beta^2}} \quad \text{and} \quad E'_y = \frac{-vB_z}{\sqrt{1 - \beta^2}}.$$

The magnetic field for A', in terms of the field for A, will change to a new value when the magnet moves relative to A, even though A' remains at the same spot on the magnet. In addition, A' will acquire an electric field. The motion of the uniform magnet is irrelevant; the significant factor is the motion of A' relative to A.

BIBLIOGRAPHY

The articles below have all appeared in the American Journal of Physics:

Chen, H. S. C.: Note on the Magnetic Pole. *33:* 563, July, 1965.
Frisch, D. H., and Wilets, L.: Development of the Maxwell-Lorentz Equations from Special Relativity and Gauss's Law. *24:* 574, Nov., 1956.
Ganley, W. P.: Forces and Fields in Special Relativity. *31:* 510, July, 1963.
Kelley, E. M.: Brief Treatment of Magnetic Poles. *33:* 507, June, 1965.
Kolb, K. B.: Relative Force between Moving Charges. *30:* 929, Dec., 1962.
McGroddy, J. C., and Stanford, J. L.: Comments on Second-Order Electric Field Due to Conduction Currents. *30:* 928, Dec., 1962.
Rindler, W., and Sciama, D. W.: Radiation Pressure on a Rapidly Moving Surface. *29:* 643, Sept., 1961.
Rohrlich, F.: Self-Energy and Stability of the Classical Electron. *28:* 639, Oct., 1960.
Rosser, W. G. V.: Second-Order Electric Field Due to a Conduction Current. *30:* 509 July, 1962.
Schlegel, R.: Radiation Pressure on a Rapidly Moving Surface. *28:* 687, Nov., 1960.
Schlegel, R.: Radiation Pressure on a Rapidly Moving Surface. *29:* 645, Sept., 1961.
Terrell, J.: Radiation Pressure on a Relativistically Moving Mirror. *29:* 644, Sept., 1961.
Volkoff, G. M.: Electric Field of a Charge Moving in a Medium. *31:* 601, Aug., 1963.
Webster, D. L.: Relativity of Moving Circuits and Magnets. *29:* 262, Apr., 1961.

Webster, D. L.: Relativity and Parallel Wires. *29:* 841, Dec., 1961.
Webster, D. L.: Schiff's Charges and Currents in Rotating Matter. *31:* 590, Aug., 1963.
Whitmer, R. M.: Calculation of Magnetic and Electric Fields from Displacement Currents. *33:* 481, June, 1965.

The following books have sections devoted to the charge on a conductor carrying conduction current:

Becker, R.: Electromagnetic Fields and Interactions. Vol. 1, Electromagnetic Theory and Relativity. New York, Blaisdell Publishing Co., 1964, p. 370. Replaces Abraham-Becker's Classical Theory of Electricity and Magnetism.
Born, M.: Einstein's Theory of Relativity. Revised ed. New York, Dover Publications, Inc., 1962, p. 294.
Panofsky, W. K. H., and Phillips, M.: Classical Electricity and Magnetism. 2nd ed. Reading, Mass., Addison-Wesley Publishing Co., Inc., 1962, p. 333.
Purcell, E. M.: Electricity and Magnetism. Vol. 2, Berkeley Physics Course. New York, McGraw-Hill Book Co., Inc., 1965, Chapter 5.

Chapter 8 FORM INVARIANCE

I. SCALARS

Up to this point in the development of the theory almost complete reliance has been placed on only one of the two basic axioms, the second—the constant value of c for Galilean observers—expressed mathematically by the invariance of the interval between arbitrary events or expressed graphically by the use of the space-time diagram. Now it is necessary to equalize in importance the first axiom—the principle of relativity, or the nonexistence of the ether. The way this is done is to demand that all physical laws which do not depend on a medium—that is, all the fundamental laws of physics—shall be written in such a way that the equations governing the laws shall have an identical form for all Galilean observers. For instance, if the force on a charge is given by $\mathbf{F} = q[\mathbf{E} + (\mathbf{v} \times \mathbf{B})]$ for one Galilean observer, then the corresponding equation for a second Galilean observer must be $\mathbf{F}' = q'[\mathbf{E}' + (\mathbf{v}' \times \mathbf{B}')]$, where the primes designate the corresponding quantities for the second observer. The equation is form invariant—no terms are altered, added, or removed. Such a property of an equation is also often called covariance, but we shall avoid using this term because of its similarity to "covariant," which has quite a different meaning. We shall consider the latter subsequently.

The statement is sometimes loosely made that all the laws of nature are to be written in this fashion. This cannot be so, however, for the principle of relativity does not apply to all physical phenomena. The propagation of a sound wave in air, for example, depends on a medium. In this case, there is a preferred observer and the principle of relativity does not apply.

Limiting ourselves, then, to such phenomena as are independent of a medium we seek a mathematical means for expressing the principle of relativity. The simplest kind of such a law is one that assigns the same number to a quantity measured by all Galilean observers: the quantity is an invariant. For instance, the charge of an electron is the same for A, with respect to whom the electron is at rest, as it is for B, with respect to whom the electron moves with velocity $\mathbf{v}$. Such a quantity is called a scalar, and any equation involving only scalars will be form invariant. A scalar is a number, but not all numbers are scalars: the kinetic energy of a particle is a number, but a number which is different for different observers; so kinetic energy is not a scalar.

It is interesting to note that the charge and the mass of an electron, two of its fundamental properties, behave quite differently in transforming their values from one observer to another. The charge is a scalar; the mass is not a scalar, since its value for an observer depends on the velocity of the electron relative to the observer.

Scalars can be generalized to scalar fields. The air density for observer A may be given as a function of position: $\rho(\mathbf{r}) = \rho_o \sin \phi$. For B, stationary but turned 90 degrees CCW relative to A, $\rho'(\mathbf{r}') = \rho_o \cos \phi'$, with $\phi' = \phi - 90°$. The two relations are not form invariant: sin is not cos. But the density is given by a scalar field: for any point, $\mathbf{r} \leftrightarrow \mathbf{r}'$ or $\phi \leftrightarrow \phi'$, we have $\rho(\mathbf{r}) = \rho'(\mathbf{r}')$. The numerical value of the function at the point is invariant for this transformation. However, if A moves relative to B then the density is not invariant. When using the term invariance it is necessary to specify the appropriate transformations. Note, also, that the equations may be made form invariant: $\rho(\mathbf{r}) = \rho_0 \sin (\phi + \alpha)$ and $\rho'(\mathbf{r}') = \rho_0 \sin (\phi' + \alpha')$.

2. CONTRAVARIANT VECTORS

Of course, only the simplest physical quantities are scalars. The position of a particle requires three quantities, not just one, to specify it, e.g., the Cartesian coordinates in 3-dimensional space (x, y, z). It is a common fallacy to assert that such an entity, constructed of several independent elements arranged in a row or column, constitutes a vector. Alternatively, the directed line segment (or arrow) pointing from the origin or some other point of space to the point (x, y, z) is considered a vector in 3-dimensional space—a 3-vector. Actually, the specification of a vector requires a definite behavior of these independent elements in transforming their values from one coordinate system to another.

In this chapter, as distinct from all others in the monograph, it is necessary to employ calculus. Suppose we consider, then, the point, P, in 3-space characterized by the coordinates (x, y, z) relative to one coordinate system. We will write this as (x^1, x^2, x^3). The same point, P, will have different coordinates $(X, Y, Z) = (X^1, X^2, X^3)$ relative to another coordinate system. It is assumed the $x^i(i = 1, 2, 3)$ are independent, single-valued, differentiable functions of the $X^J (J = 1, 2, 3)$: $x^i = x^i(X^J)$. Then, by the ordinary rules of calculus,

$$dx^i = \sum_J \frac{\partial x^i}{\partial X^J} dX^J = \sum_J A_J^i dX^J.$$

Any collection of quantities, w^i, in one coordinate system which transforms to another system in this fashion,

$$w^i = \sum_J \frac{\partial x^i}{\partial X^J} W^J = \sum_J A_J^i W^J,$$

is defined as a contravariant vector. The differential position vector at a point in ordinary 3-dimensional space is, by definition, a contravariant vector.

The inverse relation giving the components for the capitalized system in terms of the components for the uncapitalized system is obtained by multiplying the equation above by $\dfrac{\partial X^K}{\partial x^i}$ and summing over i:

$$\sum_i w^i \frac{\partial X^K}{\partial x^i} = \sum_i \frac{\partial X^K}{\partial x^i} \sum_J \frac{\partial x^i}{\partial X^J} W^J = \sum_J \sum_i \frac{\partial X^K}{\partial x^i} \frac{\partial x^i}{\partial X^J} W^J = \sum_J \delta_J^K W^J = W^K.$$

Here δ_J^K is the Kronecker delta symbol $\delta_J^K = \begin{Bmatrix} 1, J = K \\ 0, J \neq K \end{Bmatrix}$.

The symbol for the summation index, i, is immaterial. To make the result compare easily with the original expression we let $K \to I$ and $i \to j$. We then have

$$W^I = \sum_j \frac{\partial X^I}{\partial x^j} w^j$$

for the inverse relation.

The generalization to a space of 2 dimensions, or 4 dimensions, or n dimensions, is obvious. We will have occasion to employ such real-space vectors (ordinary vectors, as distinguished from space-time vectors) only in 3-dimensional space and these will, succinctly, be called 3-vectors. These are represented either by means of their coordinates w^i or, in terms of the 3-vectors themselves, by **w**. It is conceivable to consider such vectors also in a 4-dimensional real-space and these should, logically, be termed 4-vectors. We will, however, reserve that term for 4-dimensional space-time vectors where $x^1 = x$, $x^2 = y$, $x^3 = z$, and $x^4 = ct$. For a real-space 3-vector we have

$$\sum_{i=1}^{3} (x^i)^2 = \sum_{J=1}^{3} (X^J)^2 \; ;$$

the magnitude of the vector has the same value for A and for B if the two observers are at the same place at the same time but have different attitudes relative to each other; but for a space-time 4-vector we impose the condition

$$-(x^1)^2 - (x^2)^2 - (x^3)^2 + (x^4)^2 = -(X^1)^2 - (X^2)^2 - (X^3)^2 + (X^4)^2.$$

Here the interval is invariant if the two observers move relative to each other with constant velocity **v** and have a common space-time origin.

Instead of a trivial difference between 3 and 4 dimensions, therefore, there is an important and essential distinction which exists between 3-vectors and 4-vectors. We are, in effect, restricting our use of the term 4-vectors to Cartesian coordinate systems whose axes are straight lines, though these need not be orthogonal to each other; the various systems belong to different

Galilean observers. For 4-vectors the interval is an invariant; the magnitude of a 4-vector is *not* an invariant. This is the basic reason for the necessity of the nonorthogonal axes of the Loedel, Brehme, and Minkowski diagrams. If the coefficients A_j^i are constants, the equations connecting the dx^i and the dX^J may be integrated to give $x^i = \sum\limits_J A_j^i X^J$. The position vector itself is then also a contravariant vector. Such a linear relation between the coordinates is called an affine transformation. For constant coefficients A_j^i it represents a change of scale, a reversal of one or more axes, a rotation of axes, or any combination of these. This is true for Cartesian axes. Many coordinate systems in common use (such as polar, cylindrical, or spherical coordinates) do not have constant coefficients either in transformations between themselves or in transformations to Cartesian coordinates. Such transformations are nonlinear. We shall restrict ourselves to affine transformations between oblique Cartesian coordinates. One of the complications in general relativity is the necessity for employing nonlinear transformations.

We may attach a simple geometric significance to the equation defining a contravariant vector for affine transformations. Consider an oblique Cartesian reference system, as in Figure 36*a*, where the components of a vector are determined by displacements parallel to the axes. This process for obtaining coordinates is the method employed in the Loedel and Minkowski space-time diagrams. A change δW^1 in the component W^1 produces a change in $|\mathbf{W}| = W$, the magnitude of the vector, given by δW.

From similar triangles we see that

$$\frac{W}{W^1} = \frac{\delta W}{\delta W^1} = \frac{\partial W}{\partial X^1}, \quad \text{or} \quad W^1 = W\frac{\partial X^1}{\partial W}.$$

For the other components we have coorresponding equations:

$$W^2 = W\frac{\partial X^2}{\partial W} \quad \text{and} \quad W^3 = W\frac{\partial X^3}{\partial W}.$$

The same vector, $\mathbf{W}$, would have different components (w^1, w^2, w^3) in a different oblique Cartesian reference system determined in a similar fashion. Here we would have

$$w^1 = W\frac{\partial x^1}{\partial W}, \quad w^2 = W\frac{\partial x^2}{\partial W}, \quad w^3 = W\frac{\partial x^3}{\partial W}.$$

From the first of these we have:

$$w^1 = W\frac{\partial x^1}{\partial W} = W\left(\frac{\partial x^1}{\partial X^1}\frac{\partial X^1}{\partial W} + \frac{\partial x^1}{\partial X^2}\frac{\partial X^2}{\partial W} + \frac{\partial x^1}{\partial X^3}\frac{\partial X^3}{\partial W}\right)$$

$$= \frac{\partial x^1}{\partial X^1}W^1 + \frac{\partial x^1}{\partial X^2}W^2 + \frac{\partial x^1}{\partial X^3}W^3;$$

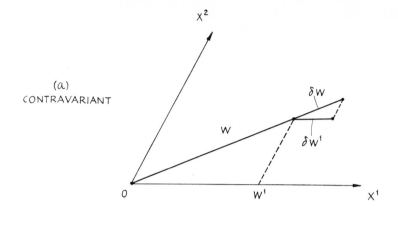

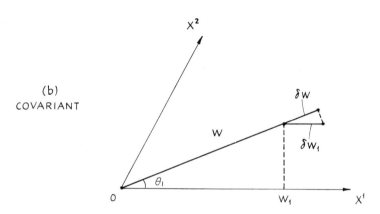

Figure 36. Connection between contravariant (Loedel) and covariant (Brehme) diagrams.

and similarly for the other two equations. Generalizing to the case of any component with an arbitrary number of dimensions: $w^i = \sum_J \dfrac{\partial x^i}{\partial X^J} W^J$. This is precisely the transformation defining contravariant vectors and shows that the Loedel and Minkowski diagrams are representations for contravariant vectors.

Any phenomenon described by equations involving only scalars or contravariant 4-vectors for one Galilean observer will be described by equations involving only such quantities for all Galilean observers. Furthermore, since the 4-vectors merely become primed (or capitalized) for another observer, the equations will be form invariant. This means that if an equation can be written exclusively with contravariant 4-vectors and scalars it is guaranteed that the phenomenon satisfies the first axiom (the principle of relativity, i.e., that there is no preferred observer). The mathematical expression of the second axiom is, then, that all relativistic equations are to be written as form invariant. Once we demand this we make the second axiom fully as important as the first. Our limitation to contravariant 4-vectors is too tight, however, and will shortly be relaxed.

We have already implicitly introduced a number of contravariant 4-vectors—space-time (invariant interval): $\{x^i\} = \{\mathbf{x}, ct\} = \{x, y, z, ct\}$; momentum-energy (invariant rest-energy): $\{p^i\} = \{c\mathbf{p}, E\} = \{cp_x, cp_y, cp_z, E\}$; current density-charge density (invariant rest-density):

$$\{j^i\} = \{\mathbf{j}, \rho c\} = \left(\frac{\rho^0 v_x}{\sqrt{1 - \beta^2}}, \frac{\rho^0 v_y}{\sqrt{1 - \beta^2}}, \frac{\rho^0 v_z}{\sqrt{1 - \beta^2}}, \frac{\rho^0 c}{\sqrt{1 - \beta^2}}\right).$$

Also, by dividing the momentum-energy 4-vector by the scalar $m^0 c$ we obtain the velocity 4-vector (invariant velocity c):

$$\{v^i\} = \left(\frac{\mathbf{v}}{\sqrt{1 - \beta^2}}, \frac{c}{\sqrt{1 - \beta^2}}\right)$$

$$= \left(\frac{v_x}{\sqrt{1 - \beta^2}}, \frac{v_y}{\sqrt{1 - \beta^2}}, \frac{v_z}{\sqrt{1 - \beta^2}}, \frac{c}{\sqrt{1 - \beta^2}}\right).$$

Sometimes the velocity 4-vector is written with dimensionless components, obtained by dividing the 4-vector above by the scalar quantity c. This is strictly a matter of personal preference, both forms being equally valid. For future reference we will add another 4-vector which we have not yet discussed, the magnetic-vector-potential—electric-scalar-potential 4-vector (invariant $c^2 A^2 - \phi^2$): $\{A^i\} = \{c\mathbf{A}, \phi\} = \{cA_x, cA_y, cA_z, \phi\}$.

On the other hand, some of the quantities we have dealt with are not 4-vectors. Force and acceleration, as we used them, were each 3-vectors and cannot, then, also be 4-vectors as they stand. By suitably multiplying the three force components and adding a fourth component, however, it is possible to form a 4-vector called the Minkowski force:

$$\{f^i\} = \left(\frac{\mathbf{F}}{\sqrt{1 - \beta^2}}, \frac{\mathbf{F} \cdot \boldsymbol{\beta}}{\sqrt{1 - \beta^2}}\right)$$

$$= \left(\frac{F_x}{\sqrt{1 - \beta^2}}, \frac{F_y}{\sqrt{1 - \beta^2}}, \frac{F_z}{\sqrt{1 - \beta^2}}, \frac{\mathbf{F} \cdot \mathbf{v}}{c\sqrt{1 - \beta^2}}\right).$$

As another example of quantities which are not 4-vectors we can mention the electromagnetic field components. Despite the fact that E_y and cB_z transform like x and ct, and can be represented by a space-time diagram, the field components $E_x, E_y, E_z, B_x, B_y, B_z$ do not form the components of a 4-vector. We will soon see that they are, instead, the components of a tensor.

3. COVARIANT VECTORS

The gradient of a scalar, ϕ, in 3-dimensional space is defined by

$$\nabla\phi = \hat{\mathbf{x}}\frac{\partial\phi}{\partial x} + \hat{\mathbf{y}}\frac{\partial\phi}{\partial y} + \hat{\mathbf{z}}\frac{\partial\phi}{\partial z}$$

with respect to a coordinate system (x, y, z). If there is another coordinate system (X, Y, Z), the original x component of the gradient, $\frac{\partial\phi}{\partial x}$, may be expressed in terms of the coordinates of the second system:

$$\frac{\partial\phi}{\partial x} = \frac{\partial\phi}{\partial X}\frac{\partial X}{\partial x} + \frac{\partial\phi}{\partial Y}\frac{\partial Y}{\partial x} + \frac{\partial\phi}{\partial Z}\frac{\partial Z}{\partial x};$$

and similarly, for the y and z components, yielding the general expression

$$\left(\frac{\partial\phi}{\partial x^i}\right) = \sum_J \frac{\partial X^J}{\partial x^i}\left(\frac{\partial\phi}{\partial X^J}\right) = \sum_J A_i^J \frac{\partial\phi}{\partial X^J}.$$

Any collection of quantities, w_i, in one coordinate system which transforms to another system in this fashion,

$$w_i = \sum_J \frac{\partial X^J}{\partial x^i} W_J = \sum_J A_i^J W_J,$$

is defined as a covariant vector. Whereas the indices of a contravariant vector are written as superscripts (or, alternatively, as subscripts with a raising bar), the indices of a covariant vector are written as subscripts. The contravariant component in the denominator of $\left(\frac{\partial\phi}{\partial x^i}\right)$ is equivalent, by definition, to the covariant component $(\nabla\phi)_i$ as a numerator.

We now show that the Brehme space-time diagram is the representation of a covariant vector. In Figure 36b we have an oblique Cartesian reference system similar to the one in Figure 36a for measuring contravariant vectors. As before, an infinitesimal change δW_1 in the covariant component W_1 of the vector produces a change δW in the magnitude W of the vector. Now, however, the value of δW is obtained by dropping a perpendicular to the extension of $\mathbf{W}$, unlike the procedure employed for contravariant vectors. Here $\delta W = \delta W_1 \cos\theta_1$ but $W_1 = W\cos\theta_1$. Thus

$$\cos\theta_1 = \frac{W_1}{W} = \frac{\delta W}{\delta W_1} = \frac{\partial W}{\partial X^1} \quad \text{or} \quad W_1 = W\frac{\partial W}{\partial X^1}.$$

The derivative is the inverse of that in the previous case. Similarly, for the other components:

$$W_2 = W\frac{\partial W}{\partial X^2} \quad \text{and} \quad W_3 = W\frac{\partial W}{\partial X^3}.$$

The same vector, $\mathbf{W}$, would have components (w_1, w_2, w_3) in a different oblique Cartesian system determined by this scheme:

$$w_1 = W\frac{\partial W}{\partial x^1}, \qquad w_2 = W\frac{\partial W}{\partial x^2}, \qquad w_3 = W\frac{\partial W}{\partial x^3}.$$

From the first we have

$$w_1 = W\frac{\partial W}{\partial x^1} = W\left(\frac{\partial W}{\partial X^1}\frac{\partial X^1}{\partial x^1} + \frac{\partial W}{\partial X^2}\frac{\partial X^2}{\partial x^1} + \frac{\partial W}{\partial X^3}\frac{\partial X^3}{\partial x^1}\right)$$

$$= \frac{\partial X^1}{\partial x^1}W_1 + \frac{\partial X^2}{\partial x^1}W_2 + \frac{\partial X^3}{\partial x^1}W_3.$$

Similar results are obtained from the other two equations. Generalizing, $w_i = \sum_J \frac{\partial X^J}{\partial x^i}W_J$. This is the transformation defining covariant vectors and shows that the Brehme diagram is a representation for covariant vectors.

An illustration of our statement that a mere collection of independent quantities does not, of itself, constitute a vector is provided by the case of $\hat{\mathbf{x}}\frac{\partial\phi}{\partial x} + \hat{\mathbf{y}}2\frac{\partial\phi}{\partial y} + \hat{\mathbf{z}}\frac{\partial\phi}{\partial z}$. This statement is significant when the components are given as functions, not numbers. But even in the latter case care is needed: the numbers apply only to one particular reference system.

A directed line segment does not necessarily constitute a vector. Such an arrow is associated with two points, its tip and its tail, unlike the usual field vectors with which we deal; the latter are associated with only one point. For nonCartesian coordinates the transformation coefficients A_J^i are not all constant so the properties at two points are different in general and the arrow does not transform like a vector. For Cartesian coordinates, however, an arrow does transform like a vector.

There are other types of vectors which are useful in some applications. The sliding vector is defined by an arrow that may be applied to any point along the straight line containing the arrow; it is only a vector for affine transformations. Also, the free vector is defined by an arrow that may be moved parallel to itself to apply to any point; it, too, requires Cartesian coordinates to actually transform as a vector. The chief application of these definitions is found in mechanics. We shall restrict ourselves to field vectors.

The addition of two vectors gives a vector defined by $S_J + T_J = U_J$ or $S^J + T^J = U^J$. This implies, first of all, that the vectors being added are both contravariant or both covariant. With rectangular Cartesian coordinates, however, there is no distinction between the two types of vectors, for the coordinates which are obtained by displacements parallel to the unit vectors are the same as the coordinates which are obtained by perpendicular projection onto the axes. An additional implication is that the individual vectors must have the same number of components.

The rule for addition is simple enough in principle. But for the case of 4-dimensional space-time, care must be taken that vector laws which are true in 3-space are not automatically assumed to be true also in 4-space. For instance, let the velocity of a body relative to A be given by

$$\{u^i\} = \left\{ \frac{u}{\sqrt{1 - \dfrac{u^2}{c^2}}}, 0, 0, \frac{c}{\sqrt{1 - \dfrac{u^2}{c^2}}} \right\}.$$

This is the 4-vector that holds when the velocity is only along the x direction. Let the velocity of A relative to B be given, correspondingly, by

$$\{v^i\} = \left\{ \frac{v}{\sqrt{1 - \dfrac{v^2}{c^2}}}, 0, 0, \frac{c}{\sqrt{1 - \dfrac{v^2}{c^2}}} \right\}.$$

Then the velocity of the body relative to B, $\{w^i\}$, is *not* the usual sum $\{w^i\} = \{u^i\} + \{v^i\}$. This equation, consisting only of 4-vectors, has the proper transformation characteristics; but it is not true. The correct law for the transformation of velocities was obtained in Chapter 5.

The multiplication of two vectors is given in a number of distinct ways. This is a matter of definition, the chief consideration being usefulness. Three common definitions for the product yield, respectively, a scalar, a pseudo-vector, and a tensor; we shall consider only the first here, deferring the others to the next section.

The dot product, or inner product, of two vectors is defined by

$$\{w^m\} \cdot \{v_n\} = \sum_i w^i v_i.$$

For 3-space this becomes

$$\mathbf{w} \cdot \mathbf{v} = w^1 v_1 + w^2 v_2 + w^3 v_3$$

although here there is actually no distinction between contravariant and covariant vectors. We keep the nomenclature, however, to make this case conform with a general rule to be introduced later. The specific case of the dot product for 4-vectors from this general rule will be given in a later section.

The index i, which appears in any summation, e.g., $\sum_i a^i a_i$, is called a running index or a dummy index; the process of summation of a dummy index is called contraction. Contraction is defined not only for vectors but also, in the next section, for tensors. In general, to contract an index it is necessary to have it appear once as a superscript and once as a subscript. We leave it to the problems to show that such a contraction for vectors results in a scalar.

The principle of relativity is satisfied if an equation can be written exclusively with covariant 4-vectors and scalars; just as, before, with contra-variant 4-vectors and scalars alone. It is not correct, however, to write an equation employing contravariant vectors, covariant vectors, and scalars except if each term in the equation is contravariant, covariant, or scalar to the same extent; otherwise different terms would transform differently.

Quadratic forms, of which the case $-x^2 - y^2 - z^2 + c^2t^2$ is a simple example, are of great importance in the development of the theory of general relativity. For that reason, and also because they can be employed in special relativity to permit a very concise notation, we consider them briefly here. Figure 37a shows the usual (x, y, z) system moving to the right in real-space (3-dimensional x, y, z space) with velocity **v** relative to the (X, Y, Z) system. The axes are designated by superscripts to indicate that the unit vectors are contravariant. By convention, contravariant axes in real-space are taken to form right-handed systems: a right-hand screw turned to bring $\bar{x}_1$ into $\bar{x}_2$, through the smaller of the two possible angles, would advance along $\bar{x}_3$. The space-time diagram is shown as a Loedel diagram. A moves toward $-\bar{x}_1$, which is also to the left in real-space, and has the outer axes in the Loedel diagram of Figure 37b.

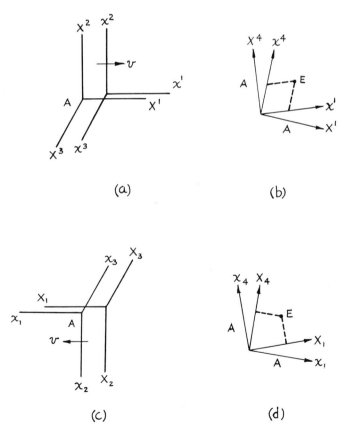

Figure 37. Contravariant and covariant vectors.

In Figure 37c each real-space axis has been reversed to give two left-handed systems. The space-time diagram is now a Brehme diagram. A still moves toward the left in real-space, but now this is toward $+X_1$; in the Brehme diagram of Figure 37d, A again has the outer axes.

An event in the Loedel diagram determines two 4-vectors:

$$\{x^j\} = \{\mathbf{x}, ct\} = \{x^1, x^2, x^3, x^4\} = \{\bar{x}_1, \bar{x}_2, \bar{x}_3, \bar{x}_4\},$$
$$\{X^J\} = \{\mathbf{X}, cT\} = \{X^1, X^2, X^3, X^4\} = \{\bar{X}_1, \bar{X}_2, \bar{X}_3, \bar{X}_4\}.$$

The same event in the Brehme diagram determines, similarly, the two 4-vectors

$$\{x_j\} = \{x_1, x_2, x_3, x_4\},$$
$$\{X_J\} = \{X_1, X_2, X_3, X_4\}.$$

With identical scales along all axes, including the orthogonal y and z axes, the following relations hold in the real-space diagrams of Figure 37a and c: $x_1 = -\bar{x}_1,\ x_2 = -\bar{x}_2,\ x_3 = -\bar{x}_3$ and $X_1 = -\bar{X}_1,\ X_2 = -\bar{X}_2,\ X_3 = -\bar{X}_3$. But, $x_4 = \bar{x}_4$ and $X_4 = \bar{X}_4$. This is useful for the quadratic form above:

$$s^2 = (ct)^2 - (x^2 + y^2 + z^2) = \bar{x}_4\bar{x}_4 - \{\bar{x}_1\bar{x}_1 + \bar{x}_2\bar{x}_2 + \bar{x}_3\bar{x}_3\}$$
$$= x_4\bar{x}_4 - \{(-x_1)\bar{x}_1 + (-x_2)\bar{x}_2 + (-x_3)\bar{x}_3\}$$
$$= \sum_{i=1}^{4} x_i\bar{x}_i = \sum_{i=1}^{4} x_i x^i.$$

Further simplification is obtained by use of the Einstein convention that any repetition of an index in a term automatically makes that index a dummy index and implies summation for all four values of the index. Then

$$s^2 = x_i\bar{x}_i = X_J\bar{X}_J = x_i x^i = X_J X^J.$$

In this simplified formulation equal emphasis is given to the covariant and contravariant 4-vectors, i.e., to the Brehme and Loedel diagrams.

4. TENSORS

In Gaussian differential geometry the square of the differential distance between two points on a surface in the ordinary space of three dimensions is given by

$$ds^2 = \sum_{i,j=1}^{2} g_{ij}\, du^i\, du^j.$$

Here u^i and u^j are two parameters which uniquely fix the values of x, y, z at any point on the surface. The coefficients g_{ij} are found to be

$$g_{ij} = \sum_{k=1}^{3} \left(\frac{\partial x_k}{\partial u^i}\right)\left(\frac{\partial x_k}{\partial u^j}\right),$$

where the x_k are functions such that $x_k = x_k(u^1, u^2)$ for $k = 1,2,3$. The 3×3 symmetric matrix of the g_{ij} coefficients, it turns out, contains within itself complete information on the geometric nature of the surface, regardless of the particular choice of the u's. This matrix is obviously fundamental and is called the metric matrix. (Subsequently we will see that this quantity is also a tensor.) Riemann extended these ideas in a natural way to n-dimensional space by proposing that

$$ds^2 = \sum_{i,j=1}^{n} g_{ij} \, du^i \, du^j \, .$$

A space for which this relation holds true is called a Riemann space. The bilinear form on the right, arising from Gauss's original 2-surface in 3-space, certainly is not the most general expression one could employ in an n-dimensional space. Why not e.g., use $(n - 1)$ differentials instead of two? The investigation of such questions by Helmholtz and by Riemann, roughly a century ago, indicated that the alternatives which were theoretically possible were in actuality ruled out by practical considerations. For example, the demand that one be able to rotate a rigid body freely about a fixed point, a somewhat modest request, leads one of necessity to a Riemann space. The bilinear form of Riemann's expression for ds^2 is therefore much more general than it appears on the face of it. Einstein consequently adopted this form for general relativity; but the g_{ij} have great significance in special relativity also.

In the 4-dimensional space-time of special relativity the expression for the interval is

$$ds^2 = -(dx^1)^2 - (dx^2)^2 - (dx^3)^2 + (dx^4)^2$$

so the values of the g_{ij} are given by $g_{11} = g_{22} = g_{33} = -1$, $g_{44} = +1$, and $g_{ij} = 0$ when $i \neq j$. The combination $(-1, -1, -1, +1)$ is called the signature of the quadratic form. Sometimes the expression is written for $-ds^2$, in which case the signature is $(1, 1, 1, -1)$. Sometimes, also, the signature is applied to the sum of the terms in the parenthesis, so the two signatures above would be -2 and $+2$, respectively. The significance of this lies in the fact that an arbitrary bilinear form may be reduced to a sum of squares,

$$a_{mn}x^m x^n \rightarrow \varepsilon_k \psi_k^2,$$

where the $\varepsilon_k = \pm 1$ and the ψ_k are homogeneous quadratic forms in the x^l; and it has been shown that the number of ε_k with value $+1$ (or -1) is an invariant of the bilinear form and is quite independent of the manner of the reduction.

We will consider the metric coefficients g_{ij} further; but first we must define a tensor.

A type of multiplication of two vectors that is more general than the inner product is provided by writing, e.g., with covariant vectors in 3-space,

$$\{W_J\} \times \{V_K\} = \begin{pmatrix} W_1V_1 & W_1V_2 & W_1V_3 \\ W_2V_1 & W_2V_2 & W_2V_3 \\ W_3V_1 & W_3V_2 & W_3V_3 \end{pmatrix}.$$

The entity on the right consists of nine independent components in 3-space. It applies to the same coordinate system as do the two original vectors and is called the outer product of the two. The component or element in the Jth row and Kth column of the resultant is given by W_JV_K.

In a new coordinate system we have $W_J = \dfrac{\partial x^i}{\partial X^J} w_i$ and $V_K = \dfrac{\partial x^l}{\partial X^K} w_l$. Consequently, in this new coordinate system the JK element becomes $W_JV_K = \dfrac{\partial x^i}{\partial X^J} \dfrac{\partial x^l}{\partial X^K} w_iw_l$. Any quantity $\{T_{JK}\}$ which transforms in this manner, i.e., such that

$$T_{JK} = \frac{\partial x^i}{\partial X^J} \frac{\partial x^l}{\partial X^K} t_{il},$$

will be called a covariant tensor of the second rank. (T_{JK} is, however, not necessarily the product of two covariant vector components. In general, an arbitrary T_{JK} is the sum of a number of such products.) The inverse transformation, obtained in a manner similar to that employed for finding the inverse of the transformation for contravariant vectors, is

$$t_{jk} = \frac{\partial X^I}{\partial x^j} \frac{\partial X^L}{\partial x^k} T_{IL}.$$

Similarly, a contravariant tensor of the second rank is one whose elements transform according to

$$T^{JK} = \frac{\partial X^J}{\partial x^i} \frac{\partial X^K}{\partial x^l} t^{il}.$$

This is the transformation obtained by the outer product of two contravariant vectors. A mixed tensor of the second rank obeys the transformation law

$$T^K_J = \frac{\partial x^i}{\partial X^J} \frac{\partial X^K}{\partial x^l} t^l_i,$$

corresponding to the outer product of a contravariant vector and a covariant vector.

A tensor of the second rank can thus appear in three different forms. A vector has only one index and is, by definition, a tensor of the first rank; it can appear in two different forms. A scalar has no indices and may be considered a tensor of zero rank; it appears in only one form. Tensors of rank higher than the second may be defined by an extension of the process above.

If the element T_{JK} of a second-order covariant tensor equals the element T_{KJ} then the tensor is called symmetric; if $T_{JK} = -T_{KJ}$ then the tensor is antisymmetric. Similar definitions hold for second-order contravariant or mixed tensors. The designations symmetric or antisymmetric have no meaning for vectors or scalars. For tensors of rank higher than two the symmetry property must be defined with respect to a given pair of indices.

A useful feature of tensor equations, similar to the property that all terms must have the same dimensions and units, is the principle of index balance. If we define a literal index as one which is not a dummy index, this principle states that the letters and positions of the literal indices must be the same in all the terms of an equation. Dummy indices are considered as canceling each other since they always appear in pairs, one as a superscript and one as a subscript. An equation $y_i = g_{ij}x^j$ may conceivably be a correct one according to this criterion; but the equations $y_i = g_{ij}x_j$ or $y_i = g^{ij}x_j$ are incorrect. To see how this principle of index balance arises, suppose we apply the transformation laws to a quantity such as $t^{jk}u_j$. Utilizing the fact that $\dfrac{\partial X^J}{\partial x^i}\dfrac{\partial x^m}{\partial X^J} = \delta_i^m = \begin{cases} 0, & m \neq i \\ 1, & m = i \end{cases}$ we obtain $T^{JK}U_J = \dfrac{\partial X^K}{\partial x^l}(t^{il}u_i)$.

So $t^{jk}u_j$ behaves exactly like a contravariant vector, $W^K = \dfrac{\partial x^K}{\partial x^l}w^l$, and the equation we started with may actually be written $\{W\} = \{T\}\{U\}$. This is only a special case of a more general statement: a product of tensors is also a tensor.

The importance of tensors rests on these transformation properties. If an equation is written exclusively with quantities which are tensors then each term in the equation is contravariant and covariant to the same extent and, under a transformation to a new coordinate system, all terms in the equation are modified in the same way. $\{W\} = \{T\}\{U\}$, an equation for one observer, would merely become $\{w\} = \{t\}\{u\}$ as the corresponding equation for another observer. The new equation is the same as the old one except that lower case $\leftrightarrow$ capitals. The equation we started with is form invariant. Note that this concept of form invariance may be applied only to an equation in which all the quantities apply to one observer; e.g., all the letters in each term are lower case to start with. The concept of form invariance is not applicable to the transformation equations themselves (say the one for $T^{JK}U_J$ above). These apply to two observers since there are capital letters only on one side while on the other side all the letters are lower case.

If the components of a matrix are scalars then the matrix is not the representation of a tensor. Suppose the matrix components are numbers, but these numbers must be determined from given functions. Is the matrix a tensor? A test of the transformation properties of all the matrix components could then be made to determine whether or not the tensor definitions above are satisfied. It is often convenient, instead, to employ the quotient theorem, which is almost the inverse of the statement above that a tensor multiplied by a tensor is also a tensor. We will give this theorem without proof: (T), the test matrix, is also a tensor $\{T\}$ if, for an *arbitrary* tensor $\{S\}$, the resultant of the product $\{R\} = \{S\}\{T\}$ is a tensor.

We may apply this test to determine whether the metric matrix (g_{ij}) is a tensor. That it is a tensor would follow immediately from $ds^2 = g_{ij}\, dx^i\, dx^j$ if the $dx^i\, dx^j$ were arbitrary, since the left side is a scalar. But the dx^i and dx^j are the components of a vector $d\mathbf{x}$ and, therefore, are not really arbitrary. Nevertheless, $d\mathbf{x}$ is itself quite arbitrary so there is no relation connecting dx^i and dx^j. The test may then be applied, yielding the result that $\{g_{ij}\}$ is a covariant tensor of rank 2. In special relativity the components of $\{g_{ij}\}$ have the values given. In general relativity the off-diagonal elements are not all zero and all the components are functions of space and time, rather than constants. The values of these functions are determined by the distribution of matter throughout space-time and general relativity thereby becomes a theory of gravitation. In going from a Galilean to a nonGalilean system the expression for the interval also gives off-diagonal elements for the g_{ij}: a system rotating with constant angular velocity about the z axis has

$$x = X \cos \omega t - Y \sin \omega t, \qquad y = X \sin \omega t + Y \cos \omega t, \qquad z = Z$$

so

$$ds^2 = [c^2 - \omega^2(X^2 + Y^2)]\, dt^2 - dX^2 - dY^2 - dZ^2 + 2\omega Y\, dX\, dt - 2\omega X\, dY\, dt.$$

It is not difficult to show that, with $ds^2 = g_{ij}\, dx^i\, dx^i$ for a Cartesian system, if we demand invariance of the interval for a new, possibly curvilinear, system then we obtain $ds^2 = g_{KL}\, dX^K\, dX^L$. It is for this reason that the expression for s^2 was written this way, rather than in the form $s^2 = g_{ii}(x^i)^2$.

We now turn to the connection between contravariant and covariant indices and to the method of conversion between them. Suppose we have a doubly contravariant matrix (T^{ij}). We may lower one of the indices by employing an arbitrary a_{ij} to form $R^i_k = a_{kj}T^{ij}$ or $S^j_k = a_{ik}T^{ij}$. But there is then no method for determining a sequence for the resultant indices; further (R) and (S) are in general unequal. These difficulties vanish if a_{ij} is symmetric. We can lower the first index by summing over that index: $a_{ik}T^{ij} = a_{ki}T^{ij} = T_k{}^j$; we can lower the second index by summing over the second: $a_{kj}T^{ij} = T^{ij}a_{jk} = T^i{}_k$. This can be carried one step further:

$$T_k{}^j a_{jl} = a_{jl}(a_{ik}T^{ij}) = a_{ki}a_{lj}T^{ij} = T_{kl},$$

$$a_{li}T^i{}_k = a_{li}(a_{kj}T^{ij}) = a_{li}a_{kj}T^{ij} = T_{lk}.$$

The two are identical: it does not matter which index was lowered first. In general, it is necessary to distinguish between $T^m{}_n$ and $T_n{}^m$; however, if the tensor is symmetric we may write T^m_n without confusion. This yields us considerable simplicity when we treat the tensor for the Lorentz transformation. This tensor is symmetric in the Minkowski, Loedel, and Brehme representations but not in the one, corresponding to the complex rotation diagram, that employs an imaginary component for the fourth coordinate of a 4-vector.

In special relativity a particular choice is made for the arbitrary symmetric matrix: g_{ij}. This explains some features of the relation between the Brehme and Loedel diagrams. In the 4-dimensional spacetime of the Loedel diagram, (x, y, z, ct) are assumed arbitrarily to form a right-hand system. The axes of the Brehme diagram are then given by $x_i = g_{ij}x^j$. So $x_1 = -x^1$, $x_2 = -x^2$, $x_3 = -x^3$, $x_4 = +x^4$. The space axes in the Brehme diagram now form a left-hand system but the time axis is unaltered. In 3-dimensional real space there is no transition from right-handed to left-handed in going from contravariant to covariant. There $ds^2 = \sum\limits_{i,j=1}^{3} g_{ij}dx^i dx^j$ has $g_{11} = g_{22} = g_{33} = 1$ with $g_{ij} = 0$, $i \neq j$. Now if we start with a right-hand contravariant system then $x_i = g^{ij}x^j$ gives a right-hand covariant system: $x_1 = x^1$, $x_2 = x^2$, $x_3 = x^3$.

To raise indices, instead of lowering them, we first define g^{ij}: $g^{ij} = C^{ij}/|g_{ij}|$, where C^{ij} is the cofactor of g_{ij}. In special relativity $(g^{ij}) = (g_{ij})$ in the particular system where the values of the letter were given. It can be shown that $\{g^{ij}\}$ is also a tensor. Assuming this to be true, we then have

$$g^{ik}T_{ij} = g^{ki}T_{ij} = T^k{}_j,$$

$$g^{kj}T_{ij} = T_{ij}g^{jk} = T_i{}^k,$$

$$T^{kl} = g^{ki}g^{lj}T_{ij}.$$

The inner product of two 4-vectors now becomes

$$\{w^m\} \cdot \{v_n\} = w^i v_i = w^i g_{ij}v^j = -w^1v^1 - w^2v^2 - w^3v^3 + w^4v^4 .$$

The interval squared is the inner product $s^2 = x_i x^i = g_{ij}x^i x^j = g^{ij}x_i x_j$.

One can now see how it is that the transformation for work, $W = W^o\sqrt{1 - \beta^2}$, differs from that for energy, $E = E^o/\sqrt{1 - \beta^2}$. Energy is a component of a 4-vector. But work is not such a component; it is related, instead, to part of an inner product of two 4-vectors—the Minkowski force and the interval. One part of $\{f^i\} \cdot \{s_i\}$ gives $-W/\sqrt{1 - \beta^2}$ for the sum of the first three terms; the last term is $+W/\sqrt{1 - \beta^2}$. Relativistically, energy and work are quite distinct quantities.

For 4-space, when the expression for s^2 is such that it can be transformed to the diagonal form used at the start of this section, the space-time is called flat and the system in which the metric tensor is diagonal is called Galilean. When this is not possible, the space-time is called curved. The space-time of special relativity is a flat space-time.

5. PSEUDOVECTORS

The antisymmetric tensor of the second rank in orthogonal, Cartesian 3-space has found wide utility. Instead of nine independent elements it has only three:

$$\{a_{ij}\} = \begin{pmatrix} 0 & a_{12} & a_{13} \\ -a_{12} & 0 & a_{23} \\ -a_{13} & -a_{23} & 0 \end{pmatrix}.$$

It is possible to make a correspondence between this tensor and a 3-vector in the following way. Consider the antisymmetric "tensor" $\{\varepsilon^{klm}\}$ defined such that, for one given 3-dimensional reference system (hence, not for all systems),

(a) $\varepsilon^{klm} = 0$ if $k = l$ or $l = m$ or $m = k$,
(b) $\varepsilon^{123} = 1$,
(c) $\varepsilon^{klm} = +1$ for $k \neq l \neq m$ with an even number of transpositions required to bring klm to 123 and
(d) $\varepsilon^{klm} = -1$ for $k \neq l \neq m$ with an odd number of transpositions required to bring klm to 123.

The word "tensor" has been put in quotation marks to show that ε^{klm} has a property which distinguishes it from a true tensor, as we are about to show. Such entities are called pseudotensors.

Suppose we have two vectors, $\mathbf{b} = \{b_i\} = \{b_1, b_2, b_3\}$ and $\mathbf{c} = \{c_j\} = \{c_1, c_2, c_3\}$. Form the antisymmetric combination $a_{ij} = b_i c_j - b_j c_i$ which has the matrix shown above. $\{a_{ij}\}$ is a tensor since

$$a_{ij} \rightarrow \left(\frac{\partial X^K}{\partial x^i} B_K\right)\left(\frac{\partial X^L}{\partial x^j} C_L\right) - \left(\frac{\partial X^M}{\partial x^j} B_M\right)\left(\frac{\partial X^N}{\partial x^i} C_N\right)$$

$$\rightarrow \frac{\partial X^K}{\partial x^i}\frac{\partial X^L}{\partial x^j} B_K C_L - \frac{\partial X^K}{\partial x^i}\frac{\partial X^L}{\partial x^j} B_L C_K = \frac{\partial X^K}{\partial x^i}\frac{\partial X^L}{\partial x^j} A_{KL}.$$

Now let

$$d^h = \tfrac{1}{2}\varepsilon^{hij} a_{ij}.$$

One may verify that $d^1 = b_2 c_3 - b_3 c_2$, $d^2 = b_3 c_1 - b_1 c_3$, $d^3 = b_1 c_2 - b_2 c_1$. If we now let $x \rightarrow -x$ then $b_1 \rightarrow -b_1$ and $c_1 \rightarrow -c_1$, the other b_i and c_i remaining the same; but this means $d^1 \rightarrow d_1$ while $d^2 \rightarrow -d^2$ and $d^3 \rightarrow -d^3$. We see that $\mathbf{d} = \mathbf{b} \times \mathbf{c}$; and also that its components behave differently, on reflection in a plane, from those of $\mathbf{b}$. For this reason $\mathbf{d}$, or the cross product of two 3-vectors, is called a pseudovector. This means ε^{hij} must be a pseudotensor; its components behave differently from a tensor's on reflection.

If both $x \rightarrow -x$ and $y \rightarrow -y$ then $\mathbf{d}$ behaves like $\mathbf{b}$ and $\mathbf{c}$; but if all three axes are reversed then $\mathbf{d}$ behaves differently from $\mathbf{b}$ and $\mathbf{c}$ again. The terminology that is often used is polar vector for vector and axial vector for pseudovector. The dot product or inner product of a polar vector and an axial vector is a pseudoscalar rather than a scalar. Because the polar vector changes sign on reversal of all three axes the resultant product also changes sign.

The axial vector **d** is said to be the first-rank dual of the antisymmetric tensor $\{a_{ij}\}$. There is also a second-rank dual of $\{a_{ij}\}$: the pseudotensor $\frac{1}{2}\varepsilon^{ijkl}a_{kl}$. Here ε^{ijkl} is a pseudotensor of the fourth rank defined in a manner analogous to that for ε^{klm}. The same pseudotensor produces a dual of the third rank for a polar vector: $\varepsilon^{ijkl}b_l$.

A direct visual picture of the distinction between polar and axial vectors is provided by a comparison of the reflected images of arrows representing the two types. Let an arrow, on the x axis and pointing toward more positive x, represent a displacement: a polar, or ordinary, vector. This arrow, as object, will form an image in a mirror placed along the plane $x = 0$; the arrow in the image will point in the opposite direction—toward more negative x. On the other hand, an arrow pointing toward $+y$ (or $+z$) will have an image also pointing toward $+y$ (or $+z$). For polar vectors, on reflection in a plane, longitudinal directions are reversed in the image while transverse directions are preserved.

Now let the object arrow along the x axis represent an axial vector such as **ω**, the angular velocity of a small ball revolving, in the yz plane about the x axis. If the arrow points toward positive x the ball is revolving clockwise as seen by an observer looking toward positive x. To obtain the image arrow we must consider the image of the ball, instant by instant, in the mirror at the yz plane. The image of the ball will revolve in the same sense, so the direction of the image arrow is also toward positive x. For an axial vector, therefore, longitudinal directions are preserved. If we let the ball revolve in the xz plane, representing an axial vector in the y direction, we find that the image ball revolves in the opposite sense, thereby giving a reversed arrow image. Similarly, revolution in the xy plane gives a reversal of an arrow along the z direction. An axial vector reverses the transverse directions on reflection in a plane. The behavior here is just the opposite of that for polar vectors.

When a man facing north looks at himself in a mirror situated in an east-west plane he sees his image facing south. This is reasonable, since displacement is a polar vector and the longitudinal north-south directions are reversed in the image. Why is it, then, that when the man winks his right eye the image (a man) returns the wink with its left eye? For a polar vector the transverse directions should be preserved.

Actually, the transverse directions are preserved. When the man winks his east eye the image, too, winks its east eye. But a complicating feature arises in the definition of right and left. Consider two vectors: **A** points from the back to the front of the man (north) and **B** points from his feet to his head (up). A man, however, has a plane of symmetry. For an object with such a plane of symmetry, **A** and **B** are well defined; but **C'**, a polar vector that points orthogonally to these in one sense, is indistinguishable from $-\mathbf{C}'$, a polar vector that points in the opposite sense, unless some restriction is imposed; this is true only because of the plane of symmetry. It is necessary to define $\mathbf{C}$ as an axial vector, left to right, in terms of $\mathbf{A}$ and $\mathbf{B}$ by setting $\mathbf{C} = \mathbf{A} \times \mathbf{B}$. For the man, right is east; but for the image, right is west. The possibility of confusion arises because of the coincidence of two imagined vectors, a polar vector (pointing from west to east) and an axial vector (pointing from left to right).

The correspondence between an antisymmetric tensor and a vector is a property peculiar to 3-space and cannot be made for 2-space, 4-space, etc. The law for transformation of the components of a tensor is, in general, different from that for the components of a vector. From $d^h = \frac{1}{2}\varepsilon^{hij}a_{ij}$, however, it may be shown that in this case the transformation laws are the same. Thus, $d^1 = \frac{1}{2}\varepsilon^{1ij}a_{ij} = \frac{1}{2}(\varepsilon^{123}a_{23} + \varepsilon^{132}a_{23}) = a_{23}$; similarly, $d^2 = a_{31}$ and $d^3 = a_{12}$. In a new coordinate system we have to check the details instead of relying on the mere appearance of a tensor equation:

$$d^h = \frac{1}{2}\left(\frac{\partial x^h}{\partial X^M}\frac{\partial x^i}{\partial X^N}\frac{\partial x^j}{\partial X^P}\varepsilon^{MNP}\right)\left(\frac{\partial X^K}{\partial x^i}\frac{\partial X^L}{\partial x^j}A_{KL}\right)$$

$$= \frac{1}{2}\frac{\partial x^h}{\partial X^M}\left(\frac{\partial x^i}{\partial X^N}\frac{\partial X^K}{\partial x^i}\right)\left(\frac{\partial x^j}{\partial X^P}\frac{\partial X^L}{\partial x^j}\right)\varepsilon^{MNP}A_{KL}$$

$$= \frac{1}{2}\frac{\partial x^h}{\partial X^M}\delta^K_N\delta^L_P\varepsilon^{MNP}A_{KL}$$

$$= \frac{1}{2}\frac{\partial x^h}{\partial X^M}\varepsilon^{MKL}A_{KL} = \frac{\partial x^h}{\partial X^M}D^M.$$

Here $D^M = \frac{1}{2}\varepsilon^{MKL}A_{KL}$ just as $d^m = \frac{1}{2}\varepsilon^{mkl}a_{kl}$. It is seen that d^m transforms like a vector even though it is actually a pseudotensor of the second rank.

We would like to mention once again that while the components of ε^{klm} are numbers they are not scalars. These numbers apply only in one coordinate system. Upon multiplication with a matrix representing rotation there results a different ε^{klm} whose components (for a given θ, ϕ) are again numbers, but different from those before. Similarly, the numbers change after multiplication by a matrix representing reflection of axes. This is also true of any tensor whose components are given as numbers in one given reference frame.

6. 4-TENSORS

The transformation of a scalar between two Galilean observers, A and b, is given by $s = s'$. The transformation of a contravariant 4-vector between A (capitalized coordinates) and b (uncapitalized coordinates) is obtained as follows. Let A and b both have right-handed space axes and let A move toward $+x$ of b with velocity v. Applying $W^J = \dfrac{\partial X^J}{\partial x^k} w^k$ to

$$X^1 = \frac{x^1 - \beta x^4}{\sqrt{1 - \beta^2}}, \qquad X^2 = x^2, \qquad X^3 = x^3, \qquad X^4 = \frac{-\beta x^1 + x^4}{\sqrt{1 - \beta^2}}$$

gives

$$
\begin{cases}
W^1 = \dfrac{1}{\sqrt{1 - \beta^2}}\, w^1 + 0\, w^2 + 0\, w^3 - \dfrac{\beta}{\sqrt{1 - \beta^2}}\, w^4, \\[2ex]
W^2 = \qquad\quad 0\, w^1 + 1\, w^2 + 0\, w^3 + \qquad\quad 0\, w^4, \\[2ex]
W^3 = \qquad\quad 0\, w^1 + 0\, w^2 + 1\, w^3 + \qquad\quad 0\, w^4, \\[2ex]
W^4 = -\dfrac{\beta}{\sqrt{1 - \beta^2}}\, w^1 + 0\, w^2 + 0\, w^3 + \dfrac{1}{\sqrt{1 - \beta^2}}\, w^4.
\end{cases}
$$

We have purposely put all the coefficients on display. We now make a matrix of these coefficients:

$$
\{L_k^J\} =
\begin{cases}
\dfrac{1}{\sqrt{1 - \beta^2}} & 0 & 0 & -\dfrac{\beta}{\sqrt{1 - \beta^2}} \\[2ex]
0 & 1 & 0 & 0 \\[1ex]
0 & 0 & 1 & 0 \\[1ex]
-\dfrac{\beta}{\sqrt{1 - \beta^2}} & 0 & 0 & \dfrac{1}{\sqrt{1 - \beta^2}}
\end{cases}.
$$

We have designated this matrix, which is symmetric, by $\{L_k^J\}$ since it is unnecessary to distinguish the rows from the columns. We will adopt the convention, however, that the subscript represents the row and the superscript represents the column. The symbol L is employed because this matrix represents the Lorentz transformation.

Our four equations may now be succinctly written

$$W^J = L_k^J w^k.$$

This tensor equation, giving the transformation of the components of a contravariant 4-vector from b to A is actually shorthand for four equations, each with four terms on the right-hand side. If we represent a 4-vector by a matrix consisting of four rows and one column,

$$
\{W^j\} =
\begin{Bmatrix} W^1 \\ W^2 \\ W^3 \\ W^4 \end{Bmatrix}
\quad \text{and} \quad
\{w^k\} =
\begin{Bmatrix} w^1 \\ w^2 \\ w^3 \\ w^4 \end{Bmatrix},
$$

then with

$$\{L_k^J\} = \begin{pmatrix} L_1^1 & L_1^2 & L_1^3 & L_1^4 \\ L_2^1 & L_2^2 & L_2^3 & L_2^4 \\ L_3^1 & L_3^2 & L_3^3 & L_3^4 \\ L_4^1 & L_4^2 & L_4^3 & L_4^4 \end{pmatrix},$$

we may write

$$(W^J) = (L_J^k)(w^k)$$

as a matrix equation, with the usual law for matrix multiplication to give the components.

For example,

$$W^2 = L_2^1 w^1 + L_2^2 w^2 + L_2^3 w^3 + L_2^4 w^4 = L_2^k w^k.$$

The element in row 2 and column 1 of W is obtained by adding the four individual products:

> (row 2, column 1 of L by row 1, column 1 of w)
> + (row 2, column 2 of L by row 2, column 1 of w)
> + (row 2, column 3 of L by row 3, column 1 of w)
> + (row 2, column 4 of L by row 4, column 1 of w).

Because of the matrix symmetry we may also write this as

$$W^2 = L_1^2 w^1 + L_2^2 w^2 + L_3^2 w^3 + L_4^2 w^4 = L_k^2 w^k,$$

which is the same as one of the four tensor equations. In matrix equations the dummy index does not always appear both top and bottom, as it does with tensors; but for symmetrical matrices this condition can be arranged.

To eliminate the necessity for the parentheses as well as to satisfy the dummy index condition, we will write all our equations as tensor relations between components; more important, however, this shows the transformation properties between the components. Braces will designate a tensor.

The tensor $\{L_k^J\}$ representing the Lorentz transformation gives the components of a contravariant 4-vector for A in terms of the contravariant 4-vector components for b. The reverse transformation, represented by

$$\{L_k^J\}^{-1} = \{L_K^j\},$$

gives the components of a contravariant 4-vector for b in terms of the contravariant 4-vector components for A. The simplest way to obtain the values of L_K^j is to replace β in L_k^J by $-\beta$: in $w^j = \dfrac{\partial x^j}{\partial X^K} W^K$ or $w^j = L_K^j W^K$ we have

$$\{L_K^j\} = \begin{cases} \dfrac{1}{\sqrt{1-\beta^2}} & 0 & 0 & \dfrac{\beta}{\sqrt{1-\beta^2}} \\ 0 & 1 & 0 & 0 \\ 0 & 0 & 1 & 0 \\ \dfrac{\beta}{\sqrt{1-\beta^2}} & 0 & 0 & \dfrac{1}{\sqrt{1-\beta^2}} \end{cases}.$$

In a similar fashion, to find the Lorentz transformation for a covariant vector between A and b, when A moves toward $+x$ of b with velocity v, we apply $W_J = \dfrac{\partial x^k}{\partial X^J}\, w_k$ to

$$x^1 = \frac{X^1 + \beta X^4}{\sqrt{1-\beta^2}}, \qquad x^2 = X^2, \qquad x^3 = X^3, \qquad x^4 = \frac{\beta X^1 + X^4}{\sqrt{1-\beta^2}}.$$

Here A and b both have left-handed space axes. This gives $W_J = l_J^k w_k$, with

$$(l_J^k) = \begin{Bmatrix} \dfrac{1}{\sqrt{1-\beta^2}} & 0 & 0 & \dfrac{\beta}{\sqrt{1-\beta^2}} \\[2mm] 0 & 1 & 0 & 0 \\[2mm] 0 & 0 & 1 & 0 \\[2mm] \dfrac{\beta}{\sqrt{1-\beta^2}} & 0 & 0 & \dfrac{1}{\sqrt{1-\beta^2}} \end{Bmatrix}.$$

The matrices representing the covariant 4-vectors are

$$\{W_J\} = \begin{Bmatrix} W_1 \\ W_2 \\ W_3 \\ W_4 \end{Bmatrix}, \qquad \{w_k\} = \begin{Bmatrix} w_1 \\ w_2 \\ w_3 \\ w_4 \end{Bmatrix}.$$

The reverse transformation, from A to b, for covariant vectors is given by

$$\{l_J^k\}^{-1} = \{l_j^K\},$$

obtained from $\{l_J^k\}$ by letting $\beta \to -\beta$:

$$\{l_j^K\} = \begin{Bmatrix} \dfrac{1}{\sqrt{1-\beta^2}} & 0 & 0 & \dfrac{-\beta}{\sqrt{1-\beta^2}} \\[2mm] 0 & 1 & 0 & 0 \\[2mm] 0 & 0 & 1 & 0 \\[2mm] \dfrac{-\beta}{\sqrt{1-\beta^2}} & 0 & 0 & \dfrac{1}{\sqrt{1-\beta^2}} \end{Bmatrix}.$$

Upon comparing the components of the four matrices representing the Lorentz transformation we find

$$L_k^J = l_j^K, \qquad L_K^j = l_J^k$$

with the second pair obtained from the first pair by letting $\beta \to -\beta$. A contravariant transformation from b to A has the same tensor as a covariant transformation from A to b. We recognize, however, that A of the contravariant case is moving right relative to b; and b of the covariant case is also moving right relative to A. Consequently, we have the result that the same matrix or tensor applies, either for contravariant or covariant vectors, for the Lorentz transformation from the left-moving observer to the right-moving observer.

7. ELECTRODYNAMICS

We can apply the Lorentz transformation to a tensor of the second rank $(T_{ij}, T^{ij}, T^i_{\ j}, \text{ or } T_i^{\ j})$ as well as to a vector. We need consider only one of them, say T_{ij}, which transforms like the product of two covariant vectors: $T'_{\ km} = L^i_k L^j_m T_{ij}$. This innocent looking equation is actually a system of 16 equations, each with 16 terms on the right-hand side. The transformation is from an observer b with a left-handed space system moving to the right relative to an observer A with a left-handed space system. The Lorentz matrix to be employed is the one having $+\beta$.

For instance, taking $k = 2$ and $m = 3$,

$$
\begin{aligned}
T'_{\ 23} = L^i_2 L^j_3 T_{ij} &= L^1_2 L^1_3 T_{11} + L^1_2 L^2_3 T_{12} + L^1_2 L^3_3 T_{13} + L^1_2 L^4_3 T_{14} \\
&+ L^2_2 L^1_3 T_{21} + L^2_2 L^2_3 T_{22} + L^2_2 L^3_3 T_{23} + L^2_2 L^4_3 T_{24} \\
&+ L^3_2 L^1_3 T_{31} + L^3_2 L^2_3 T_{32} + L^3_2 L^3_3 T_{33} + L^3_2 L^4_3 T_{34} \\
&+ L^4_2 L^1_3 T_{41} + L^4_2 L^2_3 T_{42} + L^4_2 L^3_3 T_{43} + L^4_2 L^4_3 T_{44}
\end{aligned}
$$

$$
\begin{aligned}
&= 0 + 0 + 0 \qquad\quad + 0 \\
&+ 0 + 0 + (1)(1)\, T_{23} + 0 \\
&+ 0 + 0 + 0 \qquad\quad + 0 \\
&+ 0 + 0 + 0 \qquad\quad + 0 \\
&= T_{23}.
\end{aligned}
$$

Proceeding in this manner we obtain the transformed second-rank tensor, written in matrix form, for $\{T'_{\ km}\}$:

$$
\begin{pmatrix}
\dfrac{T_{11} + \beta(T_{14} + T_{41}) + \beta^2 T_{44}}{1 - \beta^2} & \dfrac{T_{12} + \beta T_{42}}{\sqrt{1 - \beta^2}} & \dfrac{T_{13} + \beta T_{43}}{\sqrt{1 - \beta^2}} & \dfrac{T_{14} + \beta(T_{11} + T_{44}) + \beta^2 T_{41}}{1 - \beta^2} \\[3ex]
\dfrac{T_{21} + \beta T_{24}}{\sqrt{1 - \beta^2}} & T_{22} & T_{23} & \dfrac{T_{24} + \beta T_{21}}{\sqrt{1 - \beta^2}} \\[3ex]
\dfrac{T_{31} + \beta T_{34}}{\sqrt{1 - \beta^2}} & T_{32} & T_{33} & \dfrac{T_{34} + \beta T_{31}}{\sqrt{1 - \beta^2}} \\[3ex]
\dfrac{T_{41} + \beta(T_{11} + T_{44}) + \beta^2 T_{14}}{1 - \beta^2} & \dfrac{T_{42} + \beta T_{12}}{\sqrt{1 - \beta^2}} & \dfrac{T_{43} + \beta T_{13}}{\sqrt{1 - \beta^2}} & \dfrac{T_{44} + \beta(T_{14} + T_{41}) + \beta^2 T_{11}}{1 - \beta^2}
\end{pmatrix}
$$

If T'_{km} is symmetric then there are 10 independent components instead of 16. If T'_{km} is antisymmetric there are only 6 independent components:

$$\{T'_{km}\}_{\text{anti}} = \begin{pmatrix} 0 & \dfrac{T_{12} - \beta T_{24}}{\sqrt{1 - \beta^2}} & \dfrac{T_{13} - \beta T_{34}}{\sqrt{1 - \beta^2}} & T_{14} \\[3mm] -\dfrac{T_{12} - \beta T_{24}}{\sqrt{1 - \beta^2}} & 0 & T_{23} & \dfrac{T_{24} - \beta T_{12}}{\sqrt{1 - \beta^2}} \\[3mm] -\dfrac{T_{13} - \beta T_{34}}{\sqrt{1 - \beta^2}} & -T_{23} & 0 & \dfrac{T_{34} - \beta T_{13}}{\sqrt{1 - \beta^2}} \\[3mm] -T_{14} & -\dfrac{T_{24} - \beta T_{12}}{\sqrt{1 - \beta^2}} & -\dfrac{T_{34} - \beta T_{13}}{\sqrt{1 - \beta^2}} & 0 \end{pmatrix}.$$

The electromagnetic field also has 6 independent components: E_x, E_y, E_z, B_x, B_y, B_z. By comparing the transformation between the field components, obtained in the previous chapter, with the transformation for $\{T_{km}\}_{\text{anti}}$ one finds that the electromagnetic field 3-vectors are actually the components of the following antisymmetric second-rank covariant tensor:

$$\{F_{ij}\} = \begin{pmatrix} 0 & cB_z & -cB_y & E_x \\ -cB_z & 0 & cB_x & E_y \\ cB_y & -cB_x & 0 & E_z \\ -E_x & -E_y & -E_z & 0 \end{pmatrix}.$$

The mathematical expression of the second axiom of relativity is now to be modified as follows: all equations applicable to fundamental phenomena (i.e., those for which there is no medium) should be written in 4-tensor form. Whether the tensors are scalars, 4-vectors, or 4-tensors of higher rank, this requirement guarantees that the equations will be form invariant for all Galilean observers. We will see that the 12 basic differential equations of electrodynamics—Maxwell's four 3-vector equations—can be written as different components of form invariant equations involving the F_{ij}.

As an example, consider the tensor equation

$$f_i = -\frac{e}{c} F_{ij} v^j.$$

Here f_i is the covariant 4-vector Minkowski force

$$\{f_i\} = \left\{ \frac{-F_x}{\sqrt{1 - \beta^2}}, \frac{-F_y}{\sqrt{1 - \beta^2}}, \frac{-F_z}{\sqrt{1 - \beta^2}}, \frac{\mathbf{F} \cdot \mathbf{v}}{c\sqrt{1 - \beta^2}} \right\}.$$

F_{ij} is the electromagnetic field tensor given above; v^j is the contravariant 4-vector velocity

$$\{v^j\} = \left\{ \frac{v_x}{\sqrt{1 - \beta^2}}, \frac{v_y}{\sqrt{1 - \beta^2}}, \frac{v_z}{\sqrt{1 - \beta^2}}, \frac{c}{\sqrt{1 - \beta^2}} \right\}.$$

The first component of the tensor equation gives

$$\frac{-F_x}{\sqrt{1-\beta^2}} = -\frac{e}{c}[F_{11}v^1 + F_{12}v^2 + F_{13}v^3 + F_{14}v^4]$$

$$= -\frac{e}{c}\left[0 + (cB_z)\frac{v_y}{\sqrt{1-\beta^2}} + (-cB_y)\frac{v_z}{\sqrt{1-\beta^2}} + (E_x)\frac{c}{\sqrt{1-\beta^2}}\right]$$

or

$$F_x = e[E_x + (\mathbf{v} \times \mathbf{B})_x].$$

The second and third components of the tensor equation give similar y and z expressions. The space components of this tensor equation are thus identical with the Lorentz force expression for the charge e moving in the electromagnetic fields $\mathbf{E}$ and $\mathbf{B}$. For any other Galilean observer the equation becomes simply

$$f'_i = -\frac{e}{c}F'_{ij}v'^j.$$

The Lorentz force will have the same expression, in terms of the transformed variables, for the second Galilean observer as it does for the first observer.

It should be mentioned that the requirement that equations be written in 4-tensor form is a sufficient, but not a necessary, condition for the form invariance of the equations. In the example above, if F_{ij} had transformed to nF'_{ij} where n is some function $\neq 1$, then F_{ij} would not be a tensor; nevertheless, if v^j transformed to $\frac{1}{n}v'^j$, the equation would still remain form invariant.

We will now write a number of the equations of electrodynamics in a form invariant manner using MKSA units. The continuity equation,

$$\nabla \cdot \mathbf{j} + \frac{\partial \rho}{\partial t} = 0 \quad \text{or} \quad \frac{\partial j_x}{\partial x} + \frac{\partial j_y}{\partial y} + \frac{\partial j_z}{\partial z} + \frac{\partial \rho}{\partial t} = 0,$$

becomes

$$\frac{\partial j^i}{\partial x^i} = 0$$

since

$$\{j^i\} = \{j_x, j_y, j_z, c\rho\} \quad \text{and} \quad \{x^i\} = \{x, y, z, ct\}.$$

Similarly, the Lorentz condition

$$\nabla \cdot \mathbf{A} + \frac{1}{c^2}\frac{\partial \phi}{\partial t} = 0$$

becomes, since

$$\{A^i\} = \{cA_x, cA_y, cA_z, \phi\},$$

$$\frac{\partial A^i}{\partial x^i} = 0.$$

The gauge transformation

$$\left(\phi' = \phi + \frac{\partial f}{\partial t}, \qquad \mathbf{A}' = \mathbf{A} - \nabla f \right)$$

becomes

$$A'_i = A_i + c\frac{\partial f}{\partial x^i}.$$

Here $\{A_i\} = \{-cA_x, -cA_y, -cA_z, \phi\}$ while $\left\{c\frac{\partial f}{\partial x^i}\right\} = \left\{c\frac{\partial f}{\partial x}, c\frac{\partial f}{\partial y}, c\frac{\partial f}{\partial z}, c\frac{\partial f}{\partial (ct)}\right\}.$

The inhomogeneous wave equations in free space are

$$\begin{cases} \nabla^2\phi - \left(\frac{1}{c^2}\right)\frac{\partial^2\phi}{\partial t^2} = -\frac{1}{\varepsilon_0}\rho, \\[2ex] \nabla^2\mathbf{A} - \left(\frac{1}{c^2}\right)\frac{\partial^2\mathbf{A}}{\partial t^2} = -\mu_0\mathbf{j}. \end{cases}$$

Here $\nabla^2\mathbf{A}$, the Laplacian of a 3-vector, is defined as the 3-vector whose components are $\nabla^2 A_x$, $\nabla^2 A_y$, $\nabla^2 A_z$. Similarly, the D'Alembertian operator of a 3-vector, $\mathbf{A}$, is defined by the 3-vector whose components are

$$\nabla^2 A_x - \left(\frac{1}{c^2}\right)\frac{\partial^2 A_x}{\partial t^2}, \quad \nabla^2 A_y - \left(\frac{1}{c^2}\right)\frac{\partial^2 A_y}{\partial t^2}, \quad \text{and} \quad \nabla^2 A_z - \left(\frac{1}{c^2}\right)\frac{\partial^2 A_z}{\partial t^2}.$$

The two inhomogeneous wave equations may be combined into one form invariant equation. Let

$$\nabla^i = \hat{\mathbf{x}}^i\frac{\partial}{\partial x^i} = \hat{\mathbf{x}}\frac{\partial}{\partial x} + \hat{\mathbf{y}}\frac{\partial}{\partial y} + \hat{\mathbf{z}}\frac{\partial}{\partial z} + \hat{ct}\frac{\partial}{\partial (ct)}.$$

Then

$$\nabla_i = \hat{\mathbf{x}}_i\frac{\partial}{\partial x^i} = -\hat{\mathbf{x}}\frac{\partial}{\partial x} - \hat{\mathbf{y}}\frac{\partial}{\partial y} - \hat{\mathbf{z}}\frac{\partial}{\partial z} + \hat{ct}\frac{\partial}{\partial (ct)}$$

and

$$\nabla^i\nabla_i = -\frac{\partial^2}{\partial x^2} - \frac{\partial^2}{\partial y^2} - \frac{\partial^2}{\partial z^2} + \left(\frac{1}{c^2}\right)\frac{\partial^2}{\partial t^2}.$$

So

$$\nabla^i\nabla_i A^k = (\mu_0 c)j^k.$$

The Coulomb potential $\dfrac{e}{4\pi\varepsilon_0 r^0}$ produced at a point B, distant r^0 from a charge e at A and stationary relative to it, may also be made form invariant. Let

$$\{s^i\} = \{(x^B - x^A), (y^B - y^A), (z^B - z^A), (ct^B - ct^A)\};$$

so

$$\{s_i\} = \{-(x^B - x^A), -(y^B - y^A), -(z^B - z^A), (ct^B - ct^A)\}$$

and

$$s^i s_i = -(x^B - x^A)^2 - (y^B - y^A)^2 - (z^B - z^A)^2 + c^2(t^B - t^A)^2 = s^2.$$

This invariant (which may be evaluated in the rest-system where A and B are both at rest) gives the time retardation between the time at B where the potential is to be evaluated and the time at A where the potential was produced. Since the signal travels with velocity c we then have $s^2 = -r^2 + c^2t^2 = 0$ or $r = ct$; also $r^0 = ct^0$ in the rest-system.

For an observer moving with velocity $\mathbf{v}$ relative to the rest-system we may form the scalar $v^i s_i$. Its value may be obtained in the rest-system:

$$(v^i s_i)^0 = 0(-x^0) + 0(-y^0) + 0(-z^0) + \frac{c}{\sqrt{1-0}}(ct^0) = cr^0 = v^i s_i. \text{ So}$$

$r^0 = v^i s_i / c$. The 4-vector potential in the rest-system

$$\{A^i\}^0 = \left\{0, 0, 0, \frac{1}{4\pi\varepsilon_0}\frac{e}{r^0}\right\}$$

may then be written

$$\{A^i\}^0 = \left\{0, 0, 0, \frac{e}{4\pi\varepsilon_0}\left(\frac{c}{v^i s_i}\right)\right\}.$$

This can now be generalized to any Galilean observer by employing the expression for the 4-velocity:

$$\{A^i\} = \frac{e}{4\pi\varepsilon_0}\left\{\left(\frac{1}{v^i s_i}\right)\frac{v_x}{\sqrt{1-\beta^2}}, \left(\frac{1}{v^i s_i}\right)\frac{v_y}{\sqrt{1-\beta^2}}, \right.$$

$$\left.\left(\frac{1}{v^i s_i}\right)\frac{v_z}{\sqrt{1-\beta^2}}, \left(\frac{1}{v^i s_i}\right)\frac{c}{\sqrt{1-\beta^2}}\right\}$$

or

$$A^i = \frac{e}{4\pi\varepsilon_0}\frac{v^i}{v^j s_j}.$$

In this case, unlike the previous example, the conversion to form invariance results, seemingly, in greater complexity than in the classical expression. Actually, this is not so; for the form invariant equation is the equivalent of the classical Liénard-Wiechert potentials of precisely the same complexity. Since $ct = r$,

$$v^j s_j = \frac{-\mathbf{v} \cdot \mathbf{r}}{\sqrt{1-\beta^2}} + \frac{cr}{\sqrt{1-\beta^2}} = \frac{cr(1 - \boldsymbol{\beta} \cdot \hat{\mathbf{r}})}{\sqrt{1-\beta^2}} = \frac{cl}{\sqrt{1-\beta^2}}.$$

Here $l = r(1 - \boldsymbol{\beta} \cdot \hat{\mathbf{r}})$. Then

$$A^1 = \frac{e}{4\pi\varepsilon_0}\frac{v_x/\sqrt{1-\beta^2}}{cl/\sqrt{1-\beta^2}} = \frac{ev_x/c}{4\pi\varepsilon_0 l}$$

with similar expressions for A^2 and A^3, while

$$A^4 = \frac{e}{4\pi\varepsilon_0}\frac{c/\sqrt{1-\beta^2}}{cl/\sqrt{1-\beta^2}} = \frac{e}{4\pi\varepsilon_0 l}:$$

the Liénard-Wiechert potentials for a particle of charge e. These replace the distance r^0 of our original expression by $l = r(1 - \boldsymbol{\beta} \cdot \hat{\mathbf{r}})$, thereby taking into account the speed with which changes in the potential are propagated.

The relations between the potentials and fields, $\mathbf{E} = -\nabla\phi - \dfrac{\partial\mathbf{A}}{\partial t}$ and $\mathbf{B} = \nabla \times \mathbf{A}$, may be written very simply in a form invariant manner. Since $\{A_i\} = \{-cA_x, -cA_y, -cA_z, \phi\}$, we have

$$F_{ij} = \frac{\partial A_i}{\partial x^j} - \frac{\partial A_j}{\partial x^i}.$$

The ability to write the Coulomb potential in 4-vector form means that the Coulomb force ($\mathbf{F} = e\mathbf{E} = -e\nabla\phi$ with $\partial\mathbf{A}/\partial t = 0$) can be treated by special relativity. The Coulomb force $F = \dfrac{1}{4\pi\varepsilon_0}\dfrac{e_1 e_2}{r^2}$ is the basic experimental law, the foundation, of electrostatics. Similarly, the law of gravitational attraction $F = G\dfrac{m_1 m_2}{r^2}$ is the basic equation of the Newtonian theory of gravitation. But, as we have previously seen, e and m transform quite differently between Galilean observers—the mass is not a scalar. Since a Minkowski 4-force can be obtained for the electrostatic Coulomb force we are then automatically precluded from obtaining a similar expression for the gravitational Newtonian force. Thus, this Newtonian force cannot be treated by special relativity. General relativity is an outcome of the attempt to resolve this difficulty. The force between two masses in general relativity is given by a very different formalism than in Newtonian mechanics; but the results are almost identical. In fact, it is difficult to find suitable cases where the differences between the two can be tested experimentally. These tests are still inconclusive but at present seem to favor general relativity.

The transformation to form invariance may also be made for Maxwell's equations in free space:

$$\begin{cases} \nabla \cdot \mathbf{E} = \dfrac{1}{\varepsilon_0}\rho, & \nabla \times \mathbf{E} = -\dfrac{\partial\mathbf{B}}{\partial t}, \\[2ex] \nabla \cdot \mathbf{B} = 0, & \nabla \times \mathbf{B} = \mu_0\varepsilon_0\dfrac{\partial\mathbf{E}}{\partial t} + \mu_0\mathbf{j}. \end{cases}$$

With $\{A_i\} = \{-cA_x, -cA_y, -cA_z, \phi\}$, $\{x_i\} = \{-x, -y, -z, ct\}$, $\{j_i\} = \{-j_x, -j_y, -j_z, \rho c\}$, and $\mu_0\varepsilon_0 = \dfrac{1}{c^2}$ the first and fourth Maxwell equations are given by

$$\frac{\partial F_{kl}}{\partial x_l} = c\mu_0 j_k.$$

Note that a covariant vector in the denominator acts like a contravariant vector in the numerator.

The second and third equations are given, with $\{x^i\} = \{x, y, z, ct\}$, by four of the possible 64 equations represented by

$$\frac{\partial F_{kl}}{\partial x^m} + \frac{\partial F_{lm}}{\partial x^k} + \frac{\partial F_{mk}}{\partial x^l} = 0.$$

These correspond to $(k, l, m) = (1, 2, 3)$, $(1, 2, 4)$, $(1, 3, 4)$, and $(2, 3, 4)$, respectively. The other 60 equations give either repetitions of these four or else the identity $0 = 0$. By making use of the pseudotensor ε^{ijkl} introduced in a previous section we may throw the second equation into a form similar to the one preceding it. The second-rank dual of F_{kl} is the pseudotensor $P^{ij} = \frac{1}{2}\varepsilon^{ijkl}F_{kl}$. The second form invariant Maxwell equation may then be written

$$\frac{\partial P^{ij}}{\partial x^i} = 0.$$

The zero on the right-hand side here, in contrast to the j_k in the first form invariant Maxwell equation, is a reflection of the apparent physical fact that there are no magnetic monopoles or monopole current densities in nature.

BIBLIOGRAPHY

Adler, A., Bazin, M., and Schiffer, M.: Introduction to General Relativity, New York, McGraw-Hill Book Co., 1965.

Landau, L. D., and Lifshitz, E. M.: The Classical Theory of Fields. 2nd ed. London, Pergamon Press, Ltd., 1962.

Moon, P., and Spencer, D. E.: Vectors. Princeton, New Jersey, D. Van Nostrand Co., 1965.

Nicolson, M. M.: Fundamentals and Techniques of Mathematics for Scientists. New York, John Wiley & Sons, Inc., 1961.

Spain, B.: Tensor Calculus. 3rd ed. Edinburgh, Oliver & Boyd, Ltd., 1960.

Synge, J. L., and Schild, A.: Tensor Calculus. Toronto, University of Toronto Press, 1949.

Chapter 9 EXPERIMENTAL EVIDENCE

I. THE PRINCIPLE OF RELATIVITY

Both the foundation and the deductions of the theory of special relativity have been verified in numerous experiments. The tests of the two basic postulates are, of course, particularly significant. In this section we first treat the Michelson-Morley experiment. A modification of this, the Kennedy-Thorndike experiment, is considered in the process. Finally, we go briefly into a more recent type of experiment whose accuracy depends on $\frac{v}{c}$, rather than on $\left(\frac{v}{c}\right)^2$ as is the case in the preceding two experiments.

Figure 38a shows a beam of waves split into two parts, one going to the right along an arm of length L while the other goes along the other arm of length l, of approximately the same value. At the ends of the arms the two beams are reflected, retracing their paths. They are then combined at the beam splitter into one beam which goes to a detector. The entire assembly is assumed to move to the right with velocity v. In Figure 38b the assembly has been rotated through 90°.

What we have here, essentially, is a combination of our imagined experiments with reflected waves in rocket ships. In Chapter 3, Time, we considered reflection of the transverse beam; in Chapter 4, Space, we treated reflection of the longitudinal beam. Here we wish to consider the difference in time of travel for these two beams.

We will treat three distinct possibilities:

(1) sonar beams in a completely closed instrument (the air is contained within a cover, which separates the air and instrument from the rest of the universe; this is the condition treated in Chapters 3 and 4; it is also the case of 100 per cent ether drag);

(2) sonar beams in a completely open instrument (there is no separation between the instrument and the stationary air);

(3) radar beams.

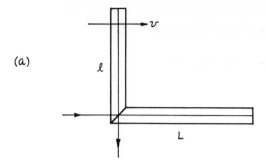

(a)

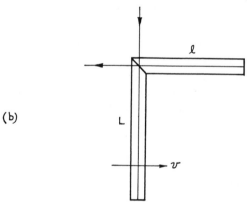

Figure 38. Interferometer for measuring v.

(b)

The resultant analysis gives the explanation for the null result of the Michelson-Morley experiment, which has become one of the classics of physics. Although the experiment probably should be considered one to select the proper law for the addition of velocities, it may also be regarded as a test of the principle of relativity, for that principle implies a lack of a medium which, in turn, leads to one combinatorial method for velocities.

We proceed, now, to treat the *first case*—a sonar beam traversing a completely enclosed instrument. As measured by an inside observer, with the instrument oriented as in Figure 38a, the time for the transverse or perpendicular beam to travel back and forth is

$$t_T = \frac{2l}{c_s}.$$

The time for the longitudinal beam to complete its journey is, correspondingly,

$$t_L = \frac{2L}{c_s}.$$

The time difference between the two journeys is

$$|t_L - t_T| = \frac{2}{c_s}|L - l|.$$

This gives an equivalent difference in distance:

$$\Delta = c_s |t_L - t_T| = 2 |L - l|.$$

With some given Δ a series of fringes is set up by interference between the two beams in the detector, with one particular fringe under the detector hairline.

When the instrument is turned through 90° the result may be obtained at once by switching l and L:

$$\Delta' = 2 |l - L| = 2 |L - l|.$$

There will then be no shift of fringes on rotating the instrument:

$$n = \frac{\Delta' - \Delta}{\lambda} = 0.$$

So, with a completely enclosed instrument there should be no observable effect upon rotation of the interferometer.

Next we treat the *second case*—a sonar beam traversing an interferometer moving through the air, with the instrument completely open relative to the stationary air. This case would also correspond to electromagnetic waves in an all-pervasive ether with no ether-drag. We will again deal with this as measured by an inside observer. With the orientation of Figure 38a the longitudinal back-and-forth time is

$$t_L = \frac{L}{c_s - v} + \frac{L}{c_s + v} = \frac{\dfrac{2L}{c_s}}{1 - \left(\dfrac{v}{c_s}\right)^2}.$$

Before calculating the transverse time we must obtain the transverse velocity with respect to the instrument. For the ray to move transversely along l when the transverse arm, itself, is moving to the right with speed v it is necessary that the velocity c_s of the ray with respect to the medium (air or ether) have a forward as well as a transverse component. Then the transverse velocity we seek is $\sqrt{c_s^2 - v^2}$. So

$$t_T = 2 \frac{l}{\sqrt{c_s^2 - v^2}} = \frac{2l/c_s}{\sqrt{1 - \left(\dfrac{v}{c_s}\right)^2}}.$$

The time difference is

$$|t_L - t_T| = \frac{2}{c_s}\left| \frac{L}{1 - \left(\dfrac{v}{c_s}\right)^2} - \frac{l}{\sqrt{1 - \left(\dfrac{v}{c_s}\right)^2}} \right|.$$

Then the equivalent distance difference is

$$\Delta = 2 \left| \frac{L}{1 - \left(\frac{v}{c_s}\right)^2} - \frac{l}{\sqrt{1 - \left(\frac{v}{c_s}\right)^2}} \right|.$$

When the instrument is rotated, l and L are interchanged in the formula for the time difference, or

$$\Delta' = 2 \left| \frac{L}{\sqrt{1 - \left(\frac{v}{c_s}\right)^2}} - \frac{l}{1 - \left(\frac{v}{c_s}\right)^2} \right|.$$

Set $\gamma = 1 / \sqrt{1 - \left(\frac{v}{c_s}\right)^2}$ and let $L > l$. Then the fringe shift will be

$n = \frac{1}{\lambda} |\Delta' - \Delta| = \frac{2\gamma}{\lambda} \left| |L - \gamma l| - |\gamma L - l| \right|$. There are 3 possibilities—

$$\gamma l < L: \quad n = \frac{2\gamma}{\lambda} |(L - \gamma l) - (\gamma L - l)| = \frac{2\gamma}{\lambda} (\gamma - 1)(L + l).$$

$$\gamma l = L: \quad n = \frac{2\gamma}{\lambda} |-(\gamma L - l)| = \frac{2\gamma}{\lambda} (\gamma L - l).$$

$$\gamma l > L: \quad n = \frac{2\gamma}{\lambda} |(\gamma l - L) - (\gamma L - l)| = \frac{2\gamma}{\lambda} (\gamma + 1)(L - l).$$

The first case is the pertinent one because, almost certainly, $v/c_s \ll 1$. But with a completely open instrument (or with ether) there should be a nonvanishing effect upon rotation of the interferometer, in any case.

It is, of course, well known that when the experiment was performed using electromagnetic waves (presumably propagating in the ether) no fringe shift was found. When we consider the third case we will see how relativity explains this fact. It is worth noting first, however, how the contraction hypothesis, made independently by Lorentz and Fitzgerald, explains this fact. If, in the expression for Δ, the quantity L is replaced by $L\sqrt{1 - \left(\frac{v}{c_s}\right)^2}$ then we may write $\Delta = \dfrac{2(L - l)}{\sqrt{1 - \left(\frac{v}{c_s}\right)^2}}$. Similarly, if in Δ' we replace l by $l\sqrt{1 - \left(\frac{v}{c_s}\right)^2}$ then $\Delta' = \dfrac{2(L - l)}{\sqrt{1 - \left(\frac{v}{c_s}\right)^2}}$. We obtain $\Delta' - \Delta = 0$ automatically if we make the ad hoc assumption that a longitudinal length must be multiplied by $\sqrt{1 - \left(\frac{v}{c_s}\right)^2}$. This change in longitudinal length cannot be measured, since the measuring rod also changes its length. It can, in fact, only be detected by the experiment it was designed to explain.

Fitzgerald made precisely this ad hoc suggestion to explain the null results of the Michelson-Morley experiment. Lorentz, however, did more than this; he derived this result by assuming only the existence of the ether and the anisotropy introduced into the electric field of a charge when the charge is moving relative to the observer. Because of this anisotropy, the equilibrium positions of the charges in a moving solid are squeezed together, in the direction of travel, by the factor $\sqrt{1 - \beta^2}$ and the equation for Δ becomes $\Delta = \dfrac{2(L - l)}{\sqrt{1 - \left(\dfrac{v}{c_s}\right)^2}}$.

It proved possible to modify the Michelson-Morley experiment in order to test this hypothesis. Suppose that, instead of L and l being very nearly equal, L and l were made quite different in magnitude. The interferometer is kept in one position when the velocity is v_1; it is turned $90°$ when the velocity is v_2. Then the last equation above becomes:

$$\Delta = \frac{2(L - l)}{\sqrt{1 - \beta_1{}^2}}, \qquad \Delta' = \frac{2(L - l)}{\sqrt{1 - \beta_2{}^2}}$$

and

$$n = \frac{|\Delta - \Delta'|}{\lambda} = \frac{2(L - l)}{\lambda} \left| \frac{1}{\sqrt{1 - \beta_1{}^2}} - \frac{1}{\sqrt{1 - \beta_2{}^2}} \right|$$

or

$$n \approx \left(\frac{L - l}{\lambda}\right) |\beta_1{}^2 - \beta_2{}^2|.$$

Using the change in velocity of the earth each 12 hours, Kennedy and Thorndike sought this effect experimentally but obtained a null result. This disproved the Lorentz hypothesis, which gave a correct answer (what we now call the Lorentz-Fitzgerald contraction) by assuming an incorrect condition (the existence of the ether). A relativistic calculation of the velocities to be inserted into the equation, however, yields the result that for the Kennedy-Thorndike experiment, also, there should be no fringe shift. This calculation is the same for the Kennedy-Thorndike and the Michelson-Morley experiments and follows immediately. It should be noted explicitly that the Kennedy-Thorndike experiment gives direct evidence for the validity of the principle of relativity and it is, therefore, a very important and basic experiment.

We now consider the *third possibility*—the relativistic explanation for electromagnetic waves obeying the principle of relativity, no ether being postulated. We will, again, look at this from the viewpoint of an inside observer. The transverse time is given by

$$t_T^0 = \frac{2l^0}{c} ;$$

the longitudinal time is given by

$$t_L^0 = \frac{2L^0}{c}.$$

Consequently,

$$\Delta = c \left| t_L^0 - t_T^0 \right| = 2 \left| L^0 - l^0 \right|.$$

When the instrument is rotated we obtain

$$\Delta' = 2 \left| l^0 - L^0 \right|,$$

and

$$n = \frac{\Delta' - \Delta}{\lambda} = 0.$$

A null result is obtained here, just as in the first case (100 per cent ether-drag), but unlike the second case (no ether-drag). But case one is eliminated by the experimental evidence of Fizeau's experiment as well as by aberration. Of the three possibilities assumed at the start of this section, only the relativistic explanation agrees with both the results of the Michelson-Morley experiment (which treats the experimenter as the inside observer and the earth as the vehicle) and the results of the Fizeau experiment.

Two criticisms that have long been leveled at the Michelson-Morley experiment should be mentioned. It is a second-order experiment in that, when a power series expansion of the various expressions is made, there are no $\frac{v}{c}$ terms; the first nonvanishing term involves $\left(\frac{v}{c}\right)^2$. Since $\frac{v}{c} \ll 1$ the effect to be measured is a small one. It would be desirable to devise an experiment in which a $\frac{v}{c}$ term appeared. This has, in fact, been done recently and is considered later. Second, it is a two-way experiment rather than a one-way experiment: in each arm of the interferometer the light goes in both directions. It would be desirable to devise an experiment in which we could traverse a path in only one direction. It does not seem possible to do this.

Today, after 80 years, the Michelson-Morley experiment still stands intact, a tribute to man's ingenuity, a beautiful work of art as well as an experiment in science.

A more recent test of the principle of relativity, with much higher accuracy, is provided by an experiment of Cedarholm, Bland, Havens, and Townes using two beam-type ammonia masers. In the ammonia molecule, NH_3, the three hydrogen atoms are situated in a plane at the vertices of an equilateral triangle. The nitrogen atom can occupy one of two positions on a line perpendicular to this triangle through its center; each position then forms a pyramid, with both pyramids having a common base. Transitions of the nitrogen atom from one position to the other may occur, but there is a slight energy difference for the NH_3 molecule between the two cases of 2.55×10^{-4} eV. This corresponds to 23,870 Mc/sec, which is in the microwave portion of the spectrum.

The original ammonia maser of Gordon, Zeiger, and Townes employed a beam of molecules which were in equilibrium for this transition: at any given moment some of the beam particles were emitting at this frequency while an equal number were absorbing at the same frequency. Either by an electric or a magnetic field it is possible to remove the lower energy particles from the beam, leaving a monoenergetic stream of molecules. The beam passed through a cavity adjusted to be precisely in resonance with the ammonia transition frequency. The beam molecules were thereby induced to radiate at 23,870 Mc/sec, the radiation from individual molecules being coherent with each other (same frequency and same phase), thereby yielding a very high total intensity. This type of maser, employed as an oscillator, has since been generally displaced by solid state types; but for this check of the principle of relativity it was the original type that was used.

The experiment compared the frequencies of two such masers, the NH_3 beams traveling with speed u in opposite directions relative to the cavities and the radiation being examined perpendicular to either direction. If the masers are stationary relative to an assumed ether then the emitted radiation is perpendicular to the beam direction and there is no Doppler frequency shift. But if a maser moves through the ether with velocity v parallel to u then the radiation must be emitted at an angle

$$\theta = \frac{\pi}{2} - \sin^{-1}\left(\frac{v}{c}\right) \approx \frac{\pi}{2} - \frac{v}{c}$$

relative to u, from the transmitter viewpoint, to be received at $90°$; similarly, if v is antiparallel to u the emission angle must be $\theta = \frac{\pi}{2} + \frac{v}{c}$ relative to u. The Doppler frequency shift in either case, calculated on a classical basis by means of the Galilean transformation, is given by

$$\frac{\Delta f}{f^0} = \frac{u}{c}\cos\theta = \frac{u}{c}\left(\frac{v}{c}\right).$$

The situation here is similar to the second case of the Michelson-Morley experiment considered above.

For thermal velocities of the molecular beam $u = 0.6 \frac{km}{sec}$; the earth's orbital velocity is $v = 30 \frac{km}{sec}$; so $\frac{\Delta f}{f^0} = 2 \times 10^{-10}$, giving $\Delta f = 4.77$ cps. Instead of attempting to measure the small change Δf against f^0 it is much simpler and also more accurate to measure the Δf of one maser against that of the other. This can be done by a heterodyne process, which multiplies the two waves to give $\cos(\omega_1 t)\cos(\omega_2 t)$. This equals

$$\tfrac{1}{2}\cos(\omega_1 + \omega_2)t + \tfrac{1}{2}\cos(\omega_1 - \omega_2)t.$$

The sum term is then rejected and the difference term selected by means of filters. There should then be a difference frequency of 2×4.77 or approximately 10 cps, a quantity which is easily measurable.

Placing the two masers, with oppositely directed beams, on a mount which is rotated 180° about a vertical axis midway between the masers, the difference frequency between the two maser oscillators should be made to change by 20 cps. The masers were adjusted to give an original difference frequency of 20 cps. No variation greater than $\pm \frac{1}{50}$ cps about the original 20 cps was found experimentally; and these were random, not correlated with the earth's orientation.

The precision obtained in this experiment by the frequency comparison was 1 part in 10^{12}. It showed any possible ether drift to be less than 10^{-3} of the earth's orbital velocity. This precision was possible because the quantity measured was of the first order in $\frac{v}{c}$; in the Michelson-Morley experiment the fringe shift is proportional to $\left(\frac{v}{c}\right)^2$.

This test constitutes excellent experimental evidence for the validity of the assumption of the principle of relativity, one of the two basic postulates.

2. THE VELOCITY OF LIGHT

The speed of electromagnetic radiation in free space, between a source and detector fixed relative to each other, has been measured by an international array of physicists for some 300 years now, employing many different types of measurements. The accompanying table (see opposite) taken, with the kind permission of the publishers, from "Physics for Students of Science and Engineering" by David Halliday and Robert Resnick,* summarizes some selected measurements. As of 1957 the accepted value for c, arrived at by weighting the different experimental results in accordance with their uncertainty, was 299,792.4 $\frac{km}{sec} \pm 0.0003$ per cent.

A proposal was made several years ago to send an atom bomb on a rocket far into outer space, where it would be exploded. This would enable a careful check to be made of the relative speed of all the different frequencies throughout the entire spectrum of electromagnetic radiation. The dangers inherent in such an experiment in the event of some malfunction, however, have mitigated against the carrying out of such an experiment and it is doubtful that it will ever be performed.

There have been many experiments designed to measure the velocity of electromagnetic radiation in a vacuum when there is relative motion between the source and the observer. They have all yielded the same value, c, as that pertaining to the case of no relative motion. The validity of all the

---

* 2nd ed. John Wiley & Sons, Inc., 1962.

DATE	EXPERIMENTER	COUNTRY	METHOD	SPEED (KM/SEC)	UNCER-TAINTY (KM/SEC)
1600?	Galileo	Italy	Lanterns and shutters	"Extraordinarily rapid"	
1675	Roemer	France	Astronomical	200,000	
1729	Bradley	England	Astronomical	304,000	
1849	Fizeau	France	Toothed wheel	313,300	
1862	Foucault	France	Rotating mirror	298,000	500
1876	Cornu	France	Toothed wheel	299,990	200
1880	Michelson	U.S.A.	Rotating mirror	299,910	50
1883	Newcomb	England	Rotating mirror	299,860	30
1883	Michelson	U.S.A.	Rotating mirror	299,853	60
1906	Rosa, Dorsey	U.S.A.	Electromagnetic theory	299,781	10
1923	Mercier	France	Standing waves on wires	299,782	15
1926	Michelson	U.S.A.	Rotating mirror	299,796	4
1928	Karolus, Mittel-staedt	Germany	Kerr cell	299,778	10
1932	Michelson, Pease, Pearson	U.S.A.	Rotating mirror	299,774	11
1940	Huettel	Germany	Kerr cell	299,768	10
1941	Anderson	U.S.A.	Kerr cell	299,776	14
1950	Bergstrand	Sweden	Geodimeter	299,792.7	0.25
1950	Essen	England	Microwave cavity	299,792.5	3
1950	Houston	Scotland	Vibrating crystal	299,775	9
1950	Bol, Hansen	U.S.A.	Microwave cavity	299,789.3	0.4
1951	Aslakson	U.S.A.	Shoran radar	299,794.2	1.9
1952	Rank, Ruth, Ven der Sluis	U.S.A.	Molecular spectra	299,776	7
1952	Froome	England	Microwave inter-ferometer	299,792.6	0.7
1954	Florman	U.S.A.	Radio inter-ferometer	299,795.1	3.1
1954	Rank, Shearer, Wiggins	U.S.A.	Molecular spectra	299,789.8	3.0
1956	Edge	Sweden	Geodimeter	299,792.9	0.2

older experiments, including the historic deSitter measurement on binary stars rotating about their center of mass, has recently been brought into question on the basis of the Ewald-Oseen extinction theorem discussed in "Principles of Optics" by M. Born and E. Wolf. A review of this argument appears in the article "Evidence Against Emission Theories" by J. G. Fox, cited in the bibliography of Chapter 1.

The extinction theorem, as employed by Fox, refers to the means by which an incoming wave $\exp i(\omega t - k'x)$, with velocity $v_1 = \dfrac{\omega}{k'}$ in vacuum, has its velocity changed by interference with the induced radiation of the electrons in any medium which the wave enters. If the induced radiation, $\exp i(\omega t - kx)$, travels with velocity $v_2 = \dfrac{\omega}{k}$ in vacuum then interference between the two waves gives a resultant

$$\left\{ 2 \cos \frac{(k - k')x}{2} \right\} \exp i\left[\omega t - \frac{(k + k')x}{2} \right].$$

The reciprocal of the velocity of the resultant wave is the mean of the reciprocals of the two original velocities. Interference occurs between the two waves, even though their velocities are different, because their frequencies are the same. The original velocity is assumed to differ from c on the basis of the Ritz emission theory, which assumes that the velocity of a wave depends on the velocity of the source. By repeated interference of the resultant wave with a new induced wave, a sequence of waves is obtained whose velocity approaches v_2. Forward scattering results in the gradual extinction of the original wave and in its replacement by a secondary wave traveling with a new velocity, the process being essentially completed in a distance called the extinction length. This is given by $\lambda/[2\pi(n - 1)]$, where λ is the wavelength and n is the index of refraction.

As applied to the binary stars of deSitter, e.g., Fox argues that the light emitted from each of the stars may be $c + v$ and $c - v$, respectively, on the basis of the Ritz theory; but in the stationary gaseous envelope that surrounds the binary stars the velocity of the light would be changed to c if the envelope were large enough. Data on this point, however, are meager. Similar criticisms are made of the validity of other experiments involving terrestrial sources; here windows, lenses, or just the atmosphere provide the extinction. In air at normal pressure and temperature the extinction length is of the order of 1 mm. Thus, he believes, almost all experiments designed to test the different predictions of the Ritz and Einstein theories are invalid.

Fox agrees, however, that there are several recent experiments to which the criticism of the extinction theorem does not apply. Furthermore, the experimental evidence here is all in favor of the prediction of relativity. An experiment by Luckey and Weil, in which 310 MeV electrons were directed at a thin target of nickel, gave 170 MeV gamma rays in coincidence with degraded 140 MeV electrons. Measurement of the velocity of the gamma rays emitted by these fast-moving particles gave 2.97×10^{10} cm/sec $\pm$ 1 per cent.

Another experiment on the speed of gamma rays, by Filippas and Fox, involved the decay of π^0 mesons and also gave evidence against the Ritz emission theory and in favor of relativity.

Babcock and Bergman measured the fringe shift in an interferometer of two beams of light which passed in opposite directions through moving glass plates. Their results also were in favor of relativity.

Finally: Alväger, Farley, Kjellman, and Wallin measured the speed of gamma rays, with an energy greater than 6 GeV, from the decay of fast

π^0 mesons of speed v. If the speed is written $c + kv$ then, they showed, $k = 0$ to an accuracy of 10^{-4}.

There is substantial experimental evidence that the velocity of electromagnetic waves in vacuum is an invariant for Galilean observers.

3. TIME DILATION

A laboratory experiment has been made verifying the existence of time dilation. It involved the subatomic particles called pi mesons or pions. These were moving with a velocity $\frac{v}{c} = 0.75$ with respect to the laboratory. The lifetime of pions at rest, independently determined by other experiments, is $t^0 = 2.6 \times 10^{-8}$ sec. The lifetime of a pion is, of course, a statistical quantity: not all pions live exactly this time before decaying to other particles. N, the number surviving at any time, t, is given by $N = N_0 \exp\left(-\frac{t}{t^0}\right)$, where N_0 is the number present when $t = 0$. So that, out of an original 10^4 pions at $t = 0$ there would survive, on the average, $\frac{10,000}{2.72} = 3680$ at the end of 2.6×10^{-8} sec; at the end of one additional lifetime $\frac{3680}{2.72} = 1350$ would remain; etc.

A curve was obtained for the number of pions remaining, as a function of distance traveled in the laboratory (instead of as a function of time). As

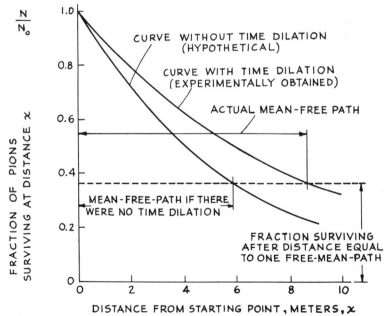

Figure 39. Experimental verification of time dilation.

shown in Figure 39, the experimentally obtained curve fits the formula $N = N_0 \exp\left(-\dfrac{x}{\lambda}\right)$. λ is the mean free path. From the curve it was determined to be 8.5 meters. Since $\lambda = vt$, the experimentally determined lifetime was $t = \dfrac{8.5}{\frac{3}{4}(3 \times 10^{-8})} = 3.8 \times 10^{-8}$ sec. Accordingly, $\dfrac{t}{t^0} = \dfrac{3.8 \times 10^{-8}}{2.6 \times 10^{-8}} = 1.5$.

The pions appeared to survive for a time interval 50 per cent longer than they would if the measurements were made on them while they were at rest. This result agreed with the value $t = \dfrac{2.6 \times 10^{-8}}{\sqrt{1 - (0.75)^2}} = 3.9 \times 10^{-8}$ required by relativity. Without time dilation λ should be 5.8 meters instead of the value 8.5 meters actually found.

4. THE LORENTZ-FITZGERALD CONTRACTION

It is an amazing fact that there does not seem to exist any direct or simple experimental verification of the Lorentz-Fitzgerald contraction. There is no reason whatever to doubt that the effect exists, precisely as called for by theory. So far, nevertheless, the difficulties—(1) of securing an object of appreciable length that moves with a speed comparable to that of light and, (2) of determining two events, one at either end, which are simultaneous for the observer—have proved insuperable. This very fundamental conclusion of the theory awaits actual proof.

5. THE DOPPLER EFFECT

The relativistic theory of the longitudinal Doppler effect gave the formulas (1) $v = v^0\sqrt{\dfrac{1 - \beta}{1 + \beta}}$ when source and observer were receding from each other, and (2) $v = v^0\sqrt{\dfrac{1 + \beta}{1 - \beta}}$ when source and observer were approaching. When these are expanded in power series they become $v \approx v^0(1 - \beta + \frac{1}{2}\beta^2)$ and $v \approx v^0(1 + \beta + \frac{1}{2}\beta^2)$, respectively. The classical theory, on the other hand, gave for the case when the source was receding from the observer $v \approx v^0(1 - \beta + \beta^2)$. The experiment of Ives and Stillwell was carried out to determine which formula was correct. Excited hydrogen ions, giving off the H_β line with $\lambda = 4861$ Å, were accelerated to a high velocity in a beam of canal rays. The light given off in the forward direction went directly to a spectrograph. The light given off in the rearward direction was reflected by a mirror into the spectrograph.

A typical spectrogram showed a central line and two side lines, slightly asymmetrically spaced, one on each side of the center. The center line was produced by stationary atoms; the bluer and redder lines, by fast-moving ions emitting in the forward and rearward directions, respectively. By measuring $\Delta\lambda$ for the side lines it was possible to determine β for the ion velocity, since on either theory $\Delta\lambda = \lambda^0\beta$ to the first order. The mean wavelength of the two side lines is given relativistically (to the second order) by

$$\lambda_m = \tfrac{1}{2}[\lambda^0(1 - \beta + \tfrac{1}{2}\beta^2) + \lambda^0(1 + \beta + \tfrac{1}{2}\beta^2)] = \lambda^0 + (1/2)\lambda^0\beta^2$$

so that

$$\lambda_m - \lambda^0 = \tfrac{1}{2}\lambda^0\beta^2.$$

Classically the mean wavelength is

$$\lambda_m = \tfrac{1}{2}[\lambda^0(1 - \beta + \beta^2) + \lambda^0(1 + \beta + \beta^2)] = \lambda^0 + \lambda^0\beta^2,$$

so that here

$$\lambda_m - \lambda^0 = \lambda^0\beta^2.$$

A small but clear-cut difference existed between the predictions of the two theories. By plotting $\Delta\lambda$ vs $(\lambda_m - \lambda^0)$ for various values of accelerating potential (i.e., $\lambda^0\beta$ versus either $\tfrac{1}{2}\lambda^0\beta^2$ or $\lambda^0\beta^2$), it was found that the data agreed quite well with the relativistic prediction.

The relativistic formula for the transverse Doppler effect is $f = f^0\sqrt{1 - \beta^2}$; for $\beta \ll 1$ this gives, approximately,

$$\frac{\Delta f}{f^0} = -\tfrac{1}{2}\beta^2.$$

Classically, there should be no frequency shift. The great precision in measurement of frequency differences made possible by the Mössbauer effect enabled Hay, Schiffer, Cranshaw, and Egelstaff to perform an experiment that gave a good correspondence with relativistic theory. The experiment may, alternatively, be considered a test of Einstein's principle of equivalence, according to which a uniformly accelerating point observer cannot be distinguished from an observer in a homogeneous gravitational field. On the basis of this principle Einstein predicted in 1907 that the frequency of a spectral line of an atom in a gravitational field would be altered. This effect is called the gravitational red shift.

In the experiment of Hay, Schiffer, Cranshaw, and Egelstaff a Co^{57} source was plated on the surface of an iron cylinder of radius $R_2 = 0.4$ cm. This cylinder was mounted on the axis of a shaft rotating with angular frequency ω. Concentric with this cylinder, and rigidly connected to it, was a cylindrical shell of Lucite of radius $R_1 = 6.64$ cm and thickness 0.31 cm. On the inside surface of the shell an iron foil, enriched in Fe^{57}, was glued. The entire assembly was rotated at angular velocities up to 500 rev/sec. A stationary xenon-filled proportional counter, with lead shielding against undesired radiation, served as the detector. Only gamma rays emitted radially by the Co^{57} and passing through the Fe^{57} absorber could reach the counter.

The cobalt nucleus has $Z = 27$. When the nucleus captures an electron this becomes iron, with $Z = 26$; the electron disappears in the process, together with one of the protons. Nine per cent of the nuclei which have captured an electron-decay directly to the stable Fe^{57} with the emission of a 137 KeV gamma ray; 91 per cent decay by emitting a 123 KeV gamma ray to an excited Fe^{57} level where, after 1.4×10^{-7} sec, a second gamma ray with 14.4 KeV energy is emitted, leaving the same stable ground state of Fe^{57}. The iron, on which the Co^{57} was plated, is in the form of a crystal lattice. It has the property that one of the excited Fe^{57} atoms resulting from the Co^{57} decay occupies a site in this lattice for a time that is long compared to the interval of 1.4×10^{-7} sec between the decay of the Co^{57} nuclide and the emission of the 14.4 KeV gamma ray.

Ordinarily there would be a recoil of the individual atom emitting the gamma ray. If the source atom were stationary originally, the emitted photon, of energy E_s, would give the atom, of mass M, a recoil momentum $\dfrac{E_s}{c}$. The atom would acquire an energy $\dfrac{E_s^2}{2Mc^2}$, so the energy of the photon becomes reduced by this amount. If E_r is the difference in energy between the excited and stable levels, the photon energy is

$$E_s = E_r - \frac{E_s^2}{2Mc^2} \simeq E_r - \frac{E_r^2}{2Mc^2} = E_r - R.$$

When the emitting atom is locked into a crystal, however, it may be not the individual atom that recoils but the entire crystal. The value of M in the denominator is tremendously increased, effectively eliminating the recoil energy shift R of the photon (0.002 eV for Fe^{57}) and leaving only the natural line width given by the Heisenberg uncertainty principle

$$\Gamma = \Delta E = \frac{h/2\pi}{\Delta t} = 4.57 \times 10^{-9} \text{ eV}.$$

Γ is roughly 10^{-6} the value of R. This is the Mössbauer effect.

When the photon emitted from the decaying Co^{57} source passes through the Fe^{57} absorber the latter can be raised from the ground state to the excited state by absorption of the photon. Subsequently, the Fe^{57} would emit a photon as scattered radiation in various directions. Ordinarily a stationary absorber atom, acting alone, would require for resonance that the absorbed photon should have an energy, E_a, given by

$$E_a = E_r + \frac{E_a^2}{2Mc^2} \simeq E_r + \frac{E_r^2}{2Mc^2} = E_r + R.$$

But when the absorbing atom is properly locked in a crystal lattice the value of R becomes effectively zero.

The assumption so far has been that the atoms were originally stationary. In the absence of the Mössbauer effect the shift $2R$ would be so large that resonant absorption would not occur. Because of the thermal motion of the atoms, however, these results must be modified. For a velocity v_s of the source atoms in the direction of the emitted photon there is a Doppler shift,

$$f = f^0 \sqrt{\frac{1 \pm \beta}{1 \mp \beta}} \simeq f^0 \left(1 \pm \frac{v_s}{c}\right).$$

So the radiated line occurs at $E_s\left(1 \pm \dfrac{v_s}{c}\right)$. In the absorber, similarly, there is a shift in the absorption line to $E_a\left(1 \pm \dfrac{v_a}{c}\right)$. Not all the atoms have the same values of v_s or v_a; there is a distribution of velocities that depends on the temperature. It can be shown that the broadening of the lines produced by the thermal Doppler effect results in a line width

$$2\Delta = \frac{2E_r}{c} \sqrt{\frac{2kT}{M}}$$

instead of the line width Γ. For Fe^{57} at room temperature $2\Delta = 0.02$ eV.

The Doppler broadening of the emission and absorption lines for unlocked Fe^{57} atoms is five times as large as the recoil shift $2R$. This is typical of some other atoms as well: for the 5890 Å line of sodium 2Δ is 3×10^4 times as large as $2R$ and optical resonance absorption followed by fluorescent resonance scattering is readily observed. For many nuclear transitions, however, $2R \gg 2\Delta$ so that resonance effects are weak. Ir^{191} is an example in which $2R < 2\Delta$, for a 129 KeV nuclear transition; it was employed by Mössbauer in 1958.

An explicit expression was derived by Mössbauer for the per cent of the emissions and absorptions, f, when free recoil of the atom is suppressed. This shows that f may be large if $R \ll k\theta_D$ and $T \ll \theta_D$, where k is Boltzmann's constant and θ_D is the Debye temperature. For Fe^{57} at room temperature the value of f is 0.71 while for Ir^{191} at 88° K its value is only 0.02. Other lattice-bound nuclei which exhibit the Mössbauer effect are Sn^{119} and Au^{197} but Fe^{57} is, by far, the most popular one with experimenters.

The usual arrangement for demonstrating the Mössbauer effect has the source mounted on a vibrator, the electronics being gated to record counts only when the vibrator has a given, but variable, value of velocity. Using a memory, one can then obtain an oscilloscope display of gamma ray absorption *versus* velocity. Pound and Rebka found that the half-width of the Fe^{57} line occurred at a source speed of $0.017 \dfrac{\text{cm}}{\text{sec}}$, corresponding to a frequency shift of $2 \dfrac{\text{Mc}}{\text{sec}}$ in the transition frequency of $3.5 \times 10^{12} \dfrac{\text{Mc}}{\text{sec}}$. Such a resolution is comparable to that obtained with beam-type masers (as in the experiment of Cedarholm, Bland, Havens, and Townes).

In the experiment considered here, however, the relative velocity of source and absorber was fixed for a given rotor angular velocity. The expected fractional shift in the frequency of the gamma rays is

$$\frac{\Delta f}{f^0} = \frac{(R_1{}^2 - R_2{}^2)\omega^2}{2c^2} .$$

The relative counting rate as a function of angular velocity rose, in the experiment of Hay, Schiffer, Cranshaw, and Egelstaff, from a value of $n = 100$ at $\omega = 0$ to $n \simeq 103.5$ at $\omega = 500 \frac{\text{rev}}{\text{sec}}$: the transmission increases with the frequency shift. A separate calibration experiment determined the absolute counting rate as a function of linear velocity and also gave the width of the resonance curve $\left(\text{only } 0.38 \frac{\text{mm}}{\text{sec}}\right)$ with the Lorentz shape $\left[(f - f^0)^2 + \frac{\gamma^2}{4}\right]^{-1}$. This information was sufficient to calculate a curve of expected relative counting rate versus angular velocity. The agreement between the data and this curve was excellent.

6. RELATIVISTIC PARTICLE DYNAMICS

The situation with regard to experimental verification of the relationships among energy, mass, and momentum is precisely the opposite of the situation regarding experimental verification of the Lorentz-Fitzgerald contraction. Here tens of thousands of experiments have confirmed the theoretical predictions of relativity in a multitude of different situations involving various kinds of particles, energies, etc. Accelerators, piles, collision experiments, rocket measurements—all provide a plethora of proof that the relativistic formulas are correct.

7. THE HOMOPOLAR GENERATOR

For our final example of experimental verification of the relativistic formulas we go to electricity and magnetism. In one sense the expression for the Lorentz force already constitutes such verification, for the Lorentz force expression follows directly from the relativistic transformation equations for force and electromagnetic field components (Problem 1, Chapter 7) and the Lorentz force expression agrees with experiment.

We will, however, take a different example—the ancient homopolar generator discussed previously. No explanation about cutting lines of force is adequate to give a classical description of the origin of the induced voltage here. Only the relativistic point of view, bringing in a transformation between observers moving relatively to each other, can remove the paradox that moving the conductor or the disc does induce a voltage but moving the magnets does not. The Faraday disc (or the homopolar generator) is, then, further experimental evidence supporting relativity.

We cannot help but add one final comment concerning an electro-magnetic verification of relativity which is actually outside the scope of this book. It has been known since the 1920's that an electron has a mechanical spin angular momentum and also a concomitant magnetic moment. Uhlen-beck and Goudsmit introduced this as a proposal which explained much spectroscopic information. In 1927 Dirac applied 4-vector relativistic con-siderations to the quantum theory of the electron. Instead of dealing with the usual 3-dimensional Schroedinger equation he wrote the Hamiltonian 4-dimensionally, to make the quantum theory conform to special relativity. When he solved the resulting four differential equations (one for each component) the electron automatically turned out to have the correct spin and magnetic moment, without any assumptions. This is the very strongest type of argument for the validity of special relativity.

BIBLIOGRAPHY

Alväger, T., Farley, F. J. M., Kjellman, J., and Wallin, I.: Test of the Second Postulate of Special Relativity in the GeV Region. Phys. Letters *12:* 260, Oct. 1, 1964.

Babcock, G. C., and Bergman, T. G.: Determination of the Constancy of the Speed of Light. J. Opt. Soc. Am. *54:* 147, Feb., 1964.

Cedarholm, J. P., Bland, G. F., Havens, B. L., and Townes, C. H.: New Experimental Test of Special Relativity. Phys. Rev. Letters *1:* 342, Nov. 1, 1958.

Durbin, R. P., Loar, H. H., and Havens, W. W.: The Lifetimes of π^+ and π^- Mesons. Phys. Rev. *88:* 179, Oct. 15, 1952.

Essen, L.: New Aether-Drift Experiment. Nature *175:* 793, May 7, 1955.

Filippas, T. A., and Fox, J. G.: Velocity of Gamma Rays from a Moving Source. Phys. Rev. *135:* B, 1071, Aug. 24, 1964.

Frisch, D. H., and Smith, J. H.: Measurement of the Relativistic Time Dilation Using μ-Mesons. Am. J. Physics *31:* 342, May, 1963.

Gordon, J. P., Zeiger, H. J., and Townes, C. H.: The Maser—New Type of Microwave Amplifier, Frequency Standard, and Spectrometer. Phys. Rev. *99:* 1264, Aug. 15, 1955.

Hay, H. J., Schiffer, J. P., Cranshaw, T. E., and Egelstaff, P. A.: Measurement of the Red Shift in an Accelerated System Using the Mössbauer Effect in Fe^{57}. Phys. Rev. Letters *4:* 165, Feb. 15, 1960.

Ives, H. E., and Stillwell, G. R.: Experimental Study of the Rate of a Moving Atomic Clock. J. Opt. Soc. Am. *28:* 215, July, 1938; *31:* 369, May, 1941.

Kennedy, R. J., and Thorndike, E. M.: Experimental Establishment of the Relativity of Time. Phys. Rev. *42:* 400, 1932.

Luckey, D., and Weil, J. W.: Velocity of 170-Mev Gamma Rays. Phys. Rev. *85:* 1060, March 15, 1952.

Michelson, A. A., and Morley, E. W.: On the Relative Motion of the Earth and the Lumin-iferous Ether. Am. J. Sci. *34:* 333, Nov., 1887.

Pound, R. V., and Rebka, G. A., Jr.: Variation with Temperature of the Energy of Recoil-free Gamma Rays from Solids. Phys. Rev. Letters *4:* 274, March 15, 1960.

Synge, J. L.: Group Motions in Space-time and Doppler Effects. Nature *198:* 679, May 18, 1963.

A number of basic articles on the theory and application of the Mössbauer effect appear in the booklet "Mössbauer Effect," published for the American Association of Physics Teachers by the American Institute of Physics, New York, 1963.

PROBLEMS

CHAPTER I

1. A rotating body has so-called fictitious forces associated with it (centrifugal force, Coriolis force) which are not present for nonrotating bodies. It would seem that one could absolutely determine whether or not a body is rotating: rotation would be an absolute motion. Comment on this.

2. An ether seems to be required for the propagation of electromagnetic energy as waves. Suppose the propagation of the energy takes place as photons. Like bullets, these do not require a medium. Why not forget about the waves? Where does the wave enter the explanation?

3. Common sense suggests that an astronaut stepping out of his space capsule should fall toward earth. Comment on this. Should not the capsule, itself, fall also?

4. Use the Galilean transformation to show that Newton's second law, $F = ma$, retains the same form for all Galilean observers. Assume that force and mass are invariant.

(Aside from those for Chapter 8, there are included a small number of problems which require a knowledge of calculus. The following is one of these.)

5. The wave equation $\dfrac{\partial^2 \phi}{\partial x^2} = \dfrac{1}{c^2} \dfrac{\partial^2 \phi}{\partial t^2}$ is a consequence of Maxwell's equations.

Here ϕ is any one of the six components of the electric and magnetic fields. Consider ϕ to be a function of x' and t'; and let x' and t' be functions of x and t, as given by the Galilean transformation. Use the chain rule of calculus (for taking derivatives of a function of functions) to show that the wave equation for the primed observer is

$$\left(1 - \frac{v^2}{c^2}\right) \frac{\partial^2 \phi}{\partial x'^2} = \frac{1}{c^2} \frac{\partial^2 \phi}{\partial t'^2} - \frac{2v}{c^2} \frac{\partial^2 \phi}{\partial x' \, \partial t'} .$$

6. Was Einstein aware of the Michelson-Morley experiment when he formulated his theory in 1905? Did he know of the existence of the Lorentz transformation?

7. Explain the differences among Lorentz, Fitzgerald, and Einstein with respect to the Lorentz transformation.

8. What were Michelson's views on relativity? Poincaré's? Lorentz's?

9. The earth has an angular velocity of $7.3 \times 10^{-5} \dfrac{\text{rad}}{\text{sec}}$ so it is not a Galilean coordinate system. Since people are earthbound, how can we verify Newtonian mechanics, which assume a Galilean system?

10. What differences exist between philosophy and science? What similarities? Why are there so few philosopher-scientists?

CHAPTER 2

1. Draw the axes of a Brehme diagram for two observers who are moving relative to each other with the following constant velocities: (a) infinitesimal; (b) a typical space rocket velocity, say $v = 18,000$ miles/hour; (c) the velocity of the earth about the sun, $v = 30$ km/sec; (d) the velocity of recession of a very distant galaxy, say $v = 0.1\,c$; (e) $v = 0.6\,c$; (f) $v = 0.8\,c$; (g) $v = c$; and (h) $v = 1.01\,c$. The tow observers are assumed to have the same spatial and temporal origins.

2. In each of the diagrams above add the world-lines for right-moving and for left-moving light rays emanating from the origin.

3. Repeat, for 2(d), with the light rays coming from the event (x, ct) given by (a) $(2, 1)$; (b) $(1, 1)$; and (c) $(1, 2)$.

4. A particle moves to the left with velocity $u = 0.7\,c$ for the (x, ct) observer, starting at $(2, 1)$. After two minutes the particle comes to rest. Draw the world-line of the particle for cases (e) and (f) in Problem 1. Use light-minutes for the units on the axes. (Coming to rest is not the same as disappearing.)

5. From the diagrams of 4(e) and 4(f) deduce whether the particle is moving to the right or left in real space for (X, cT). Also, find the speed.

6. B moves to the right in real space with $v/c = 0.6$ relative to A; C is fixed relative to B at a point in real space (i.e., 3-dimensional space, not space-time) 2 units to the right of B, so C also moves at $v/c = 0.6$ relative to A. Add dashed axes to the Brehme and Loedel diagrams for A and B so that the new axes apply to A and C. Is an interval for two events given correctly for A and C as well as for A and B?

7. Change the previous problem so that C's temporal origin $t_c = 0$ occurs at $t_b = 2$ but $x_c = 0$ where $x_b = 0$. Modify the Brehme and Loedel diagrams by adding a third set of axes to make them applicable for A, B, and C. Are intervals given correctly on the new axes?

8. B moves to the right with velocity v relative to A, while C moves to the right with velocity v' relative to B. Is it possible to modify the Brehme or Loedel diagrams for A and B so they will also be applicable to C as well?

9. Considering only intervals between an event at the origin and some other event, indicate on a Brehme diagram the region of space-time where the interval is time-like, where zero, and where space-like. How is this affected by the relative velocity between observers A and B? Repeat for a Loedel diagram.

10. An alternative proof of the equality of arbitrary intervals is obtained by considering observers A, B, and C moving with constant speeds v_{ba}, v_{cb}, and v_{ca} not along the same direction. Start with $s_b = [f(v_{ba})]s_a$, $s_c = [f(v_{cb})]s_b$, and $s_c = [f(v_{ca})]s_a$ and complete the proof, showing that $f^2 = f$. What is the physical significance of the solution $f = 0$?

11. In the complex rotation diagram of Figure 6b, p. 23, what is wrong with taking the projection of l^0 along the Ox' axis to give $l = l^0 \cos \phi$ as the measure of the rod by (x', τ')? Does this not correspond to the position measurements of the two end points at one instant for (x', τ')? Yet it gives a different answer from that in the text.

12. Prove that for the Minkowski diagram $\tan \delta = \dfrac{v}{c}$. Start with orthogonal axes for the (x, ct) observer and consider the locus of the spatial origin of the (x', ct') observer, who coincides with the first observer at $t = t' = 0$ and who moves to the right with velocity v relative to the first observer. This gives the ct' axis. Then consider the world-line for a ray of light from the origin toward the right in (x', ct'): the invariance of the interval determines the x' axis.

13. Show why $f_1 = -1$ is not permitted in the derivation of the equality of arbitrary intervals.

14. Prove, for the Minkowski diagram, that $\cos^2 \delta - \sin^2 \delta = \dfrac{1 - \beta^2}{1 + \beta^2}$.

CHAPTER 3

1. From the space-time diagram for the paradox of the twins show, for arbitrary v instead of for the specific value employed in the text, that $t_b{}^0 = t_a{}^0 \sqrt{1 - \beta^2}$.

2. It takes light 10^5 years to reach us from the most distant star in our galaxy. Could a human, traveling at constant velocity, reach this star in 50 years?

3. What is the per cent Doppler wavelength shift for light of 5000 Å if the source approaches the observer with velocity $0.7c$? if the observer recedes from the source at $0.7c$? Why do the two differ? Is the per cent shift accentuated or diminished for x-rays of 0.5 Å? (One Ångstrom unit is given by $1 \text{ Å} = 10^{-10}$ m.)

4. Suppose the traveling twin in the paradox traveled a path consisting of three segments, arranged as an equilateral triangle, with constant speed v on each. What would be the relation between the ages of the twins then? Now suppose the traveling twin took a circular path from the earth, returning from the other direction. What is the relation now?

5. For $T_A = 50$ years plot a graph of $(T_A - T_B)$ vs β in the twin paradox. Is there a reasonable hope for utilizing this effect to avoid old age?

6. What is the difference in time synchronization between A and D when D is synchronized with B, contiguous to him, if the distance between A and B is 100 miles and the velocity of D with respect to A and B is 18,000 miles/hour?

7. Suppose A remains on earth, B goes to the right and back as in the paradox of the twins, and C goes to the left and back in similar fashion. How do B's and C's clocks compare at the end of the two journeys? Explain this, considering that B and C also have relative velocity with respect to each other. A space-time diagram for A and observers R (who start with B but continue with constant velocity as Galilean observers) will be very helpful in showing the distinction between this case and the usual paradox of the twins.

8. Two events occur for (X, cT) simultaneously, in a space-time diagram with $\alpha = 37°$, but at space points separated by one unit. Find the time separation between these two events as measured by (x, ct).

9. At $T = 0$ a rocket ship (x, ct) was at $X = 1$ and moving toward greater X at a speed $\beta = 0.6$. The earth (X, cT) sent out a radar pulse at $T = 0$ which was reflected from the rocket ship, at a later time, back to earth.
(a) Draw a space-time diagram to scale.
(b) At what value of cT did the transmitted pulse reach the rocket ship?
(c) At what value of cT did the reflected pulse reach earth again?

10. In the paradox of the twins is twin B, outward bound, exactly equivalent to twin C, inward bound, at the instant they pass each other and synchronize their clocks? Consider their estimates at that instant of what time on earth is simultaneous with each.

11. In the paradox of the twins the difference in time for the two twins depends on the time taken by A. Yet whatever difference in time occurs would seem to result only from the brief turnabout time. Reconcile these statements.

CHAPTER 4

1. Calculate the Lorentz-Fitzgerald contraction, in cm, of the earth's diameter at the equator, caused by the earth's orbital motion about the sun, as measured by an observer stationary with respect to (a) the sun, (b) the earth.

2. A circle in the x-y plane moves with constant velocity v along the x axis relative to an observer. What would the observer measure? What would he see?

3. A proper-area, A^0, in a plane moves with velocity v relative to an observer. What is the nonproper-area measured by the observer? Consider all possible directions.

4. A proper-volume, V^0, moves with velocity v relative to an observer. What nonproper-volume does the observer measure? What is the effect of different directions?

5. Water flows out of a tank at a uniform rate. The proper-mass is m^0, the proper-volume is V^0 and the proper-time required to empty the tank is t^0. Compare the rate of flow with that measured by an observer moving with velocity v relative to the tank.

6. If the mean life of a meson is 2.2 microseconds when at rest and the particle moves with $v/c = 0.9$ relative to the earth, how long a distance does the meson travel between birth and death as measured by (a) the meson, (b) the earth?

7. A rocket of proper-length 600 m is moving toward the right away from earth with uniform velocity. A radar pulse is sent out from earth and is reflected by mirrors at the back end and the front end of the rocket. The first pulse is received back 200 sec after emission; the second one 20 μs later.
(a) Draw a space-time diagram (arbitrary v), labeling the emission event O, the two reflection events A and B, and the two reception events C and D.
(b) If the units for the axes are light-μs, how many units will the proper-length of the rocket take up?

8. In Problem 7, determine from the diagram the velocity of the rocket.

9. If, in Problem 7, the velocity of the rocket were known and the proper-length were unknown, would it be possible to determine the proper-length? Could this be used as an experimental test of the Lorentz contraction?

10. A string is stretched taut, to just below the breaking point, between two rockets resting on earth. The rockets accelerate identically and simultaneously, as measured by earth, until they reach velocity v, after which they continue with constant velocity. Does the string break because of the Lorentz-Fitzgerald contraction?

11. For $\dfrac{v}{c} \approx 1$ the rear face and one side of an approaching cube may be seen at certain viewing angles. What prevents the rays emitted by the front face, under these conditions, from reaching the observer? What happens to these rays?

CHAPTER 5

1. Show that for $v > c$ the angle α in the Brehme or Loedel diagrams is given by $\alpha = \dfrac{\pi}{2} + i\delta$. Find δ.

2. Two simultaneous events occur at $x = 0$ and $x = a$ when $t = 0$. What is the range in the spatial separation between these two events for all other Galilean observers? Is the interval space-like or time-like? What is the range of possible temporal separation for other observers? Is the time sequence of events preserved?

3. Show that if U is the velocity of an object with respect to (X, cT) and u is the velocity of the same object with respect to (x, ct), then

$$\sqrt{1 - \frac{U^2}{c^2}} = \frac{\sqrt{\left(1 - \frac{v^2}{c^2}\right)\left(1 - \frac{u^2}{c^2}\right)}}{1 - \frac{vu}{c^2}}.$$

Here (x, ct) moves to the right with velocity v relative to (X, cT). (The transformation equation for $\sqrt{1 - \frac{u^2}{c^2}}$ is obtained by letting v become $-v$ and capitalizing the lower case letters on the right side of the equation.)

4. B moves with velocity v toward $+X$ with respect to A; C moves toward $+y$ with respect to B; find the Lorentz transformation between A and C.

5. B' moves toward $+Y$ with respect to A; C' moves toward $+x$ with respect to B'; find the Lorentz transformation between A and C'. Compare with the answer to Problem 4. (The Lorentz transformations here may be considered rotations in the complex rotation diagram extended by the addition of one more space dimension. Rotations through finite angles about different axes are noncommutative. Consider a book rotated 90° first about x and then about y; as compared with first about y and then about x.)

6. Show that $F = \dfrac{f + \beta}{1 + \beta f}$ gives $\tanh^{-1} F = \tanh^{-1} f + \tanh^{-1} \beta$.

7. Use the Lorentz transformation to find what $F = ma$ becomes for other Galilean observers, assuming the mass and force to be invariants.

8. Is anything changed if, in Problem 7, we substitute $F = \dfrac{dp}{dt}$ for the equation to be transformed, considering the mass invariant?

9. Do this also for the wave equation $\dfrac{\partial^2 u}{\partial x^2} = \dfrac{1}{c^2}\dfrac{\partial^2 u}{\partial t^2}$. What does this equation become for another Galilean observer, using the Lorentz transformation?

10. What difference, if any, is introduced by defining the interval as $s = \pm\sqrt{c^2 t^2 - x^2}$ rather than $s = \sqrt{c^2 t^2 - x^2}$?

11. What is the equation for aberration in classical theory? How is it derived?

12. Modify the formula for light in the moving medium when the medium is dispersive, i.e., when the refractive index is a function of wavelength or frequency. This problem is lengthy.

13. B moves with velocity v toward the right with respect to A. To B an object, C, moves to the left with speed u; while to A the same object seems to move to the right with speed u. Find u. Draw C's world-line on a space-time diagram. Is the perpendicular to this not also a solution?

14. The phase of a plane wave, ϕ, is given for observer A by $\sin \phi = \sin 2\pi f\left(t - \dfrac{xn_x + yn_y + zn_z}{c}\right)$, where $\hat{n} = n_x\hat{x} + n_y\hat{y} + n_z\hat{z}$ gives the wave direction. For observer B the phase is given by $\sin \phi'$, with $\phi = \phi'$. If the source, stationary in B, moves to the left with velocity v along the x axis, use the Lorentz transformation to show that $f = f^0\left(\dfrac{\sqrt{1 - \beta^2}}{1 - \beta n_x}\right) = f^0\left(\dfrac{1 + \beta n'_x}{\sqrt{1 - \beta^2}}\right)$. This is a general formula which includes the longitudinal and transverse Doppler effect formulas as special cases.

15. Repeat the previous problem using the Galilean transformation to show there is then no transverse Doppler effect.

16. Assume the universe began as event O with an explosion or "big bang." On a space-time diagram for two observers A and B, moving relative to each other with infinitesimal velocity, draw the world-line of another particle, C, emanating from O.

(a) At a given instant for A, what is the relation between the distance of C from A and the velocity of C relative to A? At that same instant, is there a maximum distance of C from A (i.e., a radius of the universe) and, if so, what is it?

(b) What is the maximum distance of C from A at some value of proper-time, identical for both A and C? Convert proper-time to interval and draw the curve for constant interval to see this most easily.

(c) Reconcile these two answers.

17. Derive the Loedel diagram from the Minkowski diagram by considering A to move right relative to B, with B having the orthogonal axes; then B to move right relative to C, with B again having the orthogonal axes; and, finally, using the law of velocity addition between A and C.

CHAPTER 6

1. Starting from the transformation equations of the velocity derive the following transformation equations for acceleration. Here $\beta = \dfrac{v}{c}$ while $\delta_x = \dfrac{u_x}{c}$, $\delta_y = \dfrac{u_y}{c}$, $\delta_z = \dfrac{u_z}{c}$; the capitals refer to the left-moving system.

$$A_x = \frac{(1 - \beta^2)^{3/2} a_x}{(1 + \beta \delta_x)^3}$$

$$A_y = \frac{(1 - \beta^2) a_y}{(1 + \beta \delta_x)^2} - \frac{\beta \delta_y (1 - \beta^2) a_x}{(1 + \beta \delta_x)^3}$$

$$A_z = \frac{(1 - \beta^2) a_z}{(1 + \beta \delta_x)^2} - \frac{\beta \delta_z (1 - \beta^2) a_x}{(1 + \beta \delta_x)^3} .$$

2. Let $a_y = a_z = u_y = u_z = 0$ in the transformation above. Find β in terms of δ_x such that the particle has the same acceleration in both systems. Given u_x in one system, what is U_x in the other system?

3. A particle of rest-mass m_1, moving with velocity v, collides with a stationary particle of rest-mass m_2. The two particles coalesce to form a particle of rest-mass M moving with velocity V. Show that $V = \dfrac{v}{1 + \dfrac{m_2}{m_1}\sqrt{1 - \beta^2}}$.

4. In the above problem, find M. If the equations become very complicated, try a different approach.

5. If the earth receives 1.35 kw/m^2 of radiant energy from the sun, find the mass rate of loss of the sun. Take the earth-sun distance as 1.5×10^8 km.

6. Find the relativistic percentage change of the mass of an electron in the ground state of the hydrogen atom.

7. Show that $\dfrac{pv}{K} = \dfrac{\left(\dfrac{K}{m^0 c^2}\right) + 2}{\left(\dfrac{K}{m^0 c^2}\right) + 1}$.

8. Find the proper-time for a 10^{10} eV electron to pass through our galaxy, of radius 10^5 light-years. Repeat this for a proton.

9. If the rest-mass of a μ-meson is 206.8 electron rest-masses, show that the maximum kinetic energy is 52.2 MeV for the electron in $\mu \to e + \nu + \bar{\nu}$; here ν is a neutrino, $\bar{\nu}$ is an antineutrino, and both are taken to have zero rest-mass.

10. Show that $m^0 = \dfrac{c^2 p^2 - K^2}{2Kc^2}$.

11. (a) What are the transformation equations for E and p when $v \to 0$?
    (b) Express a natural unit for momentum in terms of electron-volts.
    (c) What conclusions can you draw for electrons by applying the concepts analogous to time-like and space-like intervals to the (E, cp) diagram?

12. In the photoelectric effect an incident photon, ν^0, hits a stationary atom, M^0, to form an electron, m^0, going off at an angle, θ, plus an ion, μ^0, going off at an angle ϕ. Transform this problem to a center-of-mass coordinate system, i.e., to an observer moving with such a constant velocity (both before and after the collision) that the total momentum of the system is zero for him.

13. Obtain the expressions for the momentum and energy of the ion and atom in the problem above.

14. Convert the expressions of Problem 13 back to the original laboratory system as a function of the angle θ. Compare the magnitudes of the momenta of the ion and the electron. Compare their kinetic energies.

15. Derive the expression for the Compton wavelength shift from the conservation of mass-energy and the conservation of the x and y momentum components.

16. A photon hits a stationary atom. The photon disappears, the atom acquires a velocity and an electron-positron pair is produced. Transform this problem to a C-M system.

17. An electron is accelerated from rest through a difference of potential V to give it an energy eV. For what value of V will the resultant velocity calculated classically differ from the relativistic value by 10 per cent?

18. Repeat Problem 17, solving for a proton.

19. A right-angled lever, at rest with respect to A, has a horizontal length L_x to the right from the meeting point with the vertical length. The latter is of length L_y downward, toward $-y$. A force F_y is applied upward at the right end of the horizontal arm, giving a CCW torque $F_y L_x$ about the junction. A force F_x is applied toward the left at the bottom end of the vertical arm, giving a CW torque $F_x L_y$. The two torques are equal and the lever is in equilibrium. What is the torque for an observer B moving toward $+x$ with velocity v relative to A? Explain. (Using calculus, calculate power, equivalent rate of conversion to mass, and rate of change of angular momentum.) Show $dW = \sqrt{1 - \beta^2} \, dW^0$ for a small, very-slow lever rotation θ^0.

20. Use the Lorentz transformation to find what $\mathbf{F} = \dfrac{d\mathbf{p}}{dt}$ becomes for other observers, the mass no longer being invariant. (Use calculus.)

21. What is the minimum frequency of the photon whose conversion gives pair production? Compare this to a visual photon with $\lambda = 5000$ Å.

CHAPTER 7

1. Let an electron be fixed relative to A'. A' moves to the right with velocity v relative to A. If $\mathbf{E}'$, $\mathbf{B}'$, and $\mathbf{F}'$ hold for A' then $\mathbf{F}' = e\mathbf{E}'$. From the transformation equations between $(\mathbf{E}', \mathbf{B}')$ and $(\mathbf{E}, \mathbf{B})$ as well as those between $\mathbf{F}'$ and $\mathbf{F}$ (where $\mathbf{E}$, $\mathbf{B}$, and $\mathbf{F}$ hold for A) derive the Lorentz force expression $\mathbf{F} = e[\mathbf{E} + (\mathbf{v} \times \mathbf{B})]$.

2. If ρ' and ρ are the charge densities for A' and A above, does $\mathbf{f}' = \rho \mathbf{E}'$ transform into $\mathbf{f} = \rho[\mathbf{E} + (\mathbf{v} \times \mathbf{B})]$? Here $\mathbf{f}'$ and $\mathbf{f}$ are force densities.

3. The Coulomb field of an electron fixed at the origin of A is $\mathbf{E}_A = \dfrac{q}{4\pi\varepsilon_0 R^2}\,\hat{\mathbf{R}}$.

Let A move to the right relative to B with normalized velocity β. At the instant when the origins of A and B coincide find the expression relating the distance from the origin to some field point, P, in terms of Cartesian coordinates. Then write this in polar form for B, (r,θ,ϕ). Finally, using the transformation equations between $\mathbf{E}_A$ and $\mathbf{E}_B$ show that

$$\mathbf{E}_B = \frac{q}{4\pi\varepsilon_0 r^2}\left[\frac{1-\beta^2}{(1-\beta^2\sin^2\theta)^{3/2}}\right]\hat{\mathbf{r}}.$$

4. Show that $\mathbf{E}_B$ above may also be written $\left(\dfrac{q}{4\pi\varepsilon_0}\right)\dfrac{(1-\beta^2)\mathbf{r}}{[r^2-(\mathbf{r}\times\boldsymbol{\beta})^2]^{3/2}}$. Plot E_B versus θ for values of θ between $0°$ (ahead) and $180°$ (behind) with $\beta = 0$, 0.1, and 0.5.

5. Two parallel wires, infinitely long and separated by a distance D, are each charged with λ^0 coulombs/meter stationary with respect to the conductors. Using the Coulomb force expression, find the force on unit length of one wire due to all the second wire. (This involves calculus.)

6. Find the force, in Problem 5, as measured by an observer moving parallel to the wires with velocity v. Instead of the Coulomb force expression it is now necessary to employ the results of Problems 3 or 4 above. (This problem also requires calculus.)

7. Find the proper-force between two electrons, separated by 10^{-8} m, each moving with normalized velocity $\beta = 0.99$ in a direction normal to the line of separation. Then find the nonproper-force measured by a stationary observer.

8. A charged particle moves in a uniform magnetic field. What effect does the variation of mass with velocity have on the particle motion?

9. For substances introduced into a region where there are fields $\mathbf{E}$ and $\mathbf{B}$ it is convenient to introduce auxiliary fields $\mathbf{D}$ and $\mathbf{H}$: $\mathbf{D} = K_e\varepsilon_0\mathbf{E}$ and $\mathbf{B} = K_m\mu_0\mathbf{H}$. $\mathbf{D}$ is called the displacement; K_e is the dielectric constant or the relative permittivity; K_m is the relative permeability; $\mathbf{H}$ is called the magnetic field intensity. If K_e and K_m are constants, find the transformation equations for $\mathbf{D}$ and $\mathbf{H}$ between two observers moving with velocity v relative to each other along the x axis.

10. Let the relation between the fields above be written $\mathbf{D} = \varepsilon_0\mathbf{E} + \mathbf{P}$ and $\mathbf{H} = \dfrac{1}{\mu_0}\mathbf{B} - \mathbf{M}$. Here $\mathbf{P}$ and $\mathbf{M}$ are called the polarization and magnetization vectors, respectively. What are the transformation equations for $\mathbf{P}$ and $\mathbf{M}$ for two observers moving relatively along x? (The magnetic vectors would be more analogous to the electric vectors if $\mathbf{M}$ were replaced by $\mathcal{M} = \mu_0\mathbf{M}$, but this is not customary.)

11. Show that $\mathbf{E}\cdot\mathbf{B}$ is Lorentz invariant.

12. (This problem, which supplies a proof mentioned in the text, requires calculus.) Use the results of Problem 5 to write the force on a charge q at a distance D from an infinitely long stationary line charge λ^0. Then use the following results of the Lorentz transformation

$$dF_x = dF_x{}^0,\quad dF_y = \sqrt{1-\beta^2}\,dF_y{}^0,\quad x = \sqrt{1-\beta^2}\,x^0,\quad \lambda = \frac{\lambda^0}{\sqrt{1-\beta^2}}.$$

Obtain the force on q (as measured by B moving with velocity $-\mathbf{v}$ relative to A) by integration. Finally, for q substitute line charges to obtain the expressions for $\dfrac{\text{force}}{\text{length}}$.

13. Consider two infinitely long parallel conductors, a distance D apart, and an observer A stationary relative to them. Let A measure a linear proper-charge density $\lambda_p{}^0$ of positive charges in each conductor; and also a linear nonproper-charge density λ_n of negative charges, all moving with the same velocity v, in each. For unit length of one wire find the force produced by all the second wire which is due to the force of: (a) stationary charges on stationary charges, (b) moving charges on stationary charges, (c) stationary charges on moving charges, and (d) moving charges on moving charges.

CHAPTER 8

1. Determine the contravariant 4-tensor F^{ij} that represents the electromagnetic fields.

2. Write the invariant $E^2 - c^2B^2$ in 4-tensor form.

3. Show that every 4-tensor T_{ik} can be written as the sum of a symmetric 4-tensor $T_{ik}^{(s)}$ and an antisymmetric 4-tensor $T_{ik}^{(a)}$.

4. Construct the 4-vector acceleration from the 4-vector velocity by taking the derivative with respect to the proper-time (alternatively, the interval).

5. (a). In the tensor equation for the Lorentz force, what equation is obtained from the fourth component of f_i?
(b). Write the tensor equation for f^i.

6. Show that $\nabla\phi$ is a vector while $\hat{\mathbf{x}}\dfrac{\partial\phi}{\partial x} + \hat{\mathbf{y}}2\dfrac{\partial\phi}{\partial y} + \hat{\mathbf{z}}\dfrac{\partial\phi}{\partial z}$ is not a vector.

7. Prove that the dot product of two vectors is a scalar.

8. Show algebraically that in rectangular Cartesian coordinates a contravariant vector is the same as a covariant vector.

9. If δ_j^i is the Kronecker delta symbol, is (δ_j^i) a tensor? Now let $\delta_{ij} = \delta_j^i$. Is (δ_{ij}) a tensor? How about (δ^{ij}) if $\delta^{ij} = \delta_j^i$?

10. How many independent components are there in the antisymmetric tensor a_{ijk} in 4-space? Similarly, in a_{ijkl}?

11. Show that the symmetry or antisymmetry of a second order contravariant tensor is a property independent of the reference system.

12. Consider T^{ij} in 3-space. Write the 9 components after the following reversal transformations: (a) x axis, (b) y axis, (c) z axis, (d) x and y axes, (e) y and z axes, (f) z and x axes, and (g) x, y, and z axes.

13. Show that the components of the antisymmetric unit "tensor" ε^{hij} behave like tensor components under rotations of the coordinate system.

14. Simplify to a 2-dimensional space and show that $g = |g_{ij}|$, the determinant of the metric tensor, is not a scalar.

15. Write the components of a contravariant 4-vector representing acceleration.

CHAPTER 9

1. How great a fringe shift was expected in the Michelson-Morley experiment? How great a fringe shift could be measured with the particular values in their experiment? How great a shift was obtained?

2. Describe the experimental arrangement in the Cedarholm-Bland-Havens-Townes experiment which depended on $\dfrac{v}{c}$, instead of on $\left(\dfrac{v}{c}\right)^2$ as in the Michelson-Morley experiment.

3. Describe the Pound-Rebka experiment utilizing the Mössbauer effect to measure time dilation. (The sensitivity in measuring the Doppler shift in such tests using the Mössbauer effect is high enough to detect a relative velocity of 1 mm/sec.)

4. How closely did experiments agree with the relativistic drag coefficient $\left(1 - \dfrac{1}{n^2}\right)$ in the Fizeau moving-water experiment?

5. The Essen experiment is a microwave analogue of the Michelson-Morley light-beam experiment. Outline the differences between the two experiments.

6. Compare the Durbin-Loar-Havens experiment (using pions) with the Frisch-Smith experiment (utilizing muons) for measurement of time dilation.

7. In the experiment of Hay et al. the relative velocity of source and absorber is $(R_1 - R_2)\omega$. Why should not $\dfrac{\Delta f}{f^0}$ be given by $\dfrac{(R_1 - R_2)^2 \omega^2}{2c^2}$?

APPENDIX I Nomographs

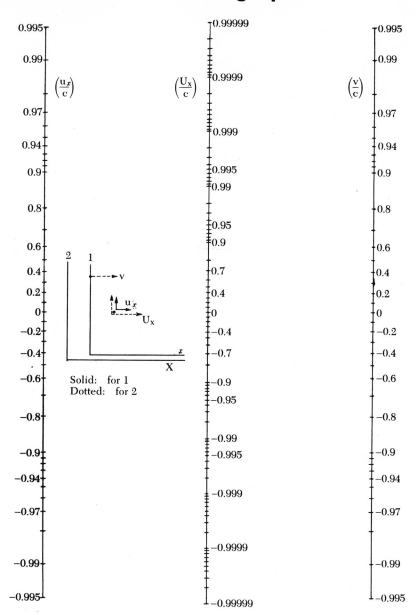

a) TRANSFORMATION OF PARALLEL VELOCITY COMPONENT

$$\left(\frac{U_X}{c}\right) = \frac{\left(\frac{u_x}{c}\right) + \left(\frac{v}{c}\right)}{1 + \left(\frac{u_x}{c}\right)\left(\frac{v}{c}\right)} \quad \text{or} \quad \tanh^{-1}\left(\frac{U_X}{c}\right) = \tanh^{-1}\left(\frac{u_x}{c}\right) + \tanh^{-1}\left(\frac{v}{c}\right)$$

Nomograph to obtain r, the ratio $\left(\dfrac{U_Y}{u_y}\right)$.

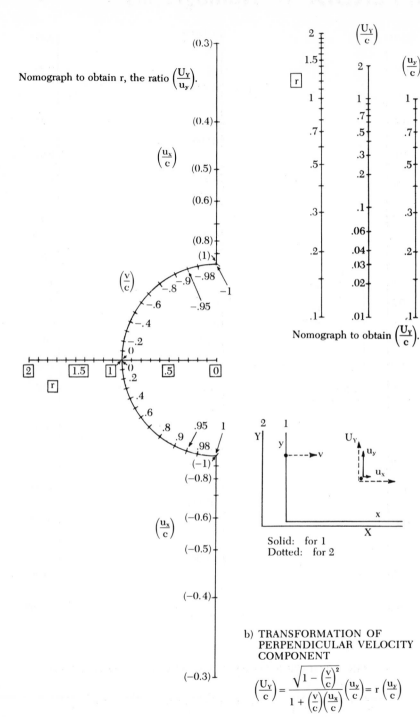

Nomograph to obtain $\left(\dfrac{U_Y}{c}\right)$.

Solid: for 1
Dotted: for 2

b) TRANSFORMATION OF
PERPENDICULAR VELOCITY
COMPONENT

$$\left(\frac{U_Y}{c}\right) = \frac{\sqrt{1 - \left(\frac{v}{c}\right)^2}}{1 + \left(\frac{v}{c}\right)\left(\frac{u_x}{c}\right)}\left(\frac{u_y}{c}\right) = r\left(\frac{u_y}{c}\right)$$

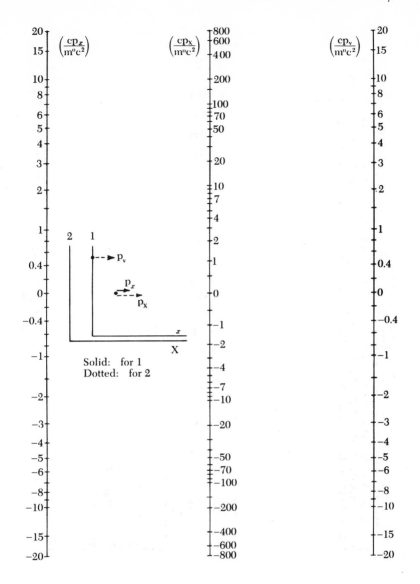

c) TRANSFORMATION OF MOMENTUM WHEN THE PARTICLE VELOCITY
   IS PARALLEL TO THE RELATIVE VELOCITY

$$\sinh^{-1}\left(\frac{cp_X}{m^0c^2}\right) = \sinh^{-1}\left(\frac{cp_x}{m^0c^2}\right) + \sinh^{-1}\left(\frac{cp_v}{m^0c^2}\right)$$

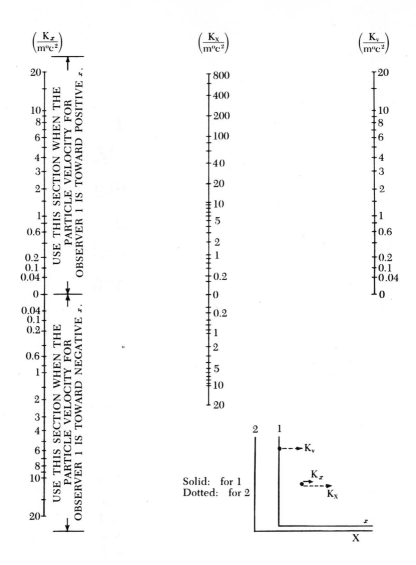

d) TRANFORMATION OF KINETIC ENERGY WHEN THE PARTICLE VELOCITY IS PARALLEL TO THE RELATIVE VELOCITY

$$\sinh^{-1}\sqrt{\frac{1}{2}\left(\frac{K_x}{m^0c^2}\right)} = \pm\sinh^{-1}\sqrt{\frac{1}{2}\left(\frac{K_x}{m^0c^2}\right)} + \sinh^{-1}\sqrt{\frac{1}{2}\left(\frac{K_v}{m^0c^2}\right)}$$

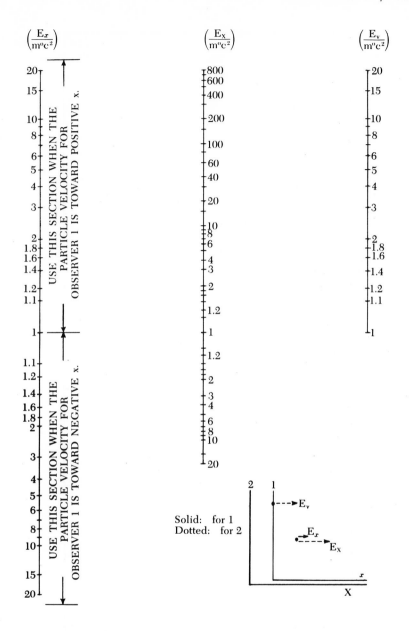

e) TRANSFORMATION OF TOTAL ENERGY WHEN THE PARTICLE
VELOCITY IS PARALLEL TO THE RELATIVE VELOCITY

$$\cosh^{-1}\left(\frac{E_X}{m^0c^2}\right) = \cosh^{-1}\left(\frac{E_x}{m^0c^2}\right) + \cosh^{-1}\left(\frac{E_v}{m^0c^2}\right)$$

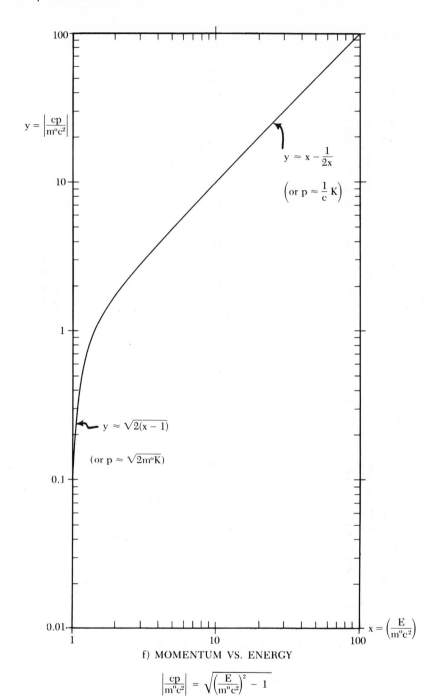

f) MOMENTUM VS. ENERGY

$$\left| \frac{cp}{m^{0}c^{2}} \right| = \sqrt{\left(\frac{E}{m^{0}c^{2}} \right)^{2} - 1}$$

APPENDIX 2 Derivation of Steady-State Values of Charge Density and Drift Velocity for the Case of Reflected Waves

From the theory of transmission lines the amplitudes of the sequence of voltage waves are given by

$$V, rV, -rV, -r^2V, r^2V, r^3V, -r^3V, \ldots$$

Here r is the reflection coefficient $r = \dfrac{R - R_o}{R + R_o}$. Figure 34a, p. 116, shows the behavior with time, for three different values of r, of the potential difference between a point P on wire a (a quarter of the way down the line) and the corresponding point on wire c. The period T is twice the time for the wave to traverse the line from one end to the other end; for lines of ordinary length T would be of the order of microseconds. The steady-state value of potential is V and is approached in a time that is small by common everyday standards.

If $I_o = \dfrac{V}{R_o}$ then the successive current wave amplitudes are:

$$I_o, -rI_o, -rI_o, r^2I_o, r^2I_o, -r^3I_o, -r^3I_o, \ldots$$

The steady-state current is $I_o(1 - 2r + 2r^2 - 2r^3 + \cdots) = I_o\left(\dfrac{1-r}{1+r}\right) = \dfrac{V}{R}.$

Figure 34b gives the behavior of the current with time at P. The transient behavior, both of the potential difference and current, are well known. We now investigate the corresponding behavior of the linear charge density and of the electron drift velocity. We will briefly consider several successive waves, one at a time, utilizing the tables of Chapter 7 for the changes in density caused by right-moving and left-moving electromagnetic waves.

As in Chapter 7, let B be a Galilean observer moving to the left relative to A with velocity $v_1 = \beta_1 c$, where v_1 is also the drift velocity to the left imparted to the electrons by the first, right-moving, wave. Before the arrival of this wave A will measure a negative linear proper-charge density λ_n; after this one wave the density will be nonproper and of magnitude $\left(\dfrac{1}{1+\beta_1}\right)\lambda_n$.

Observer B will measure, after the wave, a proper-density $\lambda_B{}^0 = \sqrt{\dfrac{1-\beta_1}{1+\beta_1}}\,\lambda_n$. The current for A will be $I'_A = \left(\dfrac{\lambda_n}{1+\beta_1}\right)(-\beta_1 c)$. Using $\lambda_n = -\lambda$, defining $f = \dfrac{I_o}{\lambda c}$, and equating the resultant to I_o gives $\beta_1 = \dfrac{f}{1-f}$. The negative linear nonproper-charge density for A may then be written $(1-f)\lambda_n$; the first wave produced an increment in the negative density for A of $-f\lambda_n$. For $\lambda_B{}^0$ we have $\lambda_B{}^0 = \sqrt{1-2f}\,\lambda_n$.

Now let C be still another Galilean observer, moving to the left relative to B with velocity $v_2 = \beta_2 c$; then, relative to A, C's normalized velocity to the left is $\beta_{CA} = \dfrac{\beta_1+\beta_2}{1+\beta_1\beta_2}$. If v_2 is also the drift velocity of the electrons, relative to B, after the passage of the second wave (left-moving from the resistor R) then the negative linear proper-charge density for C after this wave passes becomes $\lambda_C{}^0 = \sqrt{\dfrac{1+\beta_2}{1-\beta_2}}\,\lambda_B{}^0$. To calculate the corresponding nonproper-density and current for A we employ the Lorentz transformation.

$$\begin{cases} I''_A = \dfrac{I_C - (\beta_{CA}c)\lambda_C}{\sqrt{1-\beta_{CA}{}^2}} = \dfrac{-\beta_{CA}c\lambda_C{}^0}{\sqrt{1-\beta_{CA}{}^2}} \\[2ex] c\lambda''_A = \dfrac{-\beta_{CA}I_C + c\lambda_C}{\sqrt{1-\beta_{CA}{}^2}} = \dfrac{c\lambda_C{}^0}{\sqrt{1-\beta_{CA}{}^2}}. \end{cases}$$

We will not give the details of all the calculations here but will merely summarize the results, in the table, for the first five waves. The total negative density λ_A, given in the fourth column, and the total drift velocity β_A (the last column), are graphed in Figure 34c and d, respectively, for $f = 0.05$.

The steady-state values approached by these variables may now be computed. The normalized steady-state drift velocity of the electrons relative to A is

$$\beta_{ss} = [1 - 2r(1 - r + r^2 - \cdots)]\dfrac{f}{1-f} = \left(\dfrac{1-r}{1+r}\right)\left(\dfrac{f}{1-f}\right).$$

This may also be written $\beta_{ss} = \dfrac{\beta_1}{K}$, where $\beta_1 = \beta_{BA} = \dfrac{f}{1-f}$ and $K = \dfrac{R}{R_o}$.

The steady-state negative linear nonproper-charge density is the same as λ'_A:

$$\lambda_{ss} = (1-f)\lambda_n.$$

This is also $\lambda_{ss} = \dfrac{\lambda_n}{1+\beta_1} = \dfrac{-\lambda}{1+\beta_1}$.

TRANSIENTS WHEN THE FIRST WAVE IS IN THE OPPOSITE DIRECTION TO THE DRIFT VELOCITY

CURRENT		NEGATIVE LINEAR CHARGE DENSITY		$\frac{1}{c}$ (DRIFT VELOCITY)	
Change	Total	Change	Total	Change	Total
0	0	0	$\lambda_A^{\,0} = \lambda_n$	0	0
I_0	$I'_A = I_0$	$-f\lambda_n$	$\lambda'_A = (1-f)\lambda_n$	$\beta_1 = \dfrac{f}{1-f}$	$\beta_{BA} = \dfrac{f}{1-f}$
$-rI_0$	$I''_A = (1-r)I_0$	$-rf\lambda_n$	$\lambda''_A = [1-(1+r)f]\lambda_n$	$\beta_2 = \dfrac{-fr}{1-fr}$	$\beta_{CA} = \dfrac{f(1-r)}{1-(1+r)f}$
$-rI_0$	$I'''_A = (1-2r)I_0$	$+rf\lambda_n$	$\lambda'''_A = (1-f)\lambda_n$	$\beta_3 = \dfrac{-fr}{1-f(2-r)}$	$\beta_{DA} = (1-2r)\dfrac{f}{1-f}$
$r^2 I_0$	$I''''_A = (1-2r+r^2)I_0$	$+r^2 f\lambda_n$	$\lambda''''_A = [1-(1-r^2)f]\lambda_n$	$\beta_4 = \dfrac{fr^2}{1-fr(2-r)}$	$\beta_{EA} = \dfrac{f(1-r)^2}{1-(1-r^2)f}$
$r^2 I_0$	$I'''''_A = (1-2r+2r^2)I_0$	$-r^2 f\lambda_n$	$\lambda'''''_A = (1-f)\lambda_n$	$\beta_5 = \dfrac{fr^2}{1-f(2-2r+r^2)}$	$\beta_{FA} = (1-2r+2r^2)\dfrac{f}{1-f}$

The steady-state negative linear proper-charge density, calculated from the sequence $\lambda_A{}^0$, $\lambda_B{}^0$, ..., is given by

$$\lambda_{ss}{}^0 = \sqrt{1 - 2f + f^2 \left[\frac{4r}{(1+r)^2}\right]}\, \lambda_n.$$

Since $f = \dfrac{\beta_1}{1 + \beta_1}$, while $r = \dfrac{K-1}{K+1}$ and $\lambda_n = -\lambda$, this may also be written

$\lambda_{ss}{}^0 = \left(\dfrac{-\lambda}{1+\beta_1}\right)\sqrt{1 - (\beta_1/K)^2}$. The three steady-state quantities are seen to be self-consistent: $\lambda_{ss}{}^0 = \lambda_{ss}\sqrt{1 - \beta_{ss}{}^2}$.

A difficulty presented by the formula for β_{ss}, which for small enough K offers the possibility of the drift velocity exceeding c, may be explained as follows. The axial field intensity, E, set up in the terminating resistor is proportional to the difference in potential, V, between the wires; the values of the intensity established by successive waves are 0, E, $(1-r)E$, $(1-2r)E$, $(1-2r+r^2)E$, ..., all to the right. The corresponding values of normalized drift velocity from the table are, for $f \ll 1$: 0, f, $(1-r)f$, $(1-2r)f$, $(1-2r+r^2)f$, ... Therefore for small f the drift velocity is proportional to the electric field intensity. The mobility, defined by drift velocity/field intensity, is then a constant for small f. This is already known from other considerations: assuming the average forward initial velocity of an electron after a collision is zero, $eE = ma$ leads to $v_{av} = \dfrac{eE}{m}\tau$ where τ is the mean time between collisions. The mobility is then given by $\dfrac{e}{m}\tau$.

If the resistance not only of the conductors but also of the terminating resistor is made negligibly small (and if the source is capable of providing the necessary power), E grows to be a very large value and, given sufficient time, the drift velocity approaches c. But $F = ma$ is then invalid unless one uses the so-called longitudinal mass introduced in Chapter 6: $m = \dfrac{m^0}{(1 - \beta^2)^{3/2}}$. The solution to this equation is

$$\frac{\beta_{av}}{\sqrt{1 - \beta_{av}{}^2}} = \frac{eE\tau}{m^0 c} \qquad \text{or} \qquad \beta_{av} = \frac{eE\tau}{\sqrt{(m^0 c)^2 + e^2 E^2 \tau^2}}.$$

For $eE\tau \ll m^0 c$ this gives the previous results; but for $eE\tau \gg m^0 c$ we now obtain $\beta_{av} \to 1$. For $\tau = 10^{-14}$ the value of E that gives equality between the two terms in the denominator is about 10^{11} v/m. Using such a very large value of electric field intensity is not the only way, however, of obtaining this result. The resistance could also be made small by employing single crystals without impurities, by superconductivity, by lowering the temperature, etc.; this would correspond to increasing the mean time between collisions. For $\tau = 10^{-8}$ sec the critical value of E is 10^5 v/m; for $\tau = 10^{-2}$ sec the critical E is only 0.1 v/m. The theory above is not applicable to these cases.

APPENDIX 3 The Case of Parallel Conductors for Real (Nonideal) Metals

In Chapter 7, in dealing with parallel conduction currents, we have considered only ideal conductors. The situation is quite changed when we consider real, lossy conductors.

What produces the power loss in ordinary metals? In the absence of any external field the free electrons of the metal ($\sim 10^{23}$ cm^{-3}) move in a random fashion at a very high speed ($\sim 2 \times 10^8$ cm/sec $= 0.007c = 4.7 \times 10^6$ miles/hr) but change their course often in collisions, the mean free path ($\sim 4 \times 10^{-6}$ cm) and the mean free time ($\sim 2 \times 10^{-14}$ sec) being quite small. The collisions are only rarely with ions or other electrons; they are predominantly with phonons, packets of vibration energy similar in many ways to photons of electromagnetic energy. There is no net current in a conductor without an electric field because, on the average, equal numbers of electrons cross a given plane going one way as going in the opposite direction. But when a field is established within the lossy conductor a small drift velocity (~ 0.03 cm/sec) is superimposed on the random electron motion. Then a constant velocity, rather than a constant acceleration, is produced by a constant electric field because of the collisions. The situation is somewhat analogous to the terminal velocity of falling raindrops produced by air molecule collisions in the earth's gravitational field. This small drift velocity causes an excess of electrons to cross a plane (perpendicular to the wire axis) going in one sense. An excess of electron crossings going left over crossings going right gives an equivalent current to the right. The energy lost in collisions that maintain the drift velocity appears as the Joule heat in the conductor.

For a lossy conductor, the electromagnetic wave traveling down the wire has components both outside the wire and inside the wire. The wave outside is predominantly transverse but has a small axial component; inside the wire the wave is chiefly axial but has a small transverse component. The inside magnitude is usually much smaller than that outside. Several factors combine to make the procedure we employed above, for ideal conductors, much more difficult to apply to the present case. The wave is attenuated along the length of the conductor; it is also attenuated with depth from the surface; dispersion effects quickly alter the appearance of the wavefront. Different frequency components in the wave have widely varying velocities, some of which are very much less than c. A different approach is thus required for the case of the lossy conductors.

Starting with the continuity equation* (which expresses the conservation of charge) one may substitute $\mathbf{j} = \sigma\mathbf{E}$ (Ohm's law), $\mathbf{D} = \varepsilon\mathbf{E}$ (a so-called constitutive equation), and Gauss's law (one of Maxwell's equations which says that free charge is the source and the sink for lines of $\mathbf{D}$) to derive the following equation for the charge density at any point in the interior of the metal:

$$\rho = \rho_0 \exp\left(-\frac{\sigma}{\varepsilon}t\right) = \rho_0 \exp\left(-\frac{t}{\tau}\right).$$

Here σ is the conductivity and ε is the permittivity of the metal; ρ and ρ_0 are the charge density at time t and time zero, respectively; τ is called the relaxation time. For copper $\sigma = 5.8 \times 10^7$ mhos/meter; ε is approximately the value of ε_0 in vacuum 8.87×10^{-12} farad/meter. Thus $\tau \approx 10^{-19}$ sec. Inside a good conductor like copper within an extremely short time (about 10^{-19} sec), any free charge density decreases to $\frac{1}{e}$ its original value. In 10^{-6} sec, for example, the value of ρ is essentially zero within the conductor, and if there is any net charge it must lie on the surface.

For the lossy conductor we have the steady-state conditions $\lambda_p = \lambda$ and $\lambda_n = -\lambda$, the same as the conditions before the conduction current started. Observer A, at rest with respect to the wire, measures the interiors of the conductors as uncharged; but what about the surface charge? The capacitance between the wires gives a surface charge density to the wires here also. Now, however, the difference of potential between the wires drops continuously as one moves away from the battery because of the IR drop in potential along the wires. Consequently, the surface charge density also decreases as one moves away from the battery end.

Even if we limit ourselves to the interior of the metal, however, disregarding all surface effects, the lack of net charge when current is flowing is true only for a stationary observer. For an observer moving with velocity v relative to the wire the Lorentz transformation gives

$$c\rho' = \frac{c\rho + \beta j_x}{\sqrt{1 - \beta^2}}.$$

---

* $\nabla \cdot \mathbf{j} + \dot{\rho} = 0,$ $\qquad \nabla \cdot (\sigma\mathbf{E}) + \dot{\rho} = 0,$ $\qquad \frac{\sigma}{\varepsilon}\nabla \cdot \mathbf{D} + \dot{\rho} = 0,$ $\qquad \frac{\sigma}{\varepsilon}\rho + \dot{\rho} = 0,$
$\rho = \rho_0 \exp\left(-\frac{\sigma}{\varepsilon}t\right).$

For $\rho = 0$ we then have $\rho' = (vj_x/c^2)(1 - \beta^2)^{-\frac{1}{2}}$, which differs from zero. The question of whether an effect is really electrostatic or not depends on the observer for its answer.

For lossy conductors and a stationary observer we can make the electrostatic repulsion forces (caused exclusively by the surface charges) negligibly small compared to the magnetic forces. This we can do simply by removing the return conductor c to a very large distance from both a and b. This situation is seen to be very different from that of the ideal conductors, where removal of the return lead has no effect whatever when $R = R_o$.

The feature that distinguishes conduction currents from convection currents is the sign of the invariant characteristic of the current-charge density 4-vector. For conduction currents the invariant $(c\lambda)^2 - I^2 = -(I_o^2)$ so the sign is always negative; two parallel conduction currents attract each other if they flow in the same sense. On the other hand, for convection currents the invariant is $(c\lambda)^2 - I^2 = (c\lambda^0)^2$, i.e., it is always positive; two convection currents, parallel in the same sense, repel each other. It is not correct to call the two terms of the Lorentz transformation,

either of $I' = \dfrac{I + (v/c)c\lambda}{\sqrt{1 - (v/c)^2}}$ or of $j' = \dfrac{j + (v/c)c\rho}{\sqrt{1 - (v/c)^2}}$, the conduction and

convection components. This is analogous to the situation in space-time. There an interval is called time-like or space-like; but there is no meaningful way to distinguish the two terms of the transformed space coordinate

$x' = \dfrac{x + (v/c)ct}{\sqrt{1 - (v/c)^2}}$ as the space component and the time component.

In the section on Parallel Conductors we showed that ideal surface currents, such as superconductor currents, have a 4-vector invariant which may be either positive, negative, or zero. In terms of the positive ion charge density, λ, the net steady-state surface charge density is now $f\lambda$, so the 4-vector invariant $c^2(f\lambda)^2 - I^2 = I_o^2 - I^2$. This is negative when $R < R_o$, so the ideal current is then a conduction current and two such parallel currents attract each other. For $R > R_o$, however, $I_o^2 - I^2 > 0$ so the ideal current is then a convection current and two parallel superconducting currents, in this case, will repel each other. For the special case $R = R_o$ we have $I_o^2 - I^2 = 0$. An ideal current of this kind, neither a conduction nor a convection current, belongs in a separate category; zero force is exerted between two parallel currents of this kind. While convection currents correspond to time-like intervals, and conduction currents to space-like intervals, these special ideal currents correspond to an interval lying on the lightcone.

INDEX